The Old Place

Twixt Thames and Chilterns

Angela Spencer-Harper

With Love and Thanks

Angela

Published by
Robert Boyd Publications
260 Colwell Drive, Witney
Oxfordshire OX28 5LW

First published 2007

ISBN: 978 1 899536 83 2

By the same author
The Write Analysis
Understanding People Through Their Handwriting

Dipping into the Wells
The story of the two Chiltern villages of
Stoke Row and Highmoor seen through
the memories of their inhabitants

Both these books are available from the author,
who is the sole distributor, telephone 01491 641379

Printed and bound at The Alden Press
De Havilland Way, Witney
Oxfordshire OX29 0YG

Table of Contents

Acknowledgements

For my wonderful husband, Bob, without whose delicious meals this book would never have been written!

I also owe a great debt of gratitude to:

The late Mr Noel Baker for permission to use extracts from the books written by his father, Mr John H Baker.

Mrs Yvonne Bax, for proof-reading parts of this book.

Mr David Beasley for all his help and extensive knowledge of Wallingford.

The late Mr Sydney Blow, for excerpts from *The Ghost Walks on Fridays.*

Mr Robert Boyd, my publisher, for all his wise advice, born of a long experience in printing and publishing.

Members of the staff of the British Museum.

Mr Dennis Clark for use of his *Memoirs*, collected by the author.

Stuart and Judy Dewey authors of *Window on Wallingford.*

Mrs Beattie Evans, for use of her husband's *Memoirs*, collected by the author.

Mrs Judy Fraser, for her attractive watercolour on the front cover.

Dr Malcolm Graham, Head of the Centre for Oxfordshire Studies and his staff.

Mr Tony Hall for proof-reading parts of this book.

Mr Jack Heath for use of his *Memoirs*, collected by the author.

Mr J K Hedges, author of *History of Wallingford.*

Mr Charles Keevil of the Fire Brigades Society.

Dr Cathy E King of Heberden Coin Room at Ashmolean Museum, Oxford.

Mr Paul Lacey, author of many books on transport.

The Librarians at Henley, Reading, Wallingford and Watlington Libraries.

Mr Mike Macleod, author of *Land of the Rotherbeast.*

Mr David Miles of Oxford Archaeological Unit.

Mrs Juliet Noel (nee Reade) for permission to quote from the Reade manuscripts.

The ever-helpful staff at the Oxfordshire Archives.

Bernice and David Pedgley, authors of *History of Crowmarsh.*

Mrs Daphne Phillips, author of the *Story of Reading*.

Mr Robert Phillips for permission to quote from his *Henley and the English Civil War.*

Mrs Patricia Preece, researcher and writer on local woodlands.

John and Betty Searby (author of *In for a Penny*), for use of their *Memoirs,* collected by the author.

Miss Margaret Sheward for proof-reading parts of this book.

Quentin Spencer-Harper for designing the maps.

Mrs Mavis Stevens for use of her husband's *Memoirs*, collected by the author.

The Victoria and Albert Museum, especially Dr Catherine Dingwall.

I hope I have not omitted anyone. If I have, as to so many others, my deepest gratitude.

Also, to my husband, Bob, this time for his painstaking proof-reading.

Any errors that remain are, of course, all mine.

Introduction

This is the story of the cottage in which we live and its surrounding area. My love of the history of these villages was inspired when we first came here by the finding of a number of old objects as my husband and I dug out dead trees and bushes in our efforts to recreate the once beautiful garden. Later I met with older villagers and particularly a woman who lived here for the best part of the first thirty years of her life in the early part of the 20th century. The conversations I had with her and many other folk, particularly the sixty-four who were born in the two villages on whose boundary this cottage lies, together with the photographs which they and other people lent me, enabled me to write *Dipping into the Wells*, which comprises about a quarter of these photographs as well as the many facts and anecdotes that I learned from them. To all of these people and countless others who have helped me in many ways, I am deeply indebted.

Now, with other artefacts I have been given and documents which I have found in the archives, I have been spurred on to write a book which would give a larger picture, based on facts but with likely stories to go with them. So this book spans a period from the Mesolithic Age to about fifty years hence and covers a much wider area; Henley in the east, Wallingford in the west, Watlington in the north and Reading in the south.

I have based the early part on the facts very lengthily set out in the History of Stoke Row, hand-written in the mid-1860s by Edward Anderdon Reade, instigator of the Maharajah's Well. He researched this work between 1860 and 1864 in the Bodleian and Magdalen College libraries at Oxford and also had access to Reade manuscripts that date back to Edward I.

The Old Place is an historical novel and each chapter is based on at least one known fact and usually on much recorded knowledge about the locality. In essence, it starts as pure fiction, but becomes more factual as it proceeds. It begins fictionally in the future, in the year 2068 and then, by a literary device, suddenly goes back immediately to the Mesolithic Age and then proceeds through the centuries and becomes more factual as it does so.

By the time we reach the twentieth century it is almost purely based on known facts and eye-witness descriptions. Certainly the account of our life here in The Old Place is all true, with the exception of the fictional character, Jania. I make no apologies for this mini-biography because I believe that the story of today is the history of tomorrow.

The book endeavours to tell the story of the many different people who lived hereabouts, their lives and adventures, set against the background of known history, but it could really be the tale of almost any cottage and village in southern England. For this reason, if no other, I hope that it will give pleasure and interest to all those who love England, especially rural England, and its history as much as I do.

Angela Spencer-Harper
The Old Place
Witheridge Hill
Henley-on-Thames
Oxfordshire

The Ancient Parishes of South Oxfordshire

From the Reade Manuscripts

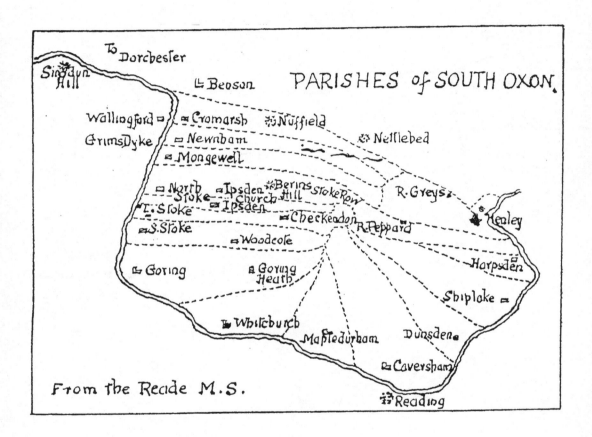

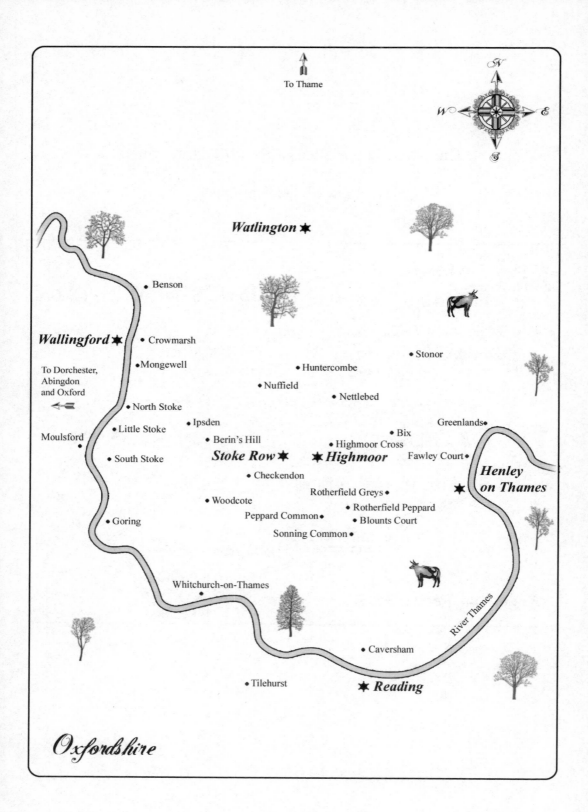

To Thame

Watlington ✦

• Benson

Wallingford ✦

• Crowmarsh

•Mongewell

To Dorchester,
Abingdon
and Oxford

• North Stoke

• Little Stoke

Moulsford
•

• South Stoke

• Goring

• Ipsden

• Berin's Hill

Stoke Row ✦

• Checkendon

• Woodcote

Peppard Common•

Sonning Common •

• Stonor

• Huntercombe

• Nuffield

• Nettlebed

• Bix

• Highmoor Cross

✦ Highmoor

Rotherfield Greys •

• Rotherfield Peppard

• Blounts Court

Greenlands•

Fawley Court •

Henley
on Thames
✦

Whitchurch-on-Thames
•

River Thames

• Caversham

• Tilehurst

✦ Reading

Oxfordshire

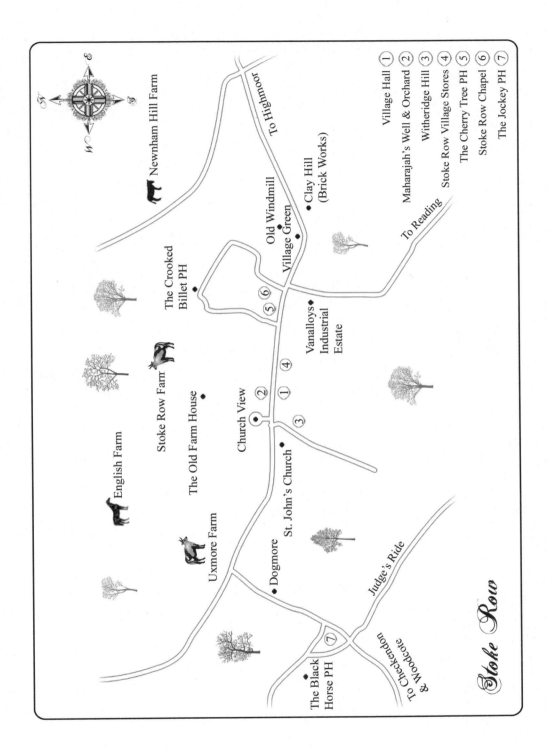

Stoke Row

1. Village Hall
2. Maharajah's Well & Orchard
3. Witheridge Hill
4. Stoke Row Village Stores
5. The Cherry Tree PH
6. Stoke Row Chapel
7. The Jockey PH

Newnham Hill Farm

To Highmoor

Old Windmill
Village Green

Clay Hill
(Brick Works)

To Reading

The Crooked
Billet PH

Vanalloys
Industrial
Estate

Stoke Row Farm

The Old Farm House

Church View

English Farm

St. John's Church

Uxmore Farm

Dogmore

Judge's Ride

To Checkendon
& Woodcote

The Black
Horse PH

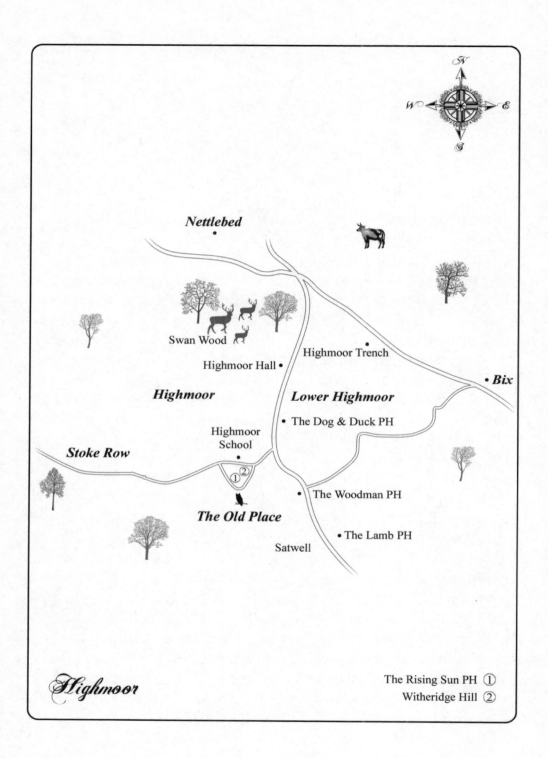

Nettlebed

Swan Wood

Highmoor Hall

Highmoor Trench

Highmoor

Lower Highmoor

• The Dog & Duck PH

• Bix

Highmoor School

Stoke Row

① ②

The Old Place

• The Woodman PH

• The Lamb PH

Satwell

Highmoor

The Rising Sun PH ①
Witheridge Hill ②

12

Chapter 1. The Puddingstone: AD 2068

Even by the standards of the mid-twenty-first century, Wednesday 22nd August 2068 seemed to be hotter than anyone could ever remember and the records of the Meteorological Office proved it to be so. When Jania Wellesbourne looked at her thermometer later that morning, it registered 48 degrees Celsius. The realisation startled Jania, as it was the first time this had happened in the nine years that she and her husband Jeremy had lived at The Old Place.

Since Jania had been born in January 2000, the year the Millennium was celebrated, average temperatures throughout the world had risen gradually by over three degrees. By this time the Millennium had become something of a watershed in that people spoke of 'since the Millennium' or 'before the Millennium'.

This rise had meant a considerable change in both the surroundings and the lifestyle of everyone in the world. For millions it had meant starvation and death from the heat, lack of water and the many natural disasters that had occurred over this period. But the comfortable middle-classes of England had learnt to adapt to the changes over the years and, though their cottage and its environs would hardly have been recognisable to those who had lived there in the twentieth century, the Wellesbournes had adapted to their surroundings and were very happy in their home. As she turned away from thoughts of the weather, Jania found herself remembering how she and Jeremy had found The Old Place in 2059, only nine years before, just by a fluke.

When they returned from almost a lifetime spent in Dubai, where Jeremy had worked as an electrical engineer for a building company and Jania had been personal assistant to an architect, they came back, as they had done so many times over the years, to their flat in Notting Hill Gate, London. This time, however, they were retiring and had finally been able to realise their dream of living back in England permanently.

Jania, who was tall and kept herself slim, had grey hair but she was still lively and had many interests. Moreover, she always became passionate about anything she undertook to do. She particularly wanted to try and find a house somewhere in the Chiltern Hills, preferably between Henley and Wallingford, where she recalled spending many happy school holidays with her Godmother, 'Auntie' Angela and her husband, 'Uncle' Bob.

The Wellesbournes had looked at several properties when, all of a sudden, they found that The Old Place at the foot of Witheridge Hill, between the villages of Stoke Row and Highmoor, had just come on the market. They examined it through their virtual reality scanner and, although Jania soon noticed many differences, she was also happy to find that the basic cottage she recalled from her childhood was still the same. "We must go out there at once – I really would love to buy that house!" she exclaimed.

It had all proved to be surprisingly easy. Notwithstanding the asking price of seven and a half million pounds, Norman and Barbara Hodgson were happy to sell it at slightly less as they were now very elderly and were finding such a large property difficult to upkeep. House prices had risen steeply in the previous ten years as more and more people had been forced to flee parts of East Anglia when the coastal land had been eroded by the sea. England had become narrower at this point and the shape of the country had altered somewhat. Also, in the thirty-eight years the Hodgsons had lived there they had made considerable alterations and improvements, both to the house and the garden

As Jania and Jeremy surveyed the property, Jania kept up a constant dialogue on the changes that she observed. It began as they drove down the hill from Highmoor and turned the bend to see the house on the left-hand side ahead of them, "There used to be a hedge all along the side of the garden and now there is a brick wall. I don't like that but I suppose they had to put it up to save on the hedge-cutting."

14

"More likely it died in one of the drought years." Jeremy commented. "Still, I like the flint panels and the rounded tiles on the top, that softens it a bit."

"And the hill, look at the hill!" Jania observed, almost unable to take in the fact that the green woods she remembered as a child had all gone and in their place rows of vines had been planted. This had been done in many parts of the south and English wines were now being accepted as being among some of the best, especially dry white wines.

As they came round to the front, they found a space to park, walked up to the security gate and pressed the buzzer. The Hodgsons were very hospitable and delighted to learn of Jania's former connection with their home.

"We are so sorry to have to sell up." Barbara explained. "We have loved this house so much over all these years. In fact, although it is quite large now, we still think of it as a cottage. The dictionary definition is 'a dwelling constructed of local materials', and we have tried to keep as much to the original style as possible, but we've had to add bits here and there."

Over a cup of coffee Jania told the owners that the Spencer-Harpers, from whom they had bought the cottage in 2021, were, in fact, Jania's Godmother, Angela and her husband, Bob. Before the owners took the prospective buyers over the house, Jania told them of how she used to come to the old cottage when she was a child.

On the tour of the house, the Hodgsons detailed the many changes they had made over the years. "We'll start in here, if you like." Norman suggested, taking the Wellesbournes through the kitchen-cum-dining-room.

"These two rooms used to be separate." Jania recalled.

"That's true," Norman admitted, "But to us, used to large rooms, they seemed too small, so we made them into one. Even when we have friends or relations to dinner, we all prefer to eat in here. It's so much more convenient than having two rooms, but we kept the old Aga for a while until we did the alterations, it was then we bought the new, electric one."

They went through a door and into a new large gabled section. The ground floor was used as an office for Norman and a study for his wife. He took them up the stairs to show them the personal gym, spare bedroom and en-suite bathroom. "We usually use this only when we have our grandchildren to stay," he explained. "They like to be in this wing on their own."

"I remember this whole area as having been occupied by a workshop which was much used by my Uncle Bob and a crazy-paved terraced where my Auntie Angela used to hang her washing."

"Were they really your aunt and uncle?" Barbara asked.

"No, they were not, actually, but my mother was very old-fashioned in these matters. In the 1930s the announcers on *Children's Hour* were called 'Uncle', so this set a fashion. Also a name like Spencer-Harper was very difficult for a young child but she felt that to allow her daughter to call adults by their Christian names was too modern!" Jania explained. Looking around her she added: "There was also a brick and flint conservatory – I loved it in there. Very cosy! When did you have this extension built?"

"Most of the improvements were done in the '30s." Barbara explained. "Norman and I both retired in 2032 and we knew that if we were going to live here permanently we had to do something to make the house more habitable. The garden had to be entirely landscaped, too, as most of the old lawn had long since dried up and most of the plants and shrubs had died. It was a pity we had to demolish the conservatory as it was still in very good condition but we needed to build on an office for Norman because he continued for some time as a consultant. Although it was a great mess for several years, we had more energy then, and we did enjoy having it all done."

She turned and led them back through the kitchen/dining-room past the sitting-room and up the two steps to the rooms at the top of the lower landing. "I remember this part!" Jania exclaimed. "This room on the left was known as the Garden Bedroom. I used to sleep in here. What I really remember about staying in this room was the amazing collection of souvenirs that my Auntie and Uncle had brought back from their travels. They used to go on cruises, you know. Auntie used to lecture about graphology and about the history of these villages. Apart from the memorabilia and the furniture, it hasn't changed that much, except for the diamond lattice windows."

Norman was quick to respond. "Yes, believe it or not, there was no air-conditioning when we came here. I think your 'Auntie' and 'Uncle' as you call them, were really too old to face a lot of alterations and I am of the opinion that's why they sold the house to us in 2021 and went to live in one of those new state-of-the-art retirement cottages that had just been built at Rush Court, near Wallingford. At that time we were working out in southern China and only needed a *pied a terre* to come home to every now and then. We just put in some basic improvements to make it more comfortable and waited until we came home for good."

"Rather like us then!" Jeremy laughed. "Except that it looks as if we shan't have to do too much to this house now. You seem to have done it all!"

"Oh, you'll find enough to do." Norman predicted. "There's always work to be done to upkeep a house in England and remember, there aren't the servants available here that we got used to having at our beck and call in China and you probably had too, out in Dubai; it's quite a different life back here. Nevertheless, there is much voluntary work you can do. Stoke Row and even little Highmoor are very active villages in which to live – there's a lot going on here and people are very friendly."

He then led the way through what Jania recalled as having been her Auntie Angela's study and was now a passageway, lined with books. "I'm glad you've got lots of bookshelves." Jania observed. "We shall need these, we've loads of books. It seems appropriate that you keep them in here, because this is where my Auntie wrote her three books and did so much of her research into the history of these two villages."

"Yes," Barbara said, pointing up to copies of the books on one of the shelves. "We do sometimes need to look up some fact or other and still occasionally refer to them today. Of course, as you no doubt know, her last book was a history of this house; it seems it had originally been a squatters' cottage, a beer-house and even home to an actress who was very famous at the time." Jania nodded, trying to remember what she had done with her copy of the book and resolving to find it as soon as she could.

The Hodgsons led the way through the 'Library' as they called it and through a door in the far wall into a small covered passageway which led up to the garages where they kept their electric cars and re-charging equipment. Beside them were also a small tool-shed and a workshop. Jania was enchanted with the 'Cloister' as the Hodgsons had named it. Also, because she had been secretary to an architect for many years, she noted with particular pleasure that flint panels had been inserted in the wall to match the back of the house.

On the right-hand side, this wall was pierced with small latticed openings through which she was able to peep out into the lane whilst on the left it was open with brick pillars, enabling one to walk up to the garage area in the cool and dry and yet to be able to see clearly into the garden at the same time. "We often sit in here if it's too hot down there in the summerhouse." Barbara stated. "We loved the idea of a thatched summerhouse when we first came here but we didn't anticipate quite how hot it would become in summer."

The garden itself was beautiful, though the Wellesbournes could see that it really needed more time and effort spent on it. "We've tried to bring it up to scratch as we're selling it," Norman explained. "But it's so hard to get a gardener nowadays and we're not as active as we were!"

"But it's beautiful!" Jeremy exclaimed and indeed it was, crammed with towering palms, bananas and other sun-loving, drought-tolerant plants, such as canna lilies, cordylines, echiums, ricinus and cardoons, interspersed with gravel paths and raised circular beds, built of brick and flint. In one corner, close by the house was a large stone trough, filled with crimson ivy-leaved pelargoniums, mahogany tree aeoniums and flowering fleshy echevarias.

******

Jania was suddenly jolted out of her reminiscences by the realisation that her grandson, Crispin, was due at any time. He was coming up from Australia to study for a Doctorate in Geology at Oxford. His father, Peter, now 47 years old and his mother, Margery, Peter's life-long partner, lived near Melbourne. In the beginning this had seemed to Jania and Jeremy to be quite a long way, even from Dubai, but the new VTOL [Vertical Take Off and Landing] technology had suddenly brought the Antipodes much closer to Europe, at least for those wealthy and fit enough to travel by this revolutionary system of rocket-propelled transport.

Another modern asset was a new invention, a helicopter-type machine that was also based on VTOL. Because they were so easy to use and enabled people to hop about from place to place, they were immediately dubbed by the media as 'Grasshoppers' and later by the shorter and rather more catchy name of 'Fleas'.

So far, personal ownership was only for the more comfortably off, but people like the Wellesbournes were able to afford the taxi version and often used it for longer journeys, especially to places like Heathrow, around which the roads were still very congested. The people who lived next door had their own 'Flea', and kept it parked on a piece of land between the two gardens, which was promptly nicknamed 'The Flea Pad'. Fortunately for the Wellesbournes there was also a pad in Highmoor for the use of the public.

'Fleas' had brought about a great improvement in the nation's transport system that had become very much overburdened. Notwithstanding the fact that oil and gas had run out by the mid-century, thanks to new developments in sources of power, all cars were now electrically driven.

Jania and Jeremy's daughter, Charlotte, known to her friends as 'Charley' had used one of the new generation of 'Fleas' when she had come from London Airport some weeks previously. Jania thought what a pity it was that she and Crispin had just missed each other, as Charley now taught robotics in northern China and came home, Jania thought, all too rarely.

It was China's new position as a growing power in the world that had enabled many British and American people to go out there in the past fifty years, working in an advisory capacity. Charley, now aged forty-two, was one of them. She had never married and was very much a career girl who worked hard to maintain her position and enjoyed every moment of her independence.

Although she liked to visit her parents, she was not at all inter-ested in their way of life and told her friends that they still 'played' at being countrified, and keeping what they saw as the traditional English way of life. "Their furniture and furnishings are all antique-style and their ornaments and pictures are of a 'rustic' nature - not that the scenes they portrayed would be recognised by those who had lived in the cottage prior to the twenty-first century!" she laughed.

Glancing at her watch, Jania realised she had just enough time to go up to the shop at Stoke Row, before it got too hot. This Village Store, which had for some years been run by an Indian couple had more recently been taken on by an equally hardworking Chinese family. "The Chinese are everywhere these days." Jania reflected to herself when they moved in but they had maintained this useful asset which might otherwise have closed down since no English people were now willing to do this type of work.

When she mentioned to Jeremy that she was going up to the village, he said: "Good idea! I'm going over to help at Tree Tops. The old folk in Wallingford are feeling the heat very badly now and the staff need all the voluntary help they can get. Can you get my flask ready please?" Since Jania had been caught out in the heat the year before, she now always made sure they both each carried a flask of iced water and salt tablets, because even in that short distance, one never knew about becoming dehydrated.

As she drove up the hill to Stoke Row, she reflected on the beautiful dark green cypress trees, grape vines and olive groves that had replaced the beech woods she remembered from childhood. In fact, the first olive grove had been planted in Devon as far back as 2006, by an environmental consultant named Marc Diacono who had planted a hundred and twenty of these long-living trees on his seventeen-acre smallholding in Honiton. Even at that time he had also been able to grow almonds, apricots, persimmons and even exotic fruits like paw-paw.

When she had first come here to spend her school vacations with her Godmother, some fifty odd years previously, the cottage which had stood in the valley for over four hundred years, the hollow itself and the wooded hills on either side of it had basically changed little since they were first formed, except for the few cottages that had been built on them and the roads that had been created to link them.

In fact, in the early part of the 20th century, Stoke Row and Highmoor, along with a number of neighbouring hamlets, had always been looked upon by the residents of towns like Henley and Reading as being 'the hidden villages'. The sudden availability of the motorcar to almost everyone in the middle of the 20th century, and the growing popularity of information technology towards the end of it, had brought increasing changes that could never have been dreamed of when man first appeared there.

Jania again found herself wishing she had paid more attention to her History lessons, especially Social History, when she was at

Berkhamsted School for Girls. Her interest in the subject had really been aroused by her Godmother, Angela, with whom she went to stay in her teens during the school holidays while her parents, friends of the Spencer-Harpers, were working in Brazil. "What would Angela and Bob think of life here as it is now?" she wondered to herself.

Now that she and Jeremy were retired, they had more time to spend in helping with local projects. They were both involved in plans to make improvements to the little Chapel at Stoke Row, where her husband was Secretary, as her Uncle had been many years before. Among these improvements was the installation of air-conditioning in lieu of the fans that had been put in during the increasing heat waves of the '20s and '30s. Another planned step, to keep up with the times, was the erection of an illuminated panel, showing changing scenes from the Bible, as well as details of the Chapel ministry, services and events. There had been some heated discussion though at recent meetings of the Chapel Council about the 'Warm Welcome to All' strip that it was proposed should be constantly flashed along the bottom of the screen.

Both the Church and Chapel at Stoke Row had enjoyed a revival in recent years. St Paul's at Highmoor had deteriorated badly since it had been closed in the early part of the century, but a gradual growth in the number of Muslims and the opening of mosques in various parts of the country every few weeks, had slowly made many Christians realise the value of their faith. Fortunately, there had been, as yet, no confrontation between the two sects, indeed all the leaders had striven hard for ecumenicism, but it had made some people aware that they had to support their local churches in to order keep them and their Christian cultural values alive, especially that of forgiveness.

Jania and Jeremy had also worked with other people in the village, forming a Committee in order to raise money for restoring the old Maharajah's Well again, in good time for the Bicentenary which had taken place about four years earlier in 2064. Luckily they had started planning early enough to persuade a member of the Royal family to come down, as the Duke of Edinburgh had done at the time of the Centenary, back in 1964. They had hoped perhaps King William Vth would agree to do as his grandfather had done, but although the Committee received a charming letter by way of explanation, they were forced to realise that this was far too small an assignment for him. The money raised at the time was also sufficient to turn the Wellkeeper's Cottage into a Museum. Most of the artefacts that her Godmother had acquired over a period of about forty years, and many which had been donated since, were now on display there. Jania enjoyed helping out as a Museum Volunteer, dispensing knowledge and selling souvenirs.

Also many family historians were attracted to come and see the two villages once they had examined the wealth of material that her Auntie Angela had acquired during her researches and was now available electronically on the Internet. Because of the Internet2, devised in the very early part of the century, this formerly overloaded system was now functioning better and faster. Almost all computers by now were 'smart', that is to say they were operated by AI [Artificial Intelligence] and would have been unrecognisable to any computer buff of fifty years previously.

It was so hot that she decided she still had enough time to pop into the Cherry Tree for a long, cool drink. There she met Archie Baldwin, whose family had lived in one or either of the villages for generations. He had been born back in the 1980's and knew a great deal about the surrounding area. Jania asked him about the 'lump of concrete' that she had recently noticed down in the valley when she had taken her dog for a walk.

"Oh, yes, my girl," he replied. "That place used to be Greyhone Wood, full of trees and managed by the Forestry Commission. Historians say it gets its name from Saxon words *gregen* and *hane*, meaning 'grey stone'. I was told them stones used to be boundary markers at one time. There's several more puddin' stones about - two of them's up at Nettlebed. They used to be in the yard of the Bull Inn. They were used as mounting stones for horse riders in the old days. Then in the '90s, when the pub was closed down and converted into flats, the Council moved them up by the brick kiln and they're there still. The notice they put up at that time was renewed years ago and even that's almost unreadable now, but the stones are millions of years old, by all accounts. They say they were used as signposts to the old Grimes Graves flint mines up in Norfolk!"

Jania loosed his tongue with another beer and he continued, "The biggest one I know is on Stoke Row Hill, a bit more than half way down on the left hand side. It's very disappointing to look at, but it must be a bit like an iceberg, much bigger underneath than what shows on top. My grandfather told me that when he was a boy and steam engines were all the thing, some of the local lads put chains around that rock and tried to haul it out, but they couldn't shift it, not even a bit!"

Crispin arrived safely the next day and, once he had recovered from his journey, his grandmother took him around the garden and told him in more detail than she had ever been able to do by electronic means, about the time when she used to stay at The Old Place in her youth and pointed out the changes that had taken place since then.

She also showed him the Garden Book that her Uncle Bob had kept; listing all the plants he had grown there, since she knew that one of Crispin's interests was horticulture. He had often said that a study of the land was linked to the growth of trees and plants and that he found it helpful to have a physical as well as a mental occupation. "Look at this page," she pointed out, while they sipped coffee in the Cloister, "he writes about growing ferns, hostas, euphorbias and ice plants. They only grow in cold, damp shady places. You wouldn't be able to raise them here now. But he does write about the gradual increase in temperature, fewer frosts, less snow in winter, that sort of thing." she pointed out.

"Not only that, but he mentions the animals like badgers, squirrels, rabbits and foxes, most of which seemed to have been a nuisance in his garden. But here and there are mentions of the birds, too, especially the pheasants which he seems to have encouraged by putting out seeds for them to nibble." Crispin took the book from her and studied it quietly for some time, making notes into a small electronic gadget that he kept in the pocket of his *Mithril* shirt. This was a garment that adapted itself to any temperature, was easily washed and needed no ironing. [Mithril was the magical chain mail forged by the elves in the books of J R R Tolkein].

Crispin was a tall, slim young man, with a crop of very dark hair, physical traits he appeared to have inherited from his grandfather, Jeremy. But his interest in a wide variety of subjects was more likely to have been passed down through the genes of Jania and her family, all of whom had been great travellers, readers and students of various languages. Nevertheless, he was a quiet man of few words but his manner as they walked around showed that he appreciated the beauty of their garden and the lovely perfume that arose from the many colourful flowers, like hibiscus and bougainvillea. Jania always said he got his ability to focus deeply on just one subject at a time from their daughter, his Aunt Charlotte.

Jania also showed her grandson her Auntie Angela's red leather covered Diary that Jeremy had found in the loft soon after they had bought the house. "When we first took over this cottage we found it needed even more insulation and Jeremy put so much into the roof that he had to lay a raised wooden floor on top of it; otherwise we would never have been able to see where the beams were and might have fallen through one of the ceilings! When he did so, he had to move a lot of stuff that had been dumped up there by the Hodgsons and even found some items left by Auntie and Uncle."

The little book was in a very poor condition. Obviously it had started out life with a new red leather cover, with the words 'Angela's Diary' tooled in gold on the front. However, as Jania explained, it had been left open up there in the loft. The first part, which started in the summer of 2000 and continued until the summer of 2006, had become safely wedged under a box and was in relatively good condition. But the right side, which appeared to have gone on from there until 2021, had been nibbled by mice and generally suffered from damp and mould.

"I haven't looked at it for years and Charlotte didn't seem at all interested in it," Jania said, "but I thought you might like to take a look at it; you seem always more interested in the family history than she is."

"Well, they were not really our family," Crispin replied, "But as she was your Godmother and it seems you saw almost more of your 'Auntie and Uncle' as you call them than you did of your own parents in your younger years, I suppose they were, in a way, part of our family, even though they were only friends of your parents."

"That's true, and the entries are fascinating. They show you a way of life that we've almost forgotten. She seems to have started this diary after the Millennium celebrations and goes on to describe the publication of her third book, which, as you know, is a history of this house. She also noted national and world events when they seemed important to her, such as '9-11' disaster in New York in 2001."

They went on perusing the Diary, noting how the writer worked for a couple of years in a charity shop in Sonning Common and how a friend of hers, Ken Stevens, one day came into the shop, to bring her a postcard of The Old Place, taken in 1900. "He had already made them a model of the Maharajah's Well and the little Wellkeeper's Cottage. They are both part of the Museum now." Jania explained. "Auntie also had another friend, who I remember meeting on a number of occasions. His name was David Beasley and he was not only a great authority on the history of the nearby town of Wallingford but also an author of several books and a keen photographer. It was he who helped her develop her great collection of local history photographs. He enlarged that postcard into a sepia picture and framed it to match the one of the house, taken in 1938, that he had already given them. We have hung them both in the hall here, although they really need reframing."

Crispin noted, too, a paragraph about an author whose name he recognised. "I see she writes about Agatha Christie and watching her plays on television. I suppose that would have been one of those small boxy ones they used to have in those days. We still watch Agatha Christie films at home sometimes. Mum loves them, but I don't think she knew that Christie lived near here." He pointed to the bottom of the page. "See here, it says she lived in Cholsey, Wallingford and was buried there in 1975. I thought she died long before then."

They continued to read the Diary together and noticed that, over the years, Jania was often mentioned, especially about Angela's love of 'buying pretty clothes for her.' It seemed as if, having had two sons and three grandsons, of whom she was very fond, she nevertheless had quite fallen in love with this little girl who came more and more under her wing later in her life and who she loved to 'spoil'.

At one point, both Angela and Bob were mentioned as volunteering for 'tin-shaking' for Samaritans. Crispin seemed to know of this charity, but asked his grandmother for an explanation of the phrase `tin-shaking' and she was happy to inform him.

Then, when they reached the page referring to the summer of 2003 they found several lengthy entries about the tragedy of the

'Highmoor shootings'. This happened when a young man, estranged from his wife, had returned to the village with a shotgun. He killed his wife and her sister in front of their children and also very badly wounded his mother-in-law. It was an affair that deeply shocked the village and surrounding area, especially as it seemed the police were slow to act in giving the 'go-ahead' to the ambulance service to enter the house, despite reassurances from neighbours that the husband had already left the immediate area. Moreover, the horror of the situation was compounded by the husband's suicide in prison shortly after his capture.

Thereafter there were references to the wood at the side of the house being cleared of all the fully-grown beech trees and a year or so later dozens of larch trees being felled in the copse at the bottom of the garden. "That's where the Flea-pad is now." Jania stated. "It would appear that the felling of all these trees made their garden much more sunny and the house lighter inside. There is no doubt that her references here to the Asian Tsunami in January 2005 and the hurricane Katrina that summer, means people were already begin-ning to suffer from global warming, even back then."

"Not only that." Crispin pointed out. "She has written here quite an account of the Al-Quaeda bombings in London on 7th July, 2005. Perhaps that's why she offered to act as a volunteer at the local Police Station."

"Oh, no, I shouldn't think that had much to do with it. I seem to remember she had health problems when she was in charge of the books for a couple of years at a charity shop and opted to do more of a desk job instead. She was always up to something!" Jania laughed.

"You must have got to know them both pretty well as you stayed with them for most of your school holidays?" Crispin enquired.

"Yes, I did. They were both very kind to me, really and to many other people, especially those in trouble, but they were great perfec-tionists and expected a high standard from everyone, not the least themselves. Uncle Bob was a very practical man, he could mend almost anything and was never happier than when he was busy pottering in the garden or supervising maintenance work up at the Chapel. The types of people who annoyed him were those who complained about something but when they could make a move to change the situation, did nothing about it and continued to moan!" Jania recalled.

"Auntie was interesting and always very active." she continued. "Like Uncle Bob, she grew up in the Second World War and they were both very keen on recycling and on not wasting anything. Although her parents were not Catholics, she was given a convent education and one of her favourite mottoes was 'The devil finds work for idle hands.' She never wasted a single moment, always busy on the computer or in the village. For a start, she edited the twenty-page Stoke Row News every month for about twenty-five years. It seemed to me though, that she was sometimes too tense and certainly didn't suffer fools gladly. Uncle Bob was the Chairman of the magazine. It was his self-appointed task to ensure that everything ran smoothly and that there were adequate supplies of paper. I missed them both though, even if Auntie did email all the news to me for years after I left school and went out to Brazil to join my parents. I still keep in touch with their sons, Philip and Michael every Christmas, Often we recall those extended family parties we had with Auntie and Uncle. He cooked the full traditional Christmas dinner every year and she wrote and produced pantomimes for some of us to act in while the others formed the audience. Her father once said to her: 'You are the last of the Victorians, Angela!' because she devised quizzes and games or us all to play, when other families usually watched television. She also made gift containers from cardboard; they varied from fairy castles or churches to trains, rockets and one time she even recreated a gingerbread house, covered with sweets," she concluded, savouring the memory.

They finally came to some of the last entries in that part of the Diary that was still in near-perfect condition. "Here's where she says in June, 2006 that her collection of old photos of the two villages had reached over two thousand. Not long afterwards they went on another cruise. Auntie used to lecture on ships, you see, and this time they went up to Northern Norway and the Arctic Circle. It says they celebrated their Golden Wedding on board that ship. Do you know, we ourselves will have been married for fifty years next year – I can't believe it!" she exclaimed.

After a pause, she continued: "I expect she wrote another of her 'Holiday Log Books' after that. When they moved to Rush Court in

27

2021, she wrote and told me they had to destroy all forty-nine of those binders in which she had recorded most of their cruises and other holidays. It must have been heart-breaking for her." Jania said, thoughtfully.

"And here's the last entry." Crispin pointed out. "October, 2006: Today I finished my third book, *The Old Place*, and gave it to Bob Boyd to print and publish. It is the culmination of five years' work."

They then tried to decipher the scraps of paper that were all that remained of the other half of the Diary, but they could only make out a few lines here and there. "December 2015; Can't see the stars at all now...light pollution from Reading and Henley," and "Jania here again for the summer," were just two. Also noted were the events held in Stoke Row in 2014 to celebrate the 150 years since the sinking of the Maharajah's Well. This had been followed by great celebrations at the Stoke Row Chapel to mark two hundred years of continuous Christian worship since its construction.

There were various items, too, about the terrible storms between 2019 and when they finally left The Old Place in 2021. Her entry for that last year was very smudged. Jania suggested she might have been weeping at the thought of leaving the cottage they had loved for over forty years.

In the cool of the evening, Jeremy, who was now a member of the Commons Conservators, attended a meeting to decide on the fate of the oak that had recently fallen at the top of Witheridge Hill, so Jania took Crispin up to show him the old tree. 'Captain', her King Charles spaniel, ran on happily ahead, retrieving the sticks which Crispin hurled great distances for him. "The tree specialist says it may be as old as fifteen hundred years and it survived all the gales and storms of recent years. It's strange that it should suddenly keel over now. Jeremy reckons it could tell a tale or two." Jania said, puffing slightly as they mounted the hill together.

The sight of this great giant, now lying motionless, never again to feel its branches waving in the wind, moved Jania to tears. There were several other women standing about and all seemed very affected by the scene. Even some of the men were moist-eyed, not the least were the members of the Commons Conservators on whose land the tree had seemed to have stood for ever, just behind the brick and flint house that had once been the village School. Some of the men were making measurements and talking about the practicalities of cutting it up and removing it, but they, too, were speaking *sotto voce*, as if at a funeral. After a while the group broke up and Jania and Jeremy continued their walk to show their grandson around Witheridge Hill.

"That's another sad thing." Jania said, "When I first came here in my school holidays, I used to walk all around the area and there were small gates and green hedges everywhere then, not security entries and high walls like these." she said, waving her arm in the direction of one such house. "It was all much more open and friendly then," she added, sadly.

Crispin stayed for almost a week with his grandparents and during this time they had many chats on a wide variety of subjects. On the Monday, Jeremy took his grandson out to help him purchase a second-hand car and as they drove around looking at first one and then another, their conversation included the up and coming problem of global cooling. Crispin had heard quite a bit about this, even in Australia and how the melting of the Arctic Ice was causing the Gulf Stream that ran alongside the British Isles to be diverted and thus these islands were gradually about to lose its warming beneficence. This change was forecast to have catastrophic results, compounded by the cooler air requiring more fuel to warm the population than it had taken to cool them in the period of global warming. Computerised models made the future look grim.

Other matters they covered during that week were the recent decline in the power of the United States under a series of disastrous Presidents and the shortage and cost of water all over the world. This had led to a sudden growth in the building of desalination plants worldwide, though they had often been the subject of much local controversy. By now most homes in Britain had two incoming water pipes, one for drinking and cooking, known as Internal water and the other External, for flushing toilets, watering gardens, etc. Water was in very short supply and that for internal use was very expensive indeed.

Crispin was particularly interested in recent legislation in Britain, soon to be followed by Australia, which aimed at reducing the quantity of unnecessary packaging and any form of built-in obsolescence that could be proved.

He showed interest too, in the recent news about greater successes in research at Oxford into stem cell technology and gene therapy. This new generation of SCT was enabling parts of the body to be grown from even quite small samples of a patient's own tissue or hair and promised to offer great hope to people who had been involved in accidents, while the studies in genetic screening and gene therapy were helping to prevent the passing down through families of undesirable features and diseases. Science was constantly producing new cures for age-old diseases and for the alleviation of physical difficulties, such as the ever-greater perfection of 'intelligent' artificial limbs; thus greater longevity in more comfort was promised for many. Jeremy and his grandson spent quite some time discussing the ethics of these problems, the pros and cons of which were the subject of much debate in the media and in the homes of thinking people.

At other times, when Crispin and Jania were on their own, they found they had a common love of classical music and the works of Charles Dickens. Jania told her grandson about the latest passion in England for collecting original plastic items in good condition and any memorabilia about the Millennium and he told her about his visit to the Olympic Games earlier that year. She offered to take him the next day to Henley where a *Twentieth Century Exhibition* was being held and outlined several other plans she had for his visit.

One evening, when they were on their own again, she found herself confiding in him such deep matters as her faith in God, the importance to her of forgiveness, her belief in prayer and in life after death. She found his views on these subjects challenging but they gave her food for thought.

Soon after this conversation, she asked him about his love life and whether or not he yet had a regular girl-friend. She was a little disappointed in his negative reply, although she could understand his wish to complete his PhD and then to find a well-paid job in geology and buy a house of his own. What astonished her was his plan for the far future, to become a 'space tourist'. "By the time I get to that stage," Crispin explained to his amazed grandmother, "people will be able to go on a thirty to ninety minutes sub-orbital space flight for not much more than it costs now to cruise around the world in a ship and only twice that to orbit the earth in space. Of course, to take a trip to an International Space Station would be quite beyond the dreams of a mere mortal like me."

She realised then that there was little chance of her ever being a great-grandmother. Crispin was obviously showing the same spirit of independence that had driven her daughter Charlotte to become what she called a SaRaH [Single, Rich and Happy]. She reflected on what a far cry it was from the days of her youth when marriage, a home and children were what most women aspired to.

* * * * * *

On Crispin's last evening, Jania took him down the valley where she wanted to show him the 'puddingstone', which she thought he, being a geologist, would find interesting. It was a quiet, casual stroll up the road for a bit and then down the slope beyond the house next door. Finally they came down to the bottom of the valley. Here Jania told her grandson how she and her Uncle and Auntie used to walk here through the beechwoods in the spring to see the bluebells. "They were really lovely," she enthused. "I'll show you some pictures of them when we get back to the house, but they won't give you any idea of the wonderful smell they had as you walked through the woods. Those beautiful carpets of blue disappeared with the loss of the beech trees in the '40s and '50s. They gave the dappled shade the bluebells needed for their survival, you see."

As they made their way down the slope, Jania told him about a meal that she and Jeremy had enjoyed in London a couple of weeks before, at one of the new restaurants that specialised in 'atmospheric eating'. "This one was called the Florentine Piazza. It really gives you the feeling that you are in Florence", she explained, "not only is the atmosphere warm and the lights brightened with a yellow filter, but also the walls are animated with three dimensional holograms, so you really feel as if you are eating in a piazza in Florence. Of course, there is Italian music too, played softly while you eat your Spaghetti Bolognese or whatever. It was a lovely experience on a cold winter's night," she concluded, "just like an evening in Italy!"

After they had walked a considerable distance down one path in the valley that would eventually have brought them to the outskirts of Henley, they turned around and made their way back via a different route to a point where Jania confessed to being 'very tired' and suggested they might sit on the 'puddingstone' as she had done many times before. Crispin was there before her and had started to examine it. She told him all she knew: "An old boy in the village told me it's a conglomerate left over from the last Ice Age. I always used to think it was a quantity of ready-mixed concrete which had somehow been dropped here and weathered over the years but it seems there are quite a lot of others around here too."

"He's right, Nan." said Crispin, his voice taking on a more enthusiastic and firmer tone than she had heard him use since his arrival. "It may look like concrete but it certainly is not." He took from his pocket a small voice-activated computer and spoke quietly into it. Although his speech contained something of an 'Aussie twang', his upbringing in Melbourne had ensured that this was not very pronounced.

After a few moments a female voice answered: "These are Breccias, formed after the last Ice Age from deposits of accumulated loose boulders and flint pebbles which solidified naturally into conglomerates under the enormous pressure of the glaciers as they retreated."

They continued to sit there for a few more minutes but then, just as Jania was thinking of getting up and continuing their walk back home, the atmosphere began to get cooler. She rubbed her hands up and down her arms and, as it got colder and even slightly misty, Crispin involuntarily acted in a similar manner. At the same time they began to hear strange noises, a distant sound of an excited and clamorous crowd.

 Jania immediately began to rise, but Crispin held her arm and motioned her to stay seated. All the same he held on to her arm, comfortingly. As they sat there the scene before them changed gradually. The air was quite cold now, although their Mithril clothing had already started to adapt to the situation. But it was the mist and the shouting that perturbed them most. "What can it be?" Jania whispered. "We never get any crowds out here."

Her grandson put his finger to his lips and motioned her to keep quite still. At the same time he put his arm reassuringly around her shoulders. As the confused noises came nearer and nearer they were able to make out the barking of dogs, the cries of young boys and the shouting of older men. To their wonder and astonishment this crowd of hairy hunters, boys and dogs began to pass before them and yet appeared to be quite unperturbed by their presence. It was as if Jania and Crispin were invisible to them. Some of the men, clad only in loincloths, bore on a pole a large animal, rather like a coarse, black pig. Others carried simple tools, such as bows, arrows and flints that were bound to sticks with leather thongs.

Crispin and Jania looked at each other in silent wonder, each glad that the other had seen what they had seen and were therefore relieved to realise that what they were witnessing was no hallucination but a paranormal 'sighting' of times long gone, a rare privilege granted to very few human beings.

******

Almost all the material in this chapter is imaginary, with the exception of predictions for the middle of the twenty-first century, taken from articles recently published in national broadsheet newspapers.

The puddingstones can be found elsewhere in Oxfordshire and neighbouring counties and are well documented in local libraries.

The Old Place

Chapter 2.   The Mesolithic Axe: 6000 BC

Long after the death of the dinosaurs, some 63 million years previously, the last Ice Age was finally in retreat. It was one of many, and had continued for about two million years, during which time the conglomerate in the Long Valley had formed. These *breccias* became known as 'puddingstones'. By about 20,000 years before Christ the ice was beginning to melt, albeit very, very slowly. It was a terrible time when about a fifth of the earth's surface was covered in a thick layer of ice, thirty or forty feet deep in some places. The land was wild, bleak, and desolate, with very little life, just a few extremely hardy animals that managed to keep alive on what little vegetation there was. This vast area, when howling winds and freezing blizzards were not blowing, was silent, cold and, for much of the time, dim or quite dark.

But very gradually, over the millennia, the earth began to warm again and the tundra, a very thin layer of vegetation over the permafrost, appeared slowly. Rivers started to form as the glaciers melted, the seas began to rise as the ice crumbled into floes and moved southwards. Twenty thousand years ago, the land masses were huge, even though they were divided by seas and Britain still lay on the western edge of the most northerly of these continents, which stretched right across to the coast of China. About eight to ten thousand years ago, as the seas rose, Britain gradually slid away from the main Eurasian land mass, but before it had done so, waves of early men, largely nomadic hunters, had drifted over in search of better game.

By this time there were more animals and an increase in vegetation for them to live on. Elk, bison, arctic foxes, reindeer, and even small horses had begun to appear. There were grasslands and forests; the oak, willow, poplar, elm and hawthorn had been hardy enough to withstand the ice ages and they flourished as never before. As the climate grew warmer still, over the many thousands of years, birch and pine, hazel and elder grew into forests that stretched across the whole of the great northern continent, forests that were inhabited by wolves, deer and wild boar. The latter two were hunted by the nomads for their delicious, nourishing meat and for their pelts that had many uses.

These later hunter-gathers, New Stone Age men as they were to become known, were a semi-nomadic people who lived about six thousand years before Christ and hunted in small family bands. There were probably not more than a few thousand people living in Britain at this time. Most of them lived in the warmer south and were seasonal migrants, who stayed near the hills for three quarters of the year and moved to lower ground in the winter months. They lived in *benders*, dwellings made from young trees bent over, bound together to form an arch and covered with branches and bracken. One such tribal group lived for a time in the foothills of the Chiltern range.

* * * * * *

All that could be heard in the clearing was the sound of the boar as he foraged for the acorns and beech-mast that had recently fallen, for it was autumn in the Long Valley and the fruits were abundant that year. Male boars are nomadic and live with their family for only three months of the year. Its singular, pungent odour pervaded the area. No sound at all came from the hunters: the leader, Strenga and his five men. With them were two youths, Walla and Neg, and the leader's son, Skep, a boy of about twelve summers; all three were already skilled in the use of slings and stones.

They had all carefully and silently stalked the animal to this spot, some five miles from their camp to the west. They had seen its footprints in the mud created by the early autumn rains and at the sides of the muddy pools where the wild pig loved to wallow. Very unusual prints they were, rounded at the top but split into two, with a big 'V' shape, and, less distinct, two projections at the base. No other beast made such a mark and the hunters, led by their chief, Strenga, knew from the size of the prints that they were on the track of a very large male. They had followed the spoor and droppings of the boar for two days now, keeping always down wind of the breeze that floated up from the river valley below.

Then, at last, they sighted him at sundown, as he had left his lair under a fallen tree, quite skittishly, after his day's rest. They had silently watched him feeding all night and now, just as the sun began to rise in the east and give a glimmer of light, they had laid down their bows and arrows and grasped their spears at the ready, poised to throw at Strenga's command. Grazing quietly, the large hog, with its bristly pale grey to blackish hair, seemed to blend in to the shade of the trees on the edge of the glade. Its muzzle ended in a mobile snout, which enabled him to forage among the roots of trees for bulbs and tubers. There he also found worms, snails and, occasionally, small rodents.

Like all male boars, except in the rutting season, he was a solitary beast and at this time of the day, coming to the end of his night's feed, he was replete and slower than he had been the evening before.. Nevertheless, the hunters were very wary for a boar when roused could be extremely ferocious. [Later, the Celts used the boar as a symbol of war]. When it charged, its upward and outward curving canine teeth which projected as defensive tusks, could inflict great damage on an unprotected man, as Strenga had learned to his cost when he was only about the age his son, Skep, was now. A particularly fierce male had turned on him suddenly and ripped a gash in his leg, as long as a man's hand could span. It had taken a long time to heal and left a red scar, making Strenga more respectful of these savage animals. Although its legs were short the total length of the boar's body, including its head, was over five feet and it would have weighed about three hundred pounds.

"Killing a deer is simple in comparison to hunting this brute!" thought Strenga to himself as he cautiously motioned to his men to wait just a little longer. He was the oldest of the group; a man of about five foot in height, with matted, once black, hair that he kept tied at the back of his head. This hair was greying and thinning now and his skin deeply lined, weathered to a dark tan. His teeth were yellow and he had already lost a few. He had lived through more than forty winters and was already an old man. Nevertheless, he was still cunning and strong, a quality that had earned him his name, and he was the chief of the family. He could fire an arrow from a bow more accurately than any other member of his tribe and was much respected. Most of the other men were younger than him and all of them had darkened their faces with mud so that they were almost invisible in the bushes.

The chief's main dread was that his son, Skep, who still only twelve years old and who had pleaded to come on the expedition, might jeopardise the hunt at this stage by some false move. Strenga was just about to let his left hand fall, as a signal for them all to throw their spears at the same time, when his worst fears were realised. Skep changed foot and snapped a twig. Their quarry was alerted and quickly moved away. The other men were angered and one of them went for the boy, but Strenga defended him saying, "The animal was not really frightened, just made wary. We shall get him later."

So they sat down quietly, glad to be relieved of the tension of being poised for so long. Strenga fell into silence, debating with himself whether to go on now, or whether to wait another day. As head of the tribe the decision was his alone and he knew it. The others were glad of the break to stretch out their weary limbs and the boy was quite still, afraid of their anger should he move again.

Strenga began to think about what to do next, trying to form a judgement as to whether to continue the hunt in the hope of finding their quarry quickly or to spend another day and night away from the camp. The birds in the trees above his head continued to sing and chirp, ignorant of his plight; his fear that the expedition might fail. "Has the boar gone far?" he thought to himself. "I wish I knew. Will he return to his lair now that the sun is coming up? Hunting deer is easy; they forage by day, but not swine. I hate hunting these beasts. They eat at night and that means we have to stalk it at dusk and then wait until the sun rises so we can see it. This is the time when we should be sleeping." He yawned widely. "Aaah, but I am tired and wish I were with my mate, holding her warm body under the night covers!"

He glanced over at his young son. "If we go on I fear the boy will not hold out. He's almost asleep already. I can see Walla and Neg are looking weary, too, even though they were born several years before Skep. The younger men would be able to go on and they are no doubt cursing my boy for changing foot carelessly, but I can remember when they did something like that."

He looked towards the two younger men who were sitting up and looking to him for an answer, but Strenga said nothing aloud. In his mind he agonised over the decision that he would soon have to make: "Shall we go on? Hmmm! The beast may not go back to the same lair. He will be starting soon to look for a female - the rutting season is not long ahead." He glanced upwards. "The weather is holding good, though. The skies are clear and the wind is light. Perhaps if we sleep this morning we could find him again this afternoon. I am so weary, weary through to my bones. I cannot go on now!"

As he lay there, he prayed: "Oh, Goddess of the Hunt, what shall we do?" He yawned widely and stretched out his limbs. "Perhaps I could send the two younger boys back to the lair; they could let us know if the boar beds down there again - it would use their energy and enable us to rest. Mmm! That would take them about two hours. Yes, that's what we will do. The younger ones shall go. We older ones and my boy shall stay."

Relieved at having come to a conclusion, Strenga opened his eyes and whispered to his men. Stealthily the younger hunters departed on their errand, while the older ones stretched out again and, like Skep, were soon asleep. They were exhausted, not only by the exercise of the long walk, but by the tensions built up in stalking their prey and they were depressed at having lost it.

Thus they all remained motionless in the wood until the sun was high in the sky; its light dappling through the leaves, already turning shades of orange, yellow and brown. Skep woke first and, unaware of the decision that his father had made earlier in the day, wondered why they were all asleep and where the two youngest men had gone.

"Father! Wake up! Where are Walla and Neg?" His father opened one eye reluctantly, and closed it quickly as the sun streamed down.

"Quiet, boy! They have gone to find the boar. We were all so tired and you were already asleep. I decided we should stay and rest and they should track that hog back to its den. They will probably sleep a while too but they don't need their rest as much as we do." The other men were awake now, refreshed by their rest and eager to be on their way again.

Within a few minutes Walla and Neg returned and reported that the boar had returned to its lair and was sleeping soundly, about an hour's trek away. Glad to know that they would not disturb the animal if they foraged for themselves; they began to look about for berries and nuts that would keep them going for a while longer. While the youths gathered sticks dry enough for a fire, the men went off to find a deer for a meal that would be nourishing enough to enable them to continue the hunt for another day or two.

After they had eaten they all fell quiet again and Strenga slept more soundly than he had in the morning. Finally, when the sun had sunk quite low and a lopsided moon was just appearing faintly in the sky, they set off once more, having previously agreed a plan of action, darkening their faces with mud before they did so. Walla and Neg led the way as they moved silently through the forest, trailing their prey again by the droppings that he had made after his previous night's feed. Although they knew it was easier to corner their quarry in the morning, when he would be full and slower moving, they agreed this time to delay no longer and to try and get him as soon as he moved out of the hollow under the root of the fallen tree.

Silence was essential and this time Skep was as quiet as the others as they picked their way stealthily through the forest. When they were within sight of the boar's den, they took up their positions in a semicircle a little way from the entrance. Luckily for them the wind had changed direction and was now coming from the north and the rays of the setting sun gave sufficient light to enable them to watch their quarry that appeared to be still asleep. An owl, out early, hooted softly in the distance and the air around them grew moist with the hint of a mist to come. From long experience most of the older hunters knew how to stand at the ready and yet be relaxed enough not to make the pose too tiring.

Strenga and the other men were now feeling the tips of the flints that topped their spears, testing the sharpness of the stone that they hoped would pierce the tough hide of their prey. Gradually, the beast opened its eyes, moved its body and began to wake. There was still just enough light to see the movement within the lair. Strenga glanced along the line of his men, scarcely visible in the undergrowth of bracken, bushes and young trees that surrounded the spot. A shiver of fear ran through them all in their suppressed excitement as they changed from being comfortable to a state of alertness, stretching their every nerve and muscle as the huge animal rolled over, found its legs, and trotted out of its sleeping quarters.

As soon as the boar had cleared his hole Strenga let his left hand down quickly and the whole party leapt into the clearing with a loud cry, so as to startle and confuse the beast. He did not know which way to look first and started to prance and threaten, lowering its head and making ready to charge. But it was too late. Already the flint-tipped spears were raining into his body and, as soon as the men had loosed them, they grabbed their flint axes from their belts and closed in on their prey, so quickly that the animal had no time to flee or charge.

Strenga wanted to be sure that his son did not suffer from the sharp tusks as he himself had done at the same age and kept the boy well behind him as they finished off the squealing animal and made sure it was safe to pick up. They tied its feet to a thin tree trunk, so it could be carried back to the camp, swinging in the cool air.

And then it was homeward! As they came cavorting through the wood they were really excited, for had they not at last killed the prime boar that they had been stealthily tracking for three days! Now the hunting party could make as much noise as they liked; they were free from the strain and stress of stalking. It mattered not that they would frighten all the animals and that the birds would fly away as they came romping through the valley bearing their trophy, its legs tied over the long pole, the blood safe in the deerskin stretched beneath it.

The lads, Walla and Neg, carried the beast; the older ones had taken their turn in times past. Skep was not yet tall enough or strong enough, but his chance would come in a few years time. The group continued its march along a track that led up to a ridge, which was to become known as Stoke Row Hill, to a point by a pond at the top where they had made a fire on their way through the dense forest to seek their prey five nights before.

It was almost the end of the autumn now, the air was cold and still and the dead leaves scrunched beneath their feet. It was late in the day and beginning to get dark. Strenga decided that they should stay out in the forest for one more night and the men agreed with him.

As soon as they arrived at the spot by the slightly worn path the men were sent out to forage for the nuts, berries and plant roots that they knew would sustain them until the next day. Early men were accustomed to going for long periods without food and then, when the opportunity arose, they would gorge themselves for days to compensate for their loss.

Walla, Neg and Skep were ordered to gather up dry twigs, sticks and large pieces of wood and make a fire on the site of the previous one. Soon they were all sitting around it and talking again and again of the boar hunt and their hopes and fears as it had progressed.

While the men were still talking and laughing at the fears that had gripped them only a few days before, Skep approached his father respectfully. "Father! Can I use your axe? I need to make my spear better. I'm sure it doesn't balance properly." The older man was reluctant to comply with his son's request for this was his favourite tool. With it he was able to make the best bows, arrows and spears that he needed to kill animals and birds for his family group.

However, he knew in his heart that his son had to learn and was pleased that the boy had realised the value of making his spear of the right weight. "Yes, my son," he replied reluctantly, after some thought. "But use it with care for it is very sharp!"

Skep was soon at work in the light of the fire, paring the shaft of the spear until he could balance it from the centre on the tip of one finger. "This axe head is certainly very sharp. I almost cut my finger with it, and how well Father has strapped it to the haft!" he observed.

The axe was a surprisingly well-made tool. The flint had been flaked to make it oval and chipped to create a sharp edge. It had then been ground on a *sarsen* or some other rough stone to make it smooth. After that it had been chipped again along the edge to sharpen it still further and to make it fit snugly into the shaft of a wooden stick handle, about the length of a man's forearm, which gave it more leverage.

Strenga felt indulgent, not only because the hunt had gone well, but also because Skep was his only surviving male child and this was his first hunt. Often he rued the fact that the boy seemed careless and less than attentive to his teachings, but he had long since realised that there was little chance of his mate, Haema, bearing him any more children now and he felt too old to take a younger woman.

As he lay down to sleep he prayed to the Goddess of the Hunt and thanked her for their achievement. She had usually answered his prayers, always made before the start of a chase. He and the other hunters would gather in a clearing in the forest and tie pieces of dried meat to the branches of a small tree before they set out. As they did so, they danced and chanted their pleas for success. The Goddess seemed grateful for the offerings - were they not always taken by her and none left by the time they came back?

He thought too, how pleased Haema would be when they returned. She had been his woman for many years now and mother of all his offspring. She was also his friend because he had known her so long and so well. He told her everything, all his joys and sorrows. She and the other women would surely be on the look out for their homecoming.

It was usually a joyous one for they had generally caught at least one, and sometimes several animals. So many abounded in the upland woods, especially large herds of deer. As he dozed off he could hear the baying of wolves far away, but they never came near the hunters who had fire, which these creatures were afraid of, and anyway there was enough prey for all.

As soon as it was light the men began to stir and roused the young ones, who now seemed to want to sleep on forever, so tired were they by the exertions of the chase and long march that had followed. By the time the sun had arisen they had set off again, their cleaned spears in their hands and their bows and quivers of flint-tipped arrows over their shoulders.

These tools, bows and arrows, were a relatively new invention and highly suited to hunting in the dense forest, for they were slim and passed easily through the trees, though the arrows were too light to pierce the tough skin of a boar. The hunters had two types of arrow. Both were created for long flight, with goose feathers tied to one end. The tips, however, differed. One lot had very sharp, pointed flints inserted into them and they were used for killing animals on the ground and birds that flew low. The other type had a small wooden knob on the end and with these the men could knock quite large birds out of the sky high above.

As they reached the edge of the great wood and the ground levelled out they could see their camp below and stopped for a moment to watch their women folk as they went about their domestic chores. Gradually, as they descended, shouts could be heard from the camp as the women and children jumped up and ran up to meet them.

Haema, being the woman of the Headman, led the way, carrying skin bags of a brew she had made from gathered seeds. "Hail!" she called and then, seeing the boar, cried: "What a beast! If you kill a few more like this one, we shall eat well this winter." She loved the meat of the big, black pig, for it was more delicate than venison that they ate more often. This triumph called for a special feast! The other women ran to their men; Walla's and Neg's mothers ran fastest of all.

Gradually, the party returned to their homes. As they did so, the women and children admired and stroked the trophy and listened to the excited tales of how the huntsmen had fared, though no one mentioned the false move made by young Skep. They talked of the meal they would enjoy that night around the fire and of how they would dry the meat so it could be kept for some time, and perhaps traded for fish with the people who lived down below by the river.

The camp itself consisted of about a dozen tents, all made from animal skins, scraped with small flint 'scrapers', stretched over latticework frames of sticks and weighted down with boulders, wigwam fashion. A loose piece of skin hung over the narrow entrance of each tent and was fastened on the inside with a bone peg. Back home in his tent, Strenga felt the need to rest, knowing he could now safely leave the treatment of the boar carcass to the younger men and women. Before he did so, however, he called to Skep and asked him for the axe he had lent him the previous evening.

The boy came over reluctantly and immediately his father could tell that something was wrong. With his head hung down Skep confessed: "I think I must have dropped it Father, somewhere on the way down here this morning. Soon after we left the fire I noticed it was gone from my belt."

At this, Strenga became very angry. He was exhausted now and had looked forward to lying down to rest. Again Skep had been careless and now they would have to go back the next day and look for the tool; the thought displeased him greatly. "Why did you not say so as soon as you noticed it was missing? We could have gone back to look for it then!"   His face grew red and his breathing was laboured. "I have told you many times to care for your tools!" he shouted. "A hunter's life depends on his weapons and the tools with which he makes them. You <u>must</u> be more careful!"

He went for the boy with a rush and began to look around for a stick with which to hit him, but Skep ran away fast, though with some reluctance, for he was sad to incur the wrath of his father whom he admired and who was usually so patient and sometimes even indulgent.

That night, lying beside his woman, Strenga gave vent to his feeling about the lost axe. "That was a good tool, it fitted my hand so well. I have cared for it so long and now Skep has lost it in just a few hours!"

Haema let him continue his ranting, knowing that talking about it would ease her man's temper. Like most women though, she had little idea why Strenga was so attached to the tool. "After all," she thought, "he has many others."

And indeed he had. In one corner of the tent was a bag with small scraper flints, which they used for preparing animal pelts, and quite a number of spears, bows, arrows, hunting sticks and even old hand-held axes made from local flints. Finally Strenga stopped talking but he still could not sleep, he was still so cross about the loss of his beloved axe. Although he did not want to speak of it to Haema there was another reason that he mourned the loss of this object. A trader from the north-east had given it to him some fifteen summers previously as a token of gratitude.

He remembered the event well for it was when they had given their only surviving daughter into the family of the trader and he knew then that he would never see her again. Haema had borne Strenga five children in all but only two had survived. Skep was the last, but there had also been another, a girl. She had been their first-born. Despite the fact that she had not been a boy, as was every hunter's wish, the girl was pretty and had, at first, been named after the Goddess of the Hunt. But, in fact, she had always been called 'Bubbie' as this was the first name she had been able to call herself.

As each of the later children died, two girls before they were a year old and a boy at the age of four, Strenga had grown increasingly fond of Bubbie and had even talked to her of his innermost thoughts, as Haema always seemed to be too busy to listen. Strenga had a small vocabulary but he was not a stupid man. He had learned from his father about the ways of the birds and animals, trees and plants around him and how important it was to placate the spirits of these beings.

When Bubbie had reached thirteen summers, the axe trader came from the axe mines in the north east, as he usually did each spring as soon as the weather was warm and settled enough to ensure a safe journey along the ridge-top routes. Every year he brought with him not only some of the best flint tools made, but also the news of tribes to the northeast of the Chiltern hills. For some years now he had been accompanied by his son, Stanna, an upright, strong lad who had always got on well with Bubbie. "Have you noticed how Bubbie has been taking more care   of herself lately?" Haema observed to Strenga one day. "She even asked me if she could borrow my bone comb and if I would let her wear my beads, the lovely shell ones that I got from the river people!"

This particular year it was as if Bubbie had known that Stanna and his father would be coming, for she had put some wild flowers in her hair when she saw the trading party approaching. On this occasion, instead of playing hide and seek with her around the camp, the lad seemed more thoughtful, and, at times, he and Bubbie stood together, watching the women at work, cleaning the pelts. Stanna had been intrigued at how they laid out the skins, pegging them down with wooden pegs, and then scraped them with small, sharp flint tools, which they held in their hands; yet did not appear to cut themselves at all.

The pelts were used for various purposes. The finer, thinner ones, made from the skins of deer, were cut into clothes, quivers for arrows and other useful items. Bubbie had learned how to make holes with thin needles of hard bone and then sew them together with the stems of certain plants and sinews of animals. Coarser hides were used for making tents and warm, furry ones for mats and bed coverings. Horns were used to make drinking mugs, needles and pegs. No scrap of the animal was wasted.

Reluctant as Haema and Strenga were to part with their only

daughter, they were glad to see the young people happy together. They had known the trader for some years and felt sure that his family would give the girl a good home. In the hope of this and because it was the custom, they gave the older man a big bundle of skins of various types to take back with him. He, for his part, had been glad to have the girl join his tribe, for she already resembled her mother in being broad-hipped and full-breasted and this, he felt, augured well for the future of his family unit.

As a parting gift on this auspicious occasion, the trader had presented Strenga with a superb axe, one of the best that he had ever brought away from the axe factory.

Before Bubbie left the camp, her mother gave her a very special and personal gift. It was a little clay statue of a female who was obviously fully pregnant. "Put this in your bed when you sleep with your man," she instructed. "My mother gave it to me. This goddess will make you fertile."

The next morning the trading party set off, back along the ridge path. Though the trader and his son came each year and reported the birth of a child or other news from Bubbie, Strenga and Haema never actually saw their daughter again, for her role was in the camp of her new family. What saddened Strenga so much was the fact that, in a sense, he had been consoled at the loss of his daughter by the gift of the axe that Skep had now lost. Haema did what she could to understand his position. She wove him a basket to put his tools in and gradually life went on in the camp as before. She was a good mate and knew where to find the best fruits, berries and nuts and how to keep them for as long as possible and it was to her that the other women looked for advice now that she was old.

******

Despite his hope, Strenga and his kin never did return to the spot where Skep had lost the axe, for a great storm arose soon after the boar hunt and the snow fell deep. That winter Strenga died and his descendants became more interested in trying to find a more settled form of life, where hunting animals was not the only source of food. They began, for at least a part of the year, to work collectively, clearing the land and creating small farms in the area between the hills and the river, though they continued to hunt in the forests on the higher ground.

****

About eight thousand years later, on 30 January 1949, a Mr Fairey, digging a hole for a fence post in Nottwood Lane, Stoke Row, found the axe that Skep had lost. The wooden handle had long since rotted away but the flint was as sharp as ever. It is now in Reading Museum, along with several other pre-historic axes of various eras, found in these two villages during the past century. Other similar worked flints, either axes or just small scrapers, have also been found in this area.

The flint axe mines in the north east were later to become known as Grimes Graves in Norfolk, where this stone abounds and where tools are thought to have been made and traded over a great deal of Britain.

The Old Place

Chapter 3. The Highmore Trench and the Potter: 2000 BC

Although men continued to hunt in the woods on the hills, they also began to clear the land, especially the lower slopes and the area down to the river. Scattered farming communities began to come together into small tribal groups with powerful leaders. They learned to make use of the metal ores that were found in the ground far away and traded their surplus products for copper and bronze from which they made ornamental artefacts, which is how they earned the name by which we know them today, the Bronze Age men. Their finest warriors became an elite class and when they died their bodies were burnt and their cremated human remains placed in collared urns and buried in raised mounds.

Around 2000 BC, people of a fair-haired Celtic and Teuton stock began to settle hereabouts. First came the Belgic Catuvellauni, ['people good in battle'] who controlled the territory from East Anglia to the Cotswolds. In the first century BC, one of their leaders, Cassevelaunus, was one of the first Britons to have his name mentioned in historical records.

A chieftain called Tasciovanus built a town near what is now St Albans, whilst the Goring, Wallingford and Dorchester areas were also tribal centres. Later other *clans* [children of a common fore-father] came up from the south to found the kingdom of Atrebates, with their chief town at Silchester, south of Reading. The Ancalites [Old Celts] controlled the riverside near Henley and the Dobunni grew strong to the west.

As they settled here these men brought with them the skill of using iron, which in England was probably extracted from the Forest of Dean. This metal was to make them far, far superior to their predecessors for they could now cut down trees more quickly and make strong tools, like ploughs and spades with which to till the land, faster and deeper. They also made iron wheels for chariots and carts and gradually increased their expertise at farming, learning wiser ways of managing their crops and animals, though the latter were often the target for thieves. They could also make better weapons, both for hunting and for warfare. Indeed, iron bars were considered as currency and often bought and stored for use when necessary. Today we call them the Iron Age men.

Gradually, when they learned to survive the bitter winters, they could afford to make war on their neighbours, whose land they coveted, for the tribes were now growing larger. Such a group lived on the hills, on which one day the stockaded village of Stoke Row would arise, and farmed the land along the ridge. This area had been hard-won, though, in many a mighty battle and it was a constant struggle to maintain their ownership of it.

Most of the clan tilled the soil and cared for the cattle and sheep. Others were craftsmen who made exquisite artefacts. Attractive goods were fashioned from copper and bronze, pots were produced from the *Gault* clay found abundantly in the area, check cloth was woven from sheep wool and leather goods cut and tooled. All of these were used by the tribe, or traded in peaceful times along the nearby Ridgeway and Icknield Way for articles and raw materials that came from far away, especially metals.

All the while a select few, the chieftain and his nobles, to whom personal honour and courage in battle were paramount, led the stronger men and almost continually waged war on the tribes around them. These skirmishes were conducted either in defence or as raiding expeditions, capturing cattle or men, women and children who could be kept or sold as slaves. However, most of their feats of arms were in the hope of gaining more land for all the tribes were all growing apace. These warriors were an elite class, feared by the farmers and craftsmen and respected even by the Druids, the priests who held sway over the lives of the people.

******

49

"I will have it higher!" As he banged the shaft of his spear on the ground, the normally menacing growl of Manwydan ap Lyr, chief of this Celtic tribe, rose to a high pitched scream and then even the nobles knew that they would have to obey or the great iron sword would come out and threaten the heads of all there that day. He was a giant of a man with a strong weathered torso, which his slaves had painted in delicate swirling patterns with the blue of the woad plant. His long red hair blew about his head as he roared out his commands and around his neck he wore a huge *torc,* made of a flexible mixture of silver and gold, fashioned like a rope.

When he was filled with the frenzy of battle, garbed only in checked trousers, with leather thongs at the knees and at the ankles over his long boots, he was invincible and bellowed out dreadful curses on his enemies. With his iron helmet and stout leather shield, he was war-mad, high-spirited and quick to be on the offensive. Everyone feared him, for he had more skulls nailed to the doorpost of his great timber hall than any others of his clan.

As he had so often shouted, "Am I not Manwydan, who cut off the head from the body of Culwych and drank of his blood?" His people knew it was true for the older men had seen him, every so often, at the great barbaric feasts, when he was full of the drink, bring out the rotted skull from the chest in which he kept it and reaffirm how he had lain with it for fifty full moons and thus absorbed the strength and power of a mighty leader whom he had killed in the long battle near the river.

These Celts held one of their feasts at each full moon and when the feasting was finally over, and Manwydan had consumed his Champion's Portion of boiled pork, having long since established his right to carve the roast, the swaggering, boisterous, belching chieftain would wipe his greasy hands on his beard, over and over again. With his right hand at his sword hilt he would begin a long and bombastic self-dramatisation, moved by chance remarks to wordy disputes. He was a great boaster, threatening to draw his sword on any who disagreed with his will or at even the hint of an insult. However, few challenged him for they knew him well for what he was, utterly selfish and always determined to have his own way in everything.

That day they were still building a colossally high wall, taking earth from the trench they dug at the same time. This was on the east side of the next hill on which the village of Highmore would later be formed. It had been agreed that the wall would be as high as two men; it was needed to defend the hill from the Ancalite attackers who came from time to time from the fertile valley in the east, from *Han Lea* [Henley, 'old site'].

The height had been agreed by all, that is, except Manwydan, whose ambitions knew no bounds and who wanted to keep the land he had won and gain ever more. The wall was being constructed in the age-old manner by nailing together slim tree trunks to form rafts that would be laid against the low bank. On these the men would push huge boxes of earth from the ditch below up to the top of the bank, thereby making the trench deeper and the wall higher.

Higher and ever higher! There seemed no end to his need for this mountainous wall to be bigger even than that of the boundary bank called Grim's Ditch only a few miles away. The men murmured, but only under their breath, ever fearful of the wrath of Manwydan, should the work not be completed by the next new moon. When, like now, there were no battles in sight, some of the warriors were content to chase and hunt, or just to be idle, to lie about the place, drink, and retell old tales, but not Manwydan.

When the tribe was not engaged in warfare he looked to defending their land and it was he who had had the idea of constructing this enormous fortification with its steep banks on the eastern side of the hill. From behind it they could use their powerful slings to hurl the sharp flint stones that they found all around them, and, if their attackers came too close, they would use their iron headed spears to maim or kill them.

Sometimes they carried the heads of distinguished enemies whom they had killed in former battles, and which they had embalmed in cedar oil, on the tops of poles to encourage their warriors to feats of greater prowess. Trumpeters, blowing into animal horns, made a terrific din on these occasions and this noise, together with the war cries of Manwydan and his warriors, all helped to terrorise their adversaries. Gwydion, the Chief Druid, who, together with his priests, kept alive the tribe's oral tradition of history and religion, had long since sought to calm Manwydan for he feared the self-centred ambitions of this belligerent man would lead the tribe into dangerous ground.

The Druids were not only priests, but also lawmakers and medicine men, skilled in the use of herbs for healing sickness and wounds incurred in battle. They believed in an after-life and that the spirit of a dead person passed into a new-born child. They taught the people about the powers in the heavens above and in the depths below the earth. All their knowledge had to be learned by heart, over many years, and handed down from generation to generation, for they wrote nothing down.

When at last, one cold day early in the New Year, the mighty fortification was finished, Gwydion stood in the centre of the circle of nobles, each with their own group of men behind him. "I call upon the gods of earth, from which it was built, and the gods of the trees, that surround it, whose roots go deep into the ground and whose branches reach high into the heavens, to bless this great rampart and give strength to those who shall defend it!" he cried at the end of the proceedings.

And he meant it too, for he realised it was very likely that only such a fortification as this would keep out the dreaded Ancalites from the eastern valley below. They lived by the river that would one day be named by Caesar as the Thames. The Celts believed there were gods in all natural things, that they were all-powerful and had to be continually placated. These gods were thought to reside in rivers and rocks and trees, especially oaks. A few miles to the south of these hills, in an area later to become known as Sonning Common, the Druids had created, in an enormous natural pit, a great *wood-henge*, an oval of fifty-two oak tree trunks, set into the ground and on them were hung, not only trophy skulls of men defeated in battle, but also of animals, especially horses and hunting dogs, both of which were highly valued.

The oak posts, one for each week of the year, had a long axis, which had been aligned on the midsummer sunrise to enable the Druids to make their astronomical measurements and calculations. Taller posts at each quadrant marked the quarter days and there were less obvious signs that were known only to the priests and never divulged, not even to the leader of their tribe. It was here, in this wooden circle that Gwydion and the other Druids held their majestic ceremonies. In the centre of the henge was an oblong wooden building with a pitched roof and it was in this rectangular hall that the high priests read their auguries and practised their secret magic.

From it they would process forth, mysterious in their long, grey woollen robes. The cowls over their heads hid the fact that their scalps had been shaved bare. Huge, jet-black ravens stalked around the ground within the oak trunks, trained never to stray far from the central wooden hall. Their distinctive voices were thought to foretell the future and some of their actions could predict not only dark and evil times but also death. When the great trench and wall were finished to Manwydan's satisfaction he came to the sacred grove to give thanks to the gods.

As he marched to the site, his long cloak, fastened at the shoulder with a huge ornamental bronze pin brooch, filled out in the breeze and the clansfolk looked on in trepidation and with a certain amount of pride in their noble chieftain. In leather bags at the sides of the two horses he led he had brought gifts for the gods, bales of wool, cheeses and barrels of mead made from the honey of wild bees. His nobles followed him, each leading a horse. These were also laden with bags of grain, tools, horse-trappings and pots - all propitiatory gifts for the spirits that dwelt in the earth, in the water, the rocks and the trees. Manwydan and his warriors trod reverently, discreetly and soberly, cautiously even, for this was hallowed ground. Even the chief was aware that here was Gwydion's province, where the sacred rules governed the behaviour of all. "Greetings, virtuous Gwydion! We have brought offerings for the gods in solemn thanksgiving for the completion of the great dyke!"

The High Priest stepped forward, holding in his left hand a bough of the sacred mistletoe and in his right the ceremonial staff made of hazel, associated with wisdom, atop of which was a gold sunburst that shone brightly in the glade. "Bring them forth!" called Gwydion. "We have dug the pits and they shall be buried with the full rituals!" Then the ceremony began and it continued all through the day, right through the evening and until the moon rose in all its fullness. But this was not a night for feasting, and certainly not an occasion for Manwydan to show off his prowess in self-dramatisation. It was a solemn occasion, one of fasting, when the bards would recite long epics of their clan's history and sagas of heroic deeds done long ago.

When it was all over they drank, just one sip each, from the great copper double-handed cup that held the potent mead brewed with special herbs and used only at these rites. The vessel was passed from Gwydion to all the other priests and only then was it the turn of Manwydan and the nobles. Each of the skilled craftsmen took his sip at the very last, while all the peasant farmers and their families looked on in awe and wonder.

As the moon set Gwydion led Manwydan aside and showed him the constellations of the stars, which only now showed up in the black velvet of the night: the Deer, the Ram, the Auroch, the Swan and the Plough, all individually bright and, between them all, the great white Milky Way that stretched across the whole heavens like a long, wide, misty ribbon.

"I have studied these stars all my life," Gwydion confided to his leader, "and they now foretell great good fortune for our clan, especially in trade with other tribes and visitors from afar, but you and your noble warriors must learn to be more peaceful. In these latter years we have become rich and can afford to develop the skills we have in farming and craftsmanship. We should learn to make peace with our neighbours instead of constant battles. These are wasteful of our finest manpower and, though we gain a little, we lose some of our strength too. Let this great dyke be our last defence. Now it is time to turn your talents to negotiating treaties with the clans on either side of us and to trading in a peaceful manner!"

* * * * * *

Manwydan said nothing but he stored in his mind what the High Priest had advised and over the coming years he realised he was right, especially now that they had defeated the Ancalites and they all had access to the lands in the valley. It was one *Lleunasa*, the great feast giving thanks to the god Lleu for a particularly good harvest, that he came reluctantly to this decision. He was older now and his tribe had many assets in its rich farms and clever craftsmen. In the forest on the hills they hunted boar, deer and many smaller prey. On the higher slopes, where the herbage was sparse, grazed large flocks of plump, horned Soay sheep, while lower down, where the verdure was richer, hundreds of cows grew fat, and goats and pigs foraged on the stubble after the wheat, flax and barley had been harvested in the huge water meadows by the river. Powerful, yoked oxen pulled carts that were laden with baskets of corn and the whole scene was one of prosperity.

All this was great wealth indeed, even though Manwydan and his nobles could not afford to own chariots and organise chariot races as some of the larger, adjacent tribes did. Still, he wondered if it would be possible to live by the plough instead of by the sword? This question absorbed him for years after the fortification was finished. The nobles noticed a gradual change in their chief as he wrestled, not with physical enemies now, but with the problem of whether he could trust the leaders of the bordering clans to keep and honour any treaties he might make with them.

Strangely enough, it was not to his peers, but to his older and wiser sister, Begwyn, that he confided his fears. He knew that her opinions, unlike those of the nobles, would be uncluttered by personal ambition for she seemed content to supervise the crafts-men, especially the potters, and they looked to her, the only other surviving child of this privileged family, as their protector.

Manwydan and Begwyn walked together one day, and as they did so, they talked of the future of their people. Begwyn was tall, slim and fair-haired. She was calmer and wiser than her brother. "It is true what Gwydion says. We are rich now and, with your great dyke, we're well protected, even from the Atrebates who seem to be the only ones who still threaten us. Perhaps they would agree to a treaty, for they, too, are becoming more wealthy by their own efforts and realise, as we do, that war is wasteful of manpower and of valuable time that could be turned to more useful occupations."

Manwydan spoke up with a strong voice. "We would need to keep our army, though, and will fight still if needs be. Never let it be said that I lack courage, for have I not slain and beheaded more men than any chief in the history of our clan?" His sister realised quickly that he would soon be off again on one of his ravings, so she led the conversation gently back to the idea of being on the defensive instead of on the offensive.

"You see," she explained. "We have considerable assets now, not only in our farms, but, perhaps more importantly, we have this wonderful clay here and our pottery skills are increasing every year.

No other tribe near here has the type of earth that we do right at the top of the hills at the edges of the forest. It is just the right type of material for our pot making and we now make more than enough for our own needs and we could trade our surplus!"

Her voice was insistent and her enthusiasm added to the conviction that was slowly growing in her brother's mind. On the south side of the top of Stoke Row Hill is an area, known as Dogmore, [from the Saxon *dag*, clay and *mer*, a water-filled pit of pliable clay soil]. It was these deposits of clay, bound up with flints and sand, found only in this area on the west side of the Chiltern Hills, that were the great gift of the gods to Manwydan's people. At first the chieftain and the nobles were scathing of the find of the potters, but as time went by they realised its value.

After many experiments with small pots that often broke in the firing, they were eventually able to create many types of vessels, each with their own purpose. In the beginning, most of them were very simple, only about six to eight inches high, and about the same in diameter, round-bottomed and rather baggy in shape, resembling the more perishable leather and woven baskets they replaced. Later, using the potter's wheel, larger ones were made. Most of them had straight sides, but as the years progressed, the potters learned to make their products conical and bell-shaped.

The way in which they fired their pots was still very primitive, the products being placed in pits and heaped over with a fire that was not much more than a large domestic bonfire. It was Begwyn who saw the possibility of making vessels of a better quality than those that the clan had produced before. She studied the methods used by the potters, the turning of bowls and urns on simple wheels, kick-started and driven by constant movements of the foot. The skill in this work lay with the individual potter and ability often ran in families.

Begwyn herself made very good pots but more than this, it was her observations and suggestions that enabled the master craftsmen to improve on their designs and make them more sophisticated. It was she who suggested that taller necks could be made and rims to give strengths to the vessels. She pointed out that improvements could be made to the clay mixes too, for she was bright enough to realise that if flint grit was mixed in with the clay when it was *puddled* in the conical pits, it became harder when it was baked and therefore less liable to fracture in use. They made not only cooking pots, but also eating dishes, weights for looms and toys for children.

But it was the pots that occupied Begwyn's mind most of all, for she was an artistic woman and loved marking patterns on them before they were fired. However, it was when the potteries had been going for some twenty years that she hit on the idea of fastening a handle to the jugs and some of the other vessels. Most of these handles broke off in the firing, but by constant experiments, she and Hwyll, the most skilled of the potters, eventually learned the best methods of fixing them on and thus perfected their invention. Because of their ability to make these beautiful bell-like pots, this tribe and others like them became known as the Beaker Folk.

Of course, Gwydion and the other Druids commanded the best urns for funeral rites. Only Hywll was allowed to make these votive pots and Begwyn incised them carefully in triangular patterns with a bronze blade and stippled them delicately with a pointed bone. They would contain the ashes of any noble who had died and whose body would have been burnt on a funeral pyre. The engraved urn would then have been placed in a grave with the noble's favourite possessions and pots of food and wine to provide refreshment for his spirit as it made the journey to a new life.

This valuable clay was to be found nowhere else in this part of Britain and Begwyn knew that it would be possible to trade their products with visitors from afar, who could bring not only wine, salt, stone querns, copper, bronze and iron, but also flamboyant golden ornaments, intricately worked, amber, jet, and pearl necklaces, bracelets and brooches which she and her female courtiers could wear, for they loved lavish display. In her family's great hall Begwyn had a little altar and on it, in a long slender vase, she placed wild flowers in season, a gift of thanks to the gods and goddesses.

As Begwyn led Manwydan back to the settlement she felt she had convinced him of the need to try and make peace with their neighbours. She realised that she would not be able to change him entirely but felt that now that he was nearly thirty and five winters old he was gradually becoming more receptive to the idea of harmony.

They gradually made their way back to a point from where they could look upon the lower slopes, to the farms that occupied most of the land governed by Manwydan, roughly twenty square miles. "I am proud of our land and our people", the leader confided in his sister, "for we have a far better life now than our forefathers had." Begwyn was glad to hear him speak thus, for she sensed the same pride herself and knew that her father and grandfather, of whom she could recall only a little, would have been glad to see the clan so prosperous. From this high vantage point they could see across the valley below, over several of their villages, right down to the river.

Eventually, Begwyn and Manwydan reached their own, the largest of the settlements, home to about three hundred people. It was made up of circular huts, about twenty of them, erected in a group that was roughly a long oval shape along the ridge, inside a stockade. The encampment was fenced to the height of about six feet, usually on a slightly sloping site, that enabled them to dig a moat around the outside of the lower half and to fortify the upper half with a bridge over a gated entrance. From here the guard and his watch dog could hide behind the wattle and see if there were any enemies coming. In one corner of the palisade was an animal shelter, oblong in shape and somewhat crudely made, though strong enough to withstand an animal leaning against the walls of it.

In the far corner of the stockade was the forge with its huge, thick-walled, conical clay oven. In this the village blacksmith melted the iron bars which had been brought from afar, probably the Forest of Dean where it was easily found near the surface of the ground, smelted, and traded all around the country. Made into bars, it was treated like currency. When the iron was heated to a sufficient degree and was of a malleable texture the village blacksmith fashioned ploughshares, adzes, axes and other weapons.

He also made other useful articles, such as hammers, chisels, saws, files and nails. He made decorative things too, especially for the families of the nobles, such as ornamental firedogs and fire irons. In one corner of this lean-to shelter was a pile of scrap iron that had been collected on every possible occasion for it was valuable and could be melted down and reused. "We must stop at the forge," Manwydan insisted as they entered the wooden gate and made their way along the straw-strewn track, rutted by the oxen carts. "My sword needs burnishing and I must get the blacksmith to make me a new set of fire-irons."

When the business was done they made their way to the home of Hwyll, the potter, and his wife, Noona. Each of the huts was a family home, roughly thirty-six feet tall, made of thirteen oak posts, about six feet high, set into the ground on which the conical roof was constructed from poles lashed together with brambles and pitched at forty-five degrees. In the centre, right at the top, there was a cross-shaped brace, and lower down poles had been lashed to the oak posts, so as to make the whole edifice quite sturdy and able to withstand the winter winds. The roof, that overhung the wall came down to about four feet six inches from the ground, was thatched with reeds or straw, similar to the ones built by the Stone Age men, but much stronger and of a far superior design.

At one point on the west side an opening had been left in the thatch. This was a window so that a little light could be let into the home, though in winter it was often closed up and on the inside rough woollen cloths were hung over it to help keep out the cold. In between the oak posts, hazel sticks had been woven into a wattle wall and on the outside clay, mixed with straw had been daubed, leaving an opening on the south side for entry. This hole had a pair of crude plank doors made of cleft timbers with iron latches and latch lifters. Around the outside of the low walls, turf had been laid about a foot high, much more thickly on the north side so as to keep out the cold winds.

The floor was set with flint nodules to minimise the dust that, together with the smoke, was always a problem for the families despite the fact that the womenfolk swept their homes out every day with besom brooms made from hazel twigs. Just outside the door was a conical oven in which the women baked their bread. These clay ovens had very thick walls that retained the heat and were very efficient for cooking a variety of foods.

However, the fire inside the house was the centre of family life and was surrounded with a ring of clay bricks for safety. It had an iron tripod over it from which a big black cauldron was hung. It usually contained a stew, made of deer meat and vegetables. The fire was poked with iron tools, but, being made only with logs, it always gave off a lot of smoke. There was a small hole in the top of the hut. A larger aperture would have let in too much rain so the smoke tended to curl around inside the home and make the family cough a great deal. Along one part of the low circular wall were ranged cooking pots, dishes, and pitchers in which the water was carried. A stone quern stood to one side, and this was used every day to grind the corn-husks into coarse flour from which unleavened bread was made and barley porridge too, which the family ate every morning.

Their corn was kept in pits, carefully dug with iron mattocks on short wooden handles. Most of the pits were conical or bell-shaped, with very narrow mouths, just wide enough to allow a man to enter. In them, sealed tight, grain could be kept throughout the winter. These cavities were opened only for a very brief period and for most of the time corn for daily consumption was kept in the rectangular granaries that were massively built from timber and thatched, the men using wooden ladders to make the capping ridge. Each of these edifices were constructed on six stout wooden legs, so as to allow the air to circulate underneath it, although rats and mice were always a nuisance and could often be found dead and decomposing beneath them.

On the far side of the palisade, Manwydan and Begwyn came, at last, to the home of the potter Hwyll and his wife Noona. "Come and see the new baby, such a fine fellow! In him and his generation lies our future, Manwydan!" Begwyn reminded him.

As they entered, Noona, clad in a simple brown wool gown, her dark hair braided and tied with leather thongs, was seated at her loom. She was weaving the checked cloth that she would soon be making into trousers, a gown or a cloak. The pieces left over would be used for children's clothes or scarves. She had plucked the wool from the sheep during the moulting season and gathered it from bushes where the sheep had brushed past. This she had then washed, combed and spun into yarn on a simple spindle, weighted with a clay spindle-whorl. Ornamented deer bone combs for combing the wool and bone needles for sewing the finished fabric lay scattered on the floor around her.

On hearing the voices Noona rose at once, fearful as always, of her great chieftain. "Welcome, my Lord, to my humble home," she whispered. "My husband, Hwyll, is up at the pottery, but may I pour you some ale?"

Manwydan glanced around the hut with its primitive bed made with four corner posts, around which were hung woven curtains, to help keep out the draughts. It was made of skins, sheepskins mostly, and these, with woven wool blankets, kept Hwyll and Noona warm at night. On the floor were more skins of sheep and goats, for Noona's father was a shepherd and kept them well supplied.

However, it was on one thick, fresh, new lambskin that the young child lie, gurgling and playing with a little clay figure that Begwyn had given him on her last visit. "Thank you, Noona," Begwyn spoke for her brother who was clearly ill at ease. "The boy looks well and grows more like his father every time I see him!" she laughed.

"Yes, my lady," Noona agreed, "and I hope he grows up as clever with his hands, for Hwyll is now making better pots than ever before, and he owes much to your interest in his craft."

As the aristocratic brother and sister left the little home and made their way to the grander hall that was their own home, Begwyn spoke thoughts that she had been concealing for some time. "It's time you settled down, took a wife and had a family of your own," she advised him. "All this fighting and feasting are all very well but you are now getting older and the clan look to you for an heir, one who will grow to lead us all into the future times." Manwydan groaned, for he knew that this was the sort of thing that women were always on about, and yet he knew his sister's words were true, although she herself was still a virgin and on the feast of *Imbolc*, each first day of the second month of the year, she would go with her maids and offer goat's and ewe's milk to the wooden statue of this goddess of fertility with much feasting and celebration.

"You yourself are still not wed," he reminded her. "Several suitors have asked me for your hand but you have refused them. You're always up at that pottery and show no interest in domestic life!"

"Ah, but, my dear brother," she pointed out, "the future of our clan lies in you having heirs and in me perfecting our skills so that we may benefit from our unique and precious clay!" He listened with interest for such a thought had not previously occurred to him. Maybe his sister was right; perhaps it was time that he took a bride and tried to make a more peaceful life for his clan and take advantage of their great asset, the clay that lay at the edge of the forest in the hills above the farmland.

* * * * * *

61

Eventually these warlike people did settle down and though they still continued to live by the plough and the sword, it was the plough that gradually took precedence and the tribes began to make peace with one another. It was fortuitous that they did because several hundreds of years later they were to face a common enemy which was to drive them westward and, though this clan held out in the cover of the woods on the Chiltern Hills longer than any other, they too, were overcome at last and forced to conform with the more civilised ways of their new masters, the Romans.

******

Traces of the Highmoor Trench can still be seen not far from Merrimoles at Lower Highmoor. The oak trees referred to were found at Widmore Pond, near Blounts Court, Sonning Common in 1675, according to Kelly's Directory of Oxfordshire, dated 1895.

Pottery shards dating from Celtic times have been found at Dogmore End, at the far west end of Stoke Row, and a Celtic or Saxon burial ground is believed to have existed at the top of Berins Hill, although it has never been excavated. Examples of pots made by the Belgae [Beaker Folk] *can be found in the Ashmolean Museum at Oxford.*

Chapter 4. The Roman Soldier and
the Housekeeper: AD 269

Late on in the Roman occupation of Britain, the headquarters of the *Consularis Beneficiarius*, a customs patrol near what is now Dorchester, stood across a little wooden bridge over the Thames at the far end of the old Ridgeway path. By this time the need for firewood, especially for the forges and the potteries of the later Britons who still lived up in this area, meant that much of the land at the top of the hill was covered with short trees that had been coppiced and conserved for fuel. Other parts had been cleared, leaving wooded *shaws* around the edges of some of the fields.

Much of this land was being farmed by men who were now much more refined than the old Celts who had only fought and feasted and gradually had been forced to move to the west, allowing the remaining occupants of the region to become Romanised. Although they continued an agricultural way of life the Britons had largely given up their organised religious life, for the Romans had purged the Druids from the land, believing them, often quite rightly, to be the instigators of rebellions against the Roman occupation. However, provided that the ordinary people kept to the rules and paid their taxes, the Romans tended to leave them to their farming. Indeed, they were glad to purchase their meat and vegetables fresh from the producers of the locality.

* * * * * *

The two men in their early thirties, had started out early, for this day in August AD 240 [*Anno Domini,* the Year of Our Lord] promised to be as dry and hot as most others had been that summer. When they reached the area that was later to become Nuffield, they took a path to the south. Many of the farmers had been privately making offerings to the Celtic god *Ouse* who governed the rain and after whom several rivers had been named. The grass was brown and the countryside away from the river *Tamisis* [Thames] was parched bone dry and cracked open in many places.

Gaius Tullius was a foot soldier and had been in the army about fifteen years. He had been in the land of the Angles for just over a month by this time, attached to a small policing force that protected the trade route on the Tamisis and he already was finding life to be boring.

Little happened in this peaceful region and he was glad when his immediate superior designated him to accompany Porteus Cornelio, a messenger, who was to take a letter to Torugodus, the chief of a well stockaded village that lay up in the hills to the east and collect a package from a retired Roman Legate on the way back. Officers were often glad to find tasks like this for their men; it gave them something to do and showed the Roman presence in the locality.

"It'll give you an insight into how these Britons live," he told Gaius, giving him his instructions. "You are to accompany the messenger there and back. I doubt if you will have any trouble, but just occasionally one of our men has been attacked whilst out alone so it would be better if he had an escort."

The messenger was glad of the company, and as they marched at a smart pace through the cool river valley Gaius told him about day to day life in a Roman camp, the soldiers' pay and their barracks, and how they grumbled against the centurions who were responsible for maintaining discipline and were often harsh. The few higher officers were for the most part from noble families, some even from Rome itself. "Quite honestly," he said. "in some ways I'm glad to leave the camp for a while and to get away from the constant noise. I get fed up with the tramp of soldiers' feet marching and drilling, the shouting of commands and the trumpets sounding orders at all times of the day!"

A Roman camp was indeed a very noisy place, increased by the rumble of carts going in and out, the hammering from the forge where the bladesmith made and repaired weapons and the blacksmith shod the horses. "Even outside there's no peace. All those stallholders shouting their wares, they never lose an opportunity to make a sale! At the little customs post where they collect taxes from the travellers who cross the Ridgeway it's different, but even that really is too quiet for me now. To tell you the truth I'm bored!"

As they left the populated valley and began to climb the hill in the rising heat their pace became slower and their conversation more relaxed. They walked steadily and began to exchange stories about their personal backgrounds. Like most of the Romans in Britain at that time, both were from Gaul and gradually discovered that they were from the same area. "I'm from *Nemausas*!" [Nimes, France] Gaius proudly announced.

"Why, so am I!" rejoined Porteus.

They were amazed to find they both came from the same region and at once began to talk at a rapid pace of the town where they were born and of the great Pont du Gard that had been built by the Romans to bring pure water to the town from the mountains fifty miles away. In AD 212, most men of substance in the provinces had had Roman citizenship conferred on them because like many Gallic families, they had long since taken to using Roman names and customs. Indeed, Gaul had been a Roman province for so long that all but the peasantry thought of themselves as Romans. Most educated people spoke fluent Latin in the Gallic dialect, although when they were by themselves they often lapsed into their native tongue, *Langue d'Oc* [Language of the East].

Nevertheless, these two were quite different types of men. Like many an auxiliary foot soldier Gaius was somewhat coarse, his speech peppered with colourful language. "Why did you join the Army?" Porteus asked him.

"Oh, well, I was born by the riverside. Poor down there it was, but I used to hear about foreign lands from the captains of the barges that came up and down the river Gardon. I thought it sounded an adventurous life and when I was quite young I ran away and joined this Legion. It happened to be in Nemausas at the time. I thought it'd be fun but it's just bloody boring. Nothing ever happens in this stinking country, just the odd outbreak of trouble here and there!"

Porteus did not agree. "I like the country and its people," he said, "but, then, I was born in the countryside. I say I come from Nemausas, but actually I grew up in a little village at the far end of the aqueduct. My father had a small vineyard there but he died when I was six. My older brothers run the vineyard now and I joined the Army so I could send money home to my mother. I must say, I've mostly enjoyed my time. Of course I often go to interesting places in my job, taking letters and packets to all sorts of localities and I don't have to do all that drilling like you lads do."

"Oh the drilling's nothing. It's when we go on long marches that the going gets tough. All that bloody equipment! By Jupiter, you'd never be able to manage that, you and your little letter pouch!" He spat on the ground and continued: "We have to wear our armour, of course, thanks be to Mithras [the soldier's god] I didn't have to wear it today! This little errand seems peaceful enough. We have our swords and daggers, too, and our shields, but on our backs we have to carry our leather bag and in that a saw, a pick, an axe, a billhook, and several other things. Oh, and, of course, three days' rations, too. It all weighs about thirty pounds and we have to keep going for thirty miles. That takes about five hours. You can't be an infantryman if you're not damn tough, I can tell you!"

"Oh, no!" agreed his companion. "I shouldn't like that sort of life. I find mine quite agreeable. I do a bit of scribing for the Praefectus [Commander] when the official scribe is off sick and I get to know what is going on, too. I couldn't go marching and fighting like you. Ah, well! Each to his own, I suppose." He sighed in the heat and slowed down even more.

"By Mithras! You're just a softie!" Gaius ribbed his companion, for they were well away from the camp by now and felt themselves to be like old friends already. "Still I suppose when your parents named you Porteus they must have known you'd just be a messenger and not a soldier."

"Never mind about the chat!" Porteus remarked tartly, "We're nearly to the top of this impossible hill now. By Mercury, the sun is hot! I know it was even hotter at home but I've got used to the cooler climate up here in Brittania and now I find it suits me better."

They gradually reached more level ground and, following the track through a large wood, came to the village which straggled along the ridge and which had been well palisaded against marauding animals, especially the wolves that roamed wild at that time. The guard admitted them at once and as they walked over to the hall house of Torugodus they met the chief, his hunting hound at his heels. Porteus patiently waited while the tall man read the missive silently.

"Yes, I understand it all." Torugodus said, in halting Latin. He spoke grimly, for the letter bore news of more taxes. "I shall write a reply and have it sent down tomorrow. If you go to the hall kitchen, the servants will give you and your escort some food and drink."

The two left the hall house as soon as they had eaten for they did not exactly feel welcome. Although the children ran up to them shyly, glad of the diversion, some of the villagers turned away when they saw the Romans. The occupational force was still not popular.

"Look here, there's no need for us to go on just yet," Gaius pointed out. "We were lucky the chieftain was here. I vote we rest under the shade of this tree for a while. The air's cooler up here on the hill and from this spot we can watch what's going on in the village."

"Oh, no, I think we should go on now," Porteus objected. "Legate Calluta's expecting me to collect a letter, and what's more I'm supposed to report back immediately so they know the messages have been delivered safely."

"By Mithras, you're a bloody fool!" Gaius cried. "You should always try and avoid work whenever you can, especially in this heat! Tell you what, we'll toss for it!" Lifting the edge of his tunic, he put his hand in his *scriptum*, [purse] and brought out a *denarius*, a small silver alloy coin, poorly struck, so that some of the silver had been left uncut at the side.

"Can I have a look at that?" asked Porteus. "I'm always interested in coins, we seem to get different ones every pay day. There have been so many emperors in recent years they hardly ever seem to wear the purple for long."

He studied the coin carefully. The obverse bore the bearded portrait of Pupienus. Around the edge was inscribed: *Imp. Clod. Pupienus Aug.* [The Imperial Emperor Clodius Pupienus Augustus] and the reverse depicted the goddess Pax, holding an olive branch, and, as if to reinforce the message, around her image was the legend: *Pax Publica* [Public Peace]. "This is a rare one and no mistake! Pupienus was joint Emperor with Balbinus for only ninety-nine days! A couple of years ago that was, in 238, I think. Not many denarii were minted in his name; you should keep that one."

"Keep it? You must be joking! I only get about six hundred denarii a year and, anyway, I'm not interested in coins, only for what I can buy with them, good wine to quench my thirst in this heat, that's what it'll be tonight when we get back! I'll toss it and we'll let the coin decide whether we should go to the Legate's straight away" Gaius tossed the coin up into the air, shouting as he did so: "Call, then!"

"Heads says we go on," said Porteus hopefully.

"Oh, Hades! I missed it! It's gone down in the grass!" Gaius shouted and immediately began to search about for it. "Ah I see it, here it is! Oh no, eternal damnation, it's gone down a crack in the ground!" Sweating now, Gaius pulled his dagger out in a flash as he knelt down and began to separate the soil between the cracks in the dry clay. He almost had the shining coin within his reach several times and then, an inch or two at a time, it slid slowly, deeper and deeper into the ground. "By Jupiter!" He was getting really angry now and red in the face as drew his *gladius* [a short, double-edged sword] quickly from its scabbard. "I'll get it out with this. It's more than long enough!" And yet still the coin, no longer glinting, evaded him. Then, in an instant, it was gone completely.

By this time a group of fair-haired village children, fascinated by the uniforms of the soldier and the messenger and intrigued by their olive skins, dark hair and foreign conversation, had gathered around and also started to look in the grass, trying to be helpful, although they did not really know what they were looking for. The word denarius meant nothing to them. "It's probably dropped too far down to get it now." said Porteus.

Gaius exclaimed: "Damnation! I haven't got my tools with me, otherwise I'd dig for it. I suppose you realise that's half a day's salary - I have nothing left till pay day now!"

"Well, that's only two days away; you'll survive! Anyway, let's compromise and sit here a while before we go on. We shall still get to the Legate's in good time." Gaius was not consoled about the loss of his denarius but as they sat chatting about life back in Nemausas and the girls they had known there, and in other parts of the Empire, he began to cheer up again. The children, sensing the excitement was over, drifted away.

After a while Gaius made the 'thumbs up' sign and they set off to find the downward road that led to the farm of Legate Calluta, a couple of miles north west of the stockaded village. This road, unlike the military roads built by the legionaries, was not a raised one, but it was fairly substantial, having been constructed by the local people under the direction of Roman surveyors more than a hundred years previously and well maintained since.

The farm was quite large, sited on the west side of a steep slope that was later to be named Berin's Hill. The site had been a Roman staging post, on the way to what are now Harpsden and Henley. The major buildings were constructed on a series of terraces on the west side of the hill, the principal edifice being a small *villa urbana*, the home of the owner, with a small bath-house at the side. Around it was an attractive garden that had been planted out with *cerisus* [cherry] trees.

They knew they had come to it when the path down the hill started to widen and instead of beeches and oaks, there were smaller trees from which the fruits had recently been picked. The messenger recognised them at once. "By Jove, I do declare that Calluta's growing cherry trees up here!" These pretty, fruiting trees had been brought from Pontus in Asia to Rome by General Lucullus in about 73 BC and imported into Britain in about AD 50. The Romans taught the Britons how to 'bud' them and to appreciate their delicious fruit.

Between the main house and the remainder of the farm was a low separating wall. On a lower slope was the *villa rustica*, which housed the *vilicus* or farm manager. The slaves lived at the far end of this establishment. The main well that had served the staging post was also on this level, not far from the dairy, where the milk was processed into cheese. Butter was rarely used, imported oil being preferred for cooking. On a still lower slope was the *villa fructuaria*, a series of buildings that housed the grain and fruit and many of the farm implements. The stables and animal stalls were also on this level, the shepherds and herdsmen living with their animals. There were also a few similar buildings lower down on the estate nearer the river.

When they arrived at the *villa urbana*, Gaius stayed at the portal, chatting to the guard, while Porteus went up to the house. He glanced up at Legate Calluta's family motto, carved on a stone over the main door: *Floreat Veritas* [May Truth Flourish]. He saluted and respectfully bade *"Salve!"* to the retired Legate.

The Legate instantly gave the messenger a thick letter of several pages that had been rolled up and sealed. "How long do you think this will take to get to Umbria?" Calluta enquired anxiously as Porteus slipped the heavy package into his cylindrical leather pouch.

"It is hard to say, sir. Most of our post has reached Rome quite quickly recently. It all depends on the luck of the messenger and whether he encounters any trouble on the way. I should think it will be there within two months, sir," he tried to reassure the older man.

"Oh, I do hope so. This letter is to my sister and I would like it to greet her on her birthday in the middle of the eleventh month. I will pray to Mercury that it will reach her in time. Go, take it with my blessing!"

Porteus saluted and bade *"Valete!"* to the Legate before leaving and went out to the gate to join his companion.

By this time the sun was lower and the air had become cooler. Nevertheless, they were glad to see a woman drawing water from a well as they made their way down the hill. "How about a drink, then?" Gaius asked the woman as the bucket came up to the top of the well. "This has been a hot day and we are very thirsty!"

"Gladly, sir!" She obeyed at once. A Roman soldier was not one to be refused. She filled the cup and extended it to him on the full length of its chain.

Gaius drank thirstily and gave the next cupful to Porteus before both had refills, thanked the woman and continued their journey, chatting along the way. "What do you think the Legate has written in that missive?" Gaius wondered.

"Ah, I often ponder on that sort of thing, too, especially as I take these messages and packets about the place. It's very rare that anyone tells me what's in them but occasionally they do, especially if its really good or bad news and there's no one else about to tell it to."

The soldier and the messenger arrived back by the river at the end of the afternoon. As they reached the more populated area they quickened their pace to a march and made their way back to the camp.

Had the two men been able to break the seal and read the letter that Porteus bore they would have found it to be a rather touching missive, that of an old soldier who had decided to retire far from his native land:

From the House of Legate Leonius Calluta

Written the twentieth day of Augustus in the year 240.

Greetings, Honoraria, my dear Sister!

As I promised, I am sending to you the necessary papers, duly signed and sealed, to hand over to you and your husband our family farm, the farmhouse, the buildings and all the land. I also feel I must explain to you why I have decided to stay in Britannia. As I wrote to you when I was recuperating at Eboracum, my wound is such that the Senate has seen fit to retire me from the Army and this has grieved me deeply these two years past. The injury has still not properly healed and every day I curse the painted Pict who inflicted this wound upon me. Thanks be to Mithras that Hadrian saw fit to build the Murus Hadriani [Hadrian's Wall] *stout enough to keep out those trouble-makers from Caledonia!*

The choice was given to me that I could either return to our family farm in Umbria with a large pension, or take a smaller one and a piece of land here in this far away province of Britannia. After a great deal of thought I have elected to stay on here and my reasons for this are these:

After so many campaigns in Gaul and Germania, I have now been some fifteen years in this part of the Empire and, albeit the cold and wet in winter play havoc with my leg, I have become used to the country and its people. Indeed, from some reports I receive, I am not sorry to be far from Rome at this time.

71

I miss the sun in the south, of course, but now I am old I doubt whether I could stand the heat of Umbria in the summer months.

So, I have been awarded a piece of land, and it is a good one. At one end there is a short length along the bank of the River Tamisis from which we get our fish supplies. From there inland we have our water meadows and, a bit higher up, large tracts of land on soft hills. We grow corn and root vegetables and keep a few cattle and sheep. Some of this produce we trade with the British in the forest above us and they provide us with deer, boar and other meat as well as wood for our winter fires.

You will, perhaps, be glad that I have decided to settle down now and the woman I have married is good for the purpose. She is the daughter of a chieftain who lives at some distance from here. Her name is Megana and she is a fair-haired, blue-eyed Briton. She is not all that affectionate; I have to say! As you know, I have loved for a while in all the places I have been stationed. However, she is a capable woman and it is enough.

Her brother, who acts as our vilicus, lives in the villa rustica and manages the farm. Megana was married before, and although her husband, a minor chieftain, was killed in a skirmish with our troops from Sinodinium, near here, she bears we Romans no ill feeling. She has two children: a fine lad of some ten years, and a sweet little girl of seven, named Gwynneth. Megana has very few words of Latin but I have learned the language of the British and we manage well enough. She is teaching Gwynneth the skills of spinning, weaving, needlework and, above all, how to manage the household servants. We only have twenty-two slaves here, four in the house and eighteen on the land.

The boy was named as Prastugus by his parents, but I now call him Vespasian after one of my officers, a very brave fellow who was killed when we were fighting on the Wall. He is a bright boy and I have found a tutor for him. I want to be sure that he will learn Mathematics, Latin, Greek, Geography and History.

We keep ourselves to ourselves, mostly. Megana certainly runs the house well. I had it newly built of brick and insisted on having it designed in the style we have come to find practical here, with only a small 'atrium' open to the sky and a little impluvium, [pool] in which we manage to keep ornamental fish, although some died last winter. Most of the rooms around the atrium are enclosed. I have had a hypocaust put in under the whole of the floor to heat the house in winter and to provide hot water. As you may remember, I love hot baths. We have a wonderful view too, for the house and farm are on the side of a hill that overlooks our property and from here on a clear day we can see down to the river.

Mother would have been pleased to know that I have built a small lararium [prayer room] and make offerings on the altar to the gods every day; not only to Mithras, but to the other gods too, when the occasion arises. Megana does not pray with me but prefers her own earth gods and I let her do as she wills in this matter.

However, we are not entirely lacking in culture here. I often take Vespasian to the festivals at Calleva, a good-sized urbes [town] eleven miles to the south. Sometimes we travel to Londinium, which is only two days journey and where there is a great deal more life. I did go to Aqua Sulis [Bath] to take the waters, but it did little good for my leg and the journey was long and tiring.

So, I am well enough, apart from my leg and rheums [colds] in the head that we all get every winter. At the moment it is really too hot, but most of the year the climate is fairly warm and often sunny, much more so than in the north of the country. We have a good little farm and I trust Father would have approved of the way in which we run it, albeit much smaller than our one at home. We have to make allowances for the weather here. It often rains in spring and autumn and the winters can be very cold.

I entrust to you, your husband and sons the care of the whole family estate. I often think of our childhood days in the warm Umbrian sun and how carefree we were, roaming on those lovely hills. However, it does not do to dwell on these matters for too long; one must accept life as one finds it.

Take care of yourself, dear Honoraria. Continue, if you can, to write to me as often as you have always done. I value your letters and news from home - would that I were as good a scribe as you, but my travelling days have lost me the habit. Indeed this letter has taken me three days to compose! I trust it will arrive in time for your fiftieth birthday. I am sure you will all have a great feast.

Remember me to all our family and to any of our neighbours and friends who remember me.

My good wishes to Murinium and the boys. May the Nine Gods be kind to you all.

Your very caring brother
Leo

******

The following day dawned equally hot on the next hill, to the east of the stockaded village and Legate Calluta's farm. The old Celtic fortification still lay more or less intact about a mile away, but it was no longer used since the Roman administration had ensured more stability and peace.

The situation was still very much one of 'them and us', with some of the Britons being servants, who were paid very low wages but usually kept under quite good conditions, and the slaves who did the very menial work. Britons descended from the noble clansmen had been declared Roman citizens, but some of the ordinary people thought more highly of adopting the habits and fashions of their occupiers than others did.

Venutius was one who adopted a Roman name, though he secretly despised the Roman way of life. His pottery business on the hill to the east side of the stockaded village depended on their custom, so he was forced to conform, at least by an outward show. Some of his pottery was more sophisticated than those Begwyn, the Celt, had overseen. The Romans had brought with them new methods of making pots and of constructing kilns, more sophisticated than the clamp fires that the British had used for many years prior to the invasion.

The old clamp ovens were still in use, though, for baking simple kitchen wares. They were hollows in the ground into which straw and kindling was placed. The pots were then stacked on top and more fuel added before the whole was covered in turf and burned. This type of firing gave a variable surface colour, according to the position of the pot in the fire, and the circulation of air in the clamp. Some pots turned out better than others but each one was quite unique.

To the local villas household pots were very important, especially in the *culina* [kitchen]; for the Romano-British, as these people became known, had been encouraged by their rulers to enjoy a much wider range of food and new ways of cooking meat with herbs. The Romans regarded food as an aesthetic experience as well as a means of survival. Most of the tableware was ornamented in some way and usually made in sets. Fine glazed dishes came from larger potteries in other parts of the region, nearer to Oxford.

The pottery produced in the area today known as Swan Wood at Highmoor was for the most part, produced from the cream and red clay found locally and some coarser ware made from a grey clay that cracked more easily. It was by no means as fine as the *Samian* ware that the Romans imported from Gaul.

The workshops belonging to Venutius and his brother were very plain buildings, oblong in shape, and thatched with straw. Here workers made every kind of vessel, most of them being turned on a simple kick-wheel. Other skilled craftsmen ornamented them with bronze tools and made things like clay statues of gods or horses. Apprentices were probably started off on simpler jobs, such as making cressets, oblong clay blocks, with four or six concave holes, about two inches across, in each one. These would be filled with oil and have wicks floating in them. When lit they would illuminate a small room at night.

Venutius's nearby home was also quite a simple, oblong affair with a porch shaped over the main door. The corner posts were made from seasoned oak and the frame was held together with nails fourteen inches long. The wattle walls were daubed with clay and higher than those of the old circular huts and the reed roof was bound to the ash rafters with twine. There were just a couple of windows covered with thin skins to allow a little light.

The potter was not very tall but his hair was fair and though he was clean-shaven, he wore his moustache like most of his compatriots, long and drooping and this gave him a rather dolorous appearance. He wore the same Celtic style plaid trousers and tunic that his forefathers had done. His wife and children also dressed simply and lived basically.

Like the two soldiers, Venutius also set off in the cool of the early morning from his workshop, leaving his brother in charge of the kilns and pot-drying ovens, their smoke rising almost straight upwards in the still air. His cart was piled high with all types of cream and red table bowls, shallow and deep dishes, flagons for oil and wine, as well as a good selection of kitchen wares, platters, rimmed jars, jugs and *mortaria* [grit-studded bowls for grinding food]. He was off on his rounds of all the local big houses and first of all he was planning to call at a *villa urbana* belonging to Plautius Ostia at Bix, thought to have been named after the box bushes which grew there. This man Ostia was also a Briton, turned Roman.

He always enjoyed calling at this villa, for he had a soft spot for the *vilica* [housekeeper], a British woman who ran the house and whom he had known since they were children together in the stockaded village on the next hill about a mile to the west. She was always full of gossip and knew everyone in the neighbourhood. Like many of the British people who were descended from the later Celts she had little time for the Romans and their ways, although she was careful to mind her tongue in front of her employers.

The housekeeper, Boudicca, had been named by her mother in honour of the famous British leader of the Iceni tribe who had rebelled against the Romans a century earlier, but the name was not acceptable to her mistress who called her Melissa after one of the herbs that she was so fond of growing in her garden. She had renamed all her slaves after flowers.

When Venutius arrived at the rear door, he entered the kitchen and found Melissa reprimanding a slave girl who had broken a flagon. "Ah, you've arrived just in time. Young Calendula here has just broken one of those flagons you brought only last month. Really, she's such a careless girl!" So saying, she pushed the girl away from her. "Go and clean out the cressets and lamps and refill them. Don't put too much oil in them, though!"

"Now, now, Bou," Venutius calmed her with the name he had called her since they were children. "Don't forget there was a time when you were just a young slave girl and broke dishes too."

"Ah yes, perhaps. Now I am a *liberta* I tend to forget what it was like to be enslaved," sighed the woman. "I must say that receiving the Certificate last year on my fiftieth birthday was wonderful, though I'd never leave the master and mistress now, they've been so good to me."

"They have indeed! You've been here since you were quite a young girl, haven't you?"

"Yes, that's true. Now, now, that's enough of the past. You sit down here by the table. I'm sure you'd like a beaker of wine. A delivery of amphorae came yesterday. It's good wine, too, from Hispania, I'm told. See what you think of it."

"Ah, yes. I'd love a drink. It's early yet and already the sun is warm. The farmers are all grumbling about the lack of rain. It'll be another scorcher today, I shouldn't wonder. No need for a woollen *birrus* [British wool cloak] in this weather, eh?"

"Yes, that's true, though I must say I love the sun! Now, what have you brought? I need a new flagon and a small bowl."

When Venutius had stated the price she selected a key from several on the end of a chain around her waist, unlocked a small wall cupboard, took out a bag of coins and paid the potter for his wares. Looking out of the window to ensure that the girl was at work, she returned to the table. "I should keep working while you sit and rest, though, for I've got a great deal to do!" she declared loudly.

And then, lowering her voice, whispered the phrase that Venutius always looked forward to hearing, "Have you heard the latest news?"

"You mean about Plautius Ostia being made a Magistrate? Yes, I heard that in the market last week. It's a quite a leg up for him. I mean, him being just a tradesman, really."

"Oh, the master's a bit better than that. His father had him taught Latin and Greek, you know. He speaks Latin fluently and they say he has a very good ear for the language. He writes it well, too. His father's money bought him a good education and, after all, he's more than just a tradesman like his father. He shaves off all his body hair and calls himself a merchant now."

"Well, good luck to him, I say. You wouldn't catch me copying those Romans the way your master and mistress do."

"I should say they do. My mistress, particularly. She's taken to using Latin phrases in recent years. Even when she talks to me, she says things like: 'The servants try my patience *ad nauseum*.' What's the matter with 'The servants make me sick', I'd like to know? Or she'll say 'He's persona *non grata* in this house', instead of 'He's not allowed in this house'. She's even made a shrine to Juno now. She tells me that she's the wife of their god Jupiter and that she looks after women. Our language and our gods were good enough for her parents, why not for her?"

Melissa was getting quite heated by now. "She also does her hair the way she thinks is the latest fashion. And the jewellery she's got, you'd never believe it! Mind you, I think the clothes she wears in the winter are just not suited to our climate, even though she wears a wool tunic under her *stola*; no wonder she feels the cold so!" As she spoke, Melissa busied herself about the kitchen. It was a large room with tables for food preparation, shelves and cupboards for utensils and a walk-in pantry for storing food. This kitchen had the latest development, an intramural well with a hand pump that supplied water to a stone basin.

"The cook has had to learn a lot of new dishes in recent years and now that the master has been elevated in society we are to have a great banquet at the end of the month. The mistress has promised the cook some help but they want guinea-fowl, pheasants and even stuffed dormice, too. I don't know why they can't just be content with the pork and beef that we have always had, along with a bit of game and fish."

"Ah well! You see, I suppose they must show off their new-found wealth. I suppose they'll be inviting all the neighbours?"

"Oh, yes," she said, placing a *patera* [bronze skillet] on the *craticula* [gridiron] over the fire and pouring into it a small quantity of imported olive oil. "Marcus Catullus and his mother, Torugodus and his sister, the Sylvanuses, even Legate Calluta and his wife; they're all to be invited, as well as lots of the master's business friends from the town. I dread it! There'll be so much to do. Mind you, we'll need more cooking pots and dishes, so you'll do well!"

Venutius laughed. "More tableware, too, I suppose?"

"Oh, no. The master and mistress are away in Londinium now, or I wouldn't be talking to you for this length of time. They've gone to buy a lot of new things, a *Samian* ware dinner set and especially wine glasses from Cologna, which I believe," she hesitated, "is in Germania. Yes, that's right. They say that River Rhenus has very sandy shores there and that they make the best glass in the Empire. How the master and mistress will be able to afford all this new stuff, I don't know. Horn mugs were good enough for my family. Don't tell me that wine or mead taste any better out of a glass!" she said, moving a pot from the fire.

"Before they left for Londinium the mistress told me that they're even thinking of having one of those mosaic floors, like Legate Calluta has got. Going to look at patterns, they are. All I hope is that the master will be getting a good salary as a Magistrate to pay for all this new high life!" She livened the fire up with a poker. "It's awful to have to cook over a fire on hot days like this, but there's nothing else for it if I am to prepare this lamb stew for the evening. The master and mistress should be back by then so I can't sit here all day gossiping!"

Venutius rose from the table and remarked: "I can see you're busy, Bou, and I must be getting on to the Callutas' house. Let me know what extra pots and dishes you will require for preparing the feast and I'll bring them over the next day. Certainly my wares are cheaper than your mistress could buy in Londinium. Thanks for the wine. Good stuff that!"

Melissa said, sadly, "Farewell, then. I'm glad you enjoyed the wine. You'll be lucky if you get a mug of ale at the Callutas'; they're really stingy in that house!"

Venutius departed, leaving Melissa to chase up the girl outside. Most of the other house slaves had accompanied their owners to the city. "By the gods, haven't you finished yet, girl! Here, I'll give you a hand." Melissa was feeling more kindly now after her long chat with Venutius.

When work was done Melissa sent the girl out on an errand, and took herself around the garden for a little fresh air, away from the heat of the fire in the kitchen. "After all," she reflected, "there's all the afternoon to prepare the meal for the master and mistress when they return. Meantime a light salad will do for me and the girl."

The garden was a very pretty one. Lavendula Ostia, herself named after the sweet smelling mauve flower, spent a great deal of time here and had improved the plot greatly over the years that they had lived in the house. She had studied plans of Roman gardens and had created a decorative area where one could take light exercise, as well as an orchard and a vegetable garden, at the end of which by the kitchen door was a herb patch that was her pride and joy, for as well as having culinary uses, herbs provided the source of many home-made medicines.

In it she grew rosemary, thyme, mint, fennel, coriander, rue and hyssop as well as the imported ground elder, which was used in treating gout and was to become the plague of English gardens for thousands of years afterwards. In the orchard there were apple trees imported from Italy of a superior type to the native British *malus* that was hard and bitter.

There were also pear trees and, as in the garden of Legate Calluta, there were cherry trees, too. All of these trees, which could be seen from the house, provided not only delicious fruit, but also delicate pink and white blossoms in the spring and a source of nectar for the bees. Several conical hives, made from plaited osiers, were kept in the orchard. Honey, used as a preservative and in medicines, as well as for sweetening, was procured from them every year. The pleasure garden consisted mainly of lawns with low hedges of box. Bushes and statues were dotted about, and the border beds were full of flowers.

A few plants, like lavender, valerian, acanthus and various lilies had been imported, but most of them, such as the pansy, rose, violet and daffodil, were native species that had been cultivated and encouraged to grow larger. A small pool with goldfish in it provided a central ornamental feature. Of course, Lavendula didn't do any of the heavy work. Slaves were for that, but she took cuttings, grew seeds, cut off dead heads from the bushes and generally saw to it that the garden was kept in immaculate order. She hated having to go away and leave it.

Melissa stopped in the vegetable garden to pick a lettuce, some radishes, a couple of onions and some parsley for the *prandium* [lunch] as well as carrots, leeks and turnips for the *cena* [evening meal]. She returned to the house, once again berating the poor slave girl for not having finished the cressets and oil lamps. As the cook had gone to Londinium with her mistress, Melissa had little alternative but to start to prepare the meals.

******

About 150 years after this the Roman Empire was so large that it was becoming difficult to administer. This, together with political problems in Rome, led to a weakening of the Roman hold on their western territories. From about the year AD 275, Saxons from North Germany started to raid and then invade Britain. The Romans found it hard to defend the country and gradually returned southwards. Hadrian's Wall was abandoned in about 350.

The last Legion left Britain soon after 400 and little is recorded about Anglo-Saxon life in this area. Most of the buildings, being wooden, rotted away and few records were kept. For this reason the following five hundred or more years are usually referred to as the Dark Ages.

The light came with the monks who brought Christianity to the country in 596, but even then it did not come to Oxfordshire until about 635.

******

A denarius, *bearing the head of Pupienus (AD 238) was discovered when the Maharajah's Well was being dug in Stoke Row at the end of 1863.*

The Roman Well on Berin's Hill (privately owned) continued to be used for many years. Traces of it still remain.

Romano-British pottery shards can still be found on the ground in Swan Wood, Highmoor (privately owned) and in the summer of 1955 traces of a Roman villa were found at Bix, about a mile to the north-east.

The Old Place

Chapter 5. The Missionary and the Witan: AD 634

By the middle of the sixth century much of England was in Anglo-Saxon hands after a series of violent invasions from the northeast by a variety of tribes. At this time the Old English name for Wallingford was *Gualengford* [the ford of the Gauls].

This part of the country had often changed hands, sometimes being owned by West Saxons and at others by Mercians, who had also came from Northern Europe and were strong to the east. The Britons had mainly been driven northwards and westwards to Wales and those who remained were defeated in 571.

Baesingtun [Benson], one of the strongest garrisons of the West Saxon Gewissae tribe, then became subject to King Cynegils.

About six years later, around 577, after a victory over the British at Derham in Gloucestershire, the Saxons increased their lands along the Avon and the Severn and began to penetrate the valley of the 'dark river' as the Thames was known at that time. Reading, which had been until then largely protected by the former Roman garrison at Calleva, was invaded by *Reada's Ing*, [Reada's people] in 600. It was they who gave their name to the Reading we know today.

In 614 thousands of Britons died in a battle with King Cynegils, but in 633, at Hatfield, the Saxons lost a large number of their possessions and Mercia was extended under the rule of King Penda.

Meantime, in 597, St Augustine, under the direction of Pope Gregory the Great, began to convert the heathen Saxons, among the first of whom was King Ethelbert of Kent. Most of this missionary work was done by means of open air preaching, but gradually churches were built and monasteries set up.

All of this work helped to soften the belligerent ways of the Saxons. Oswald, King of Northumbria, was a Christian who had been instructed by Celtic monks in Scotland and was keen to have the whole of England converted.

In 634 the pious Birinus, a Lombardian from Italy, full of missionary zeal, was sent to England by Pope Honorius I, having been consecrated Bishop at Genoa by Asterius, Archbishop of Milan. He landed on the south coast of England in 635 and immediately travelled inland, in a northerly direction, intending to convert the British heathens in the Midlands. Instead he arrived at *Dorcic* [Dorchester] and, finding the Gewissae tribe to be entirely pagan, decided to stay and begin his missionary work here.

******

That Judith was very beautiful there was little doubt and in the mind of her father, Aethelfled, no doubt at all. As he watched her from the window of the Long Hall, he thought, with a sigh, "She is just as her mother was at that age. I first met her when she was thirteen."

Judith was tall, slender and with a well-proportioned figure, now almost fully developed. Her hair was flaxen gold and she wore it in two long plaits that she coiled around her head. Her eyes were a piercing blue, like the sky on a hot summer's day, and here lay her great attraction, for she was not just a beauty but she also had hot blood and an independent spirit. Although she was dutiful, her aunt, Brunne, thought she sometimes behaved in a way unbecoming to a daughter of a *thane* [a member of a rank between ordinary freemen and hereditary nobles]. She would often roam the countryside, unaccompanied by her brothers, or even a handmaid.

Aethelfled had three sons, to all of whom he had given a name with the same stem, as was the Saxon custom. The eldest was Aethelric and it was upon his shoulders that Aethelfled put much of the responsibility for the family farm, for one day it would all be his. Aethelred, the second son, was a warrior, proud and pig-headed, true to the family tradition and was often away in the service of King

Cynegils. However it was Aethelstaen, born much later than the other two, who was so often the companion of the tomboyish Judith.

On this sunny day in late May, 636, Judith was once more walking alone on the lovely hills that stood above the valley of the wide river. Spring had come late that year, bringing with it clear, frosty nights and sunny days. This sudden change in the weather had given Judith an urge to wander away from the stockaded village that straggled along the ridge. She was making her way down the hill past the ruin of what local people said had once been a Roman farm, stopping only to draw herself a drink from the well which her father had maintained, for it was very useful at that point.

There, where the steep part levelled out to form a shelf, she met a man in a brown garment and sandals. His head was tonsured, shaved around the centre at the top, and although his robe was plain the folds of it fell softly and she could see it was made of wool. A cowl hung loosely from the back of the neck. Around his waist he wore a rope girdle and from his neck hung a finer cord with a wooden object on it shaped like a cross with a long stem. In his hand he had a tall staff.

"Good day sir!" she politely bade the stranger. "I have not seen you before in these parts. Is there any way in which I can help you?"

"Yes, daughter, it may be that you can." answered the man. His speech was imperfect and he was obviously a foreigner. "I am Brother Paulinus and I am seeking the way to the hall of the Lord Aethelfled, who, I understand, is thane of the lands hereabouts." He could tell at once that this was no churl's daughter, for even on a working day she wore a kirtle of soft green wool with an embroidered hem.

"I can take you there, sir, for I am his daughter. My name is Judith."

"This is indeed a blessed meeting, child." The monk spoke with feeling, for he had been sent on an errand to find a man about whom he knew very little. Here, perhaps, was a chance to find out more before they met.

"Your father owns all the land between these hills and Gualengford, I believe?"

"Yes, that is so, sir. For a thane he is not rich but we are not poor either!" She spoke proudly and tossed her head as she did so. "We have many cattle in the lowland pastures and grow corn on the uplands."

Gradually they ascended the hill and came to the stockaded village. It was a great deal larger than the Iron Age village had been. The dwellings and cattle byres were not round now, but oblong and built much more strongly, many of them having sunken floors. The largest of these *steadings*, the Long Hall, stood in the middle of the ridge and it was to this, her family home, that Judith took Brother Paulinus to meet her father.

Aethelfled received the monk politely and offered him mead but the guest would only drink weak ale. "Lord Aethelfled, I have come as a messenger from Bishop Birinus." Paulinus explained. "He wishes to meet with you, wherever you will."

"Who is Bishop Birinus? What sort of title is that? Do you come from afar? Your tongue is not clear. I think you come from over the seas, you are perhaps a merchant?"

Paulinus laughed. "Slowly, slowly, friend. One question at a time! Who is Bishop Birinus?   I think that was your first question. A Bishop is one who is, like me, a servant of God. However, he has jurisdiction over many men like me and has been sent by the Holy Father to preach the Gospel of Christ."

"Which god? Speak more plainly!" said Aethelfled loudly in his guttural Saxon.

Paulinus replied: "The one God, sir. There is only one God and Bishop Birinus will tell you about him. You asked whether we come from afar. Indeed we do and the journey has been long. We come from Milano, north of Rome, where there are many churches."

Aethelfled was quick to retort: "Rome! It is a very long time since the power of Rome was felt in this land."

"Ah, I speak not of the Rome of the Empire, sir, though that still exists but it is not as powerful as it was long ago. I myself come from near Firenze, but I have been here in Saxon lands before. Some years ago I was sent with a flock of sheep by ship to Sussex. I stayed there for about a year with the flock and went through their first lambing for a thane there. Maybe you know of him? His name is Aldhelm."

"No, I have not heard of him. We lead a very quiet life here, when we can." Aethelfled sighed on the last phrase. "But I have heard about this Christ you mention. I learned at the last Witan that King Ethelbert of Kent has had some dealings with him."

"Yes, sir. That is correct." Paulinus smiled gently at the way in which the news had drifted through from the east. "But I myself am not here now to talk to you about our Saviour. I am to arrange for you to meet with Bishop Birinus. He very much hopes that you will agree to a meeting. He is staying in *Dorcic*."

"Very well. I promise no more than to be hospitable, but he shall come to dine with us and bide overnight. It shall be next Wodens-tag [Wednesday] and he and his men shall sleep here afterwards. I shall invite all the principal men hereabouts and we shall have a great feast." Aethelfled's eyes lit up at the prospect of an excuse for a banquet, when there would be much drinking, music and singing of the old saga songs.

"Thank you, sir. I am sure the Bishop will be most pleased to come, but at this stage he just wishes to speak with you and your family quietly. Just he and I will come and we shall be glad of a meal, but no wine. Perhaps just a horn of mead for friendship's sake."

Aethelfled looked disappointed. "Ah, well, perhaps later on. Meantime we shall be pleased to hear your news. We get little around here except of who has been killed or maimed in battles."

* * * * * *

And so it was arranged and the following Wednesday, Birinus and Paulinus came, both clad in their simple brown robes, mounted on a stout mare. "Only one horse?" Aethelfled asked, once he had introduced himself, as he was surprised to see the two men mounted this way, the older man obviously a nobleman.

"Yes, my Lord, we are both light and have no need of two where one will do. The journey wasn't long and we walked up the steepest part of the hill. Why have two horses when one will do? Will you arrange for her to be groomed and bedded well for the night?" Birinus requested.

"Guthlac!" Aethelfled called one of his slaves. "See to this mare. Make sure she is well fed and watered and keep her in my stable!" he ordered as he led his two visitors indoors.

"You are welcome to my house, my Lord Bishop." Aethelfled said and, conscious as ever of the Saxon rules of hospitality, he led his two visitors to the dining-hall. Aethelfled was stouter now in his old age, his beard and long fair hair were shaggier. His tunic, worn over trousers and leather shoes with thongs that laced up the legs, was of bilberry mauve, the hem and sleeves edged with bands of coloured weave. Around his waist he wore a wide leather belt, fastened with a large bronze buckle, and from the belt hung his knife, sheathed in a leather scabbard, inlaid with swirling Nordic patterns in silver. His cloak was russet and fastened at the shoulder with a huge, circular silver brooch, engraved with the design of a bird and inlaid with semi-precious stones. It was a badge of his rank.

He had sensed from Paulinus's previous visit the need for sobriety and had provided a good meal of salmon and goose, accompanied by beans, kale and peas. Loaves of freshly baked coarse bread were in plenty, and there were several dishes of butter with which to soften it. Large clay pots of honey were scattered along the table but the salt container was kept at the top end so that the host and the guests should help themselves first. Horn mugs of mead stood ready on the table, but Aethelfled had seen to it that weak ale was also provided in large pitchers.

In accordance with Birinus's wishes only the family were gathered around the long table. Aethelfled sat at the top, with his eldest son, Aethelric, the farmer, on his left. Birinus was offered the place of the chief guest on the right of the host. "My second son, Aethelred, wants to be a warrior and is now away in the service of the King," his father explained. "My daughter, Judith, you have met, and here is my youngest son, Aethelstaen. This lady is my dead brother's wife, the Lady Brunne."

"We are very pleased to meet with you all." Birinus spoke in a warm, clear voice. "We bring you greetings from our Holy Father, and are glad of this opportunity to talk with you and, we hope, the people on your lands."

"Then will you take a horn of mead with us for friendship's sake?" Aethelfled asked, picking up the Guest Horn exquisitely carved and encased in an ornamented silver holder.

"Yes, just one, for we don't normally drink much intoxicating liquor, believing that it clouds the judgement."

Although Aethelfled and his elder son drank more than that, they were quite abstemious by their standards and the meal proved to be in sharp contrast to most of their entertaining. It was more interesting, though, for these men had come, not to feast and boast, as most of their friends did, but to preach the gospel of God in such a way as to make it attractive to heathens whose pagan beliefs stretched far back into the past. Birinus did most of the talking, with occasional help from Paulinus when he needed a Saxon word that he did not know or could not remember.

"I come to tell you about the God of Love, who forgives us our sins and wants us all to love one another and live in peace and harmony." To Aethelfled and his proud, stubborn family this was a very strange idea. All the history of the Nordic people was laced with the fear of their many gods.

When they first came to Britain the Saxons were not a nation led by a king but rather a number of blood-thirsty, land-grabbing tribal chiefs. Few of these so-called kings lived on a grand scale, even in comparison with a Roman Legate. Down the years, as they fought not only the Britons, but each other, some of these leaders had become very powerful and claimed lineage from their harsh Norse gods. *Tiw* was thought to have been associated with death. *Thor* was the god of thunder and *Freyr* was the fertility god. But *Woden* was feared most for he was the father of all the deities and the most powerful, being the god of war. All these gods left their names in villages throughout the north east, the midlands and the south and, especially, in the names of four days of the week.

To the violent men of the north, these deities summoned up thoughts of fear and revenge, hatred and bloodshed. "How can a god be loving? Surely this is weakness?" suggested Aethelric. "As a farmer I know that a man has to be strong to withstand all weathers and the many setbacks of farming life. Often here we haven't enough food and many of us die in times of famine, especially children. If we don't appease the gods we shall be in trouble."

"Yes, it is true that life is not easy," agreed Paulinus. "I was once a shepherd and know it can be dangerous, for I have often been out with my ewes when they were lambing on the Tuscan hills in winter and the snow came unexpectedly." Aethelfled and Aethelric looked on him as more one of themselves from that moment on and

Paulinus, although he had spoken little, could tell that these words had counted for much.

"God tests us in many ways." Birinus explained. "But most of the problems we have we bring upon ourselves. Ill-health and quarrels are often brought about by too much drinking. Many men ignore the nature's signs because they are too busy wining and dining. Lead a sober life and you will find God will help you with your work."

Aethelric flushed for he recalled the time when he had been so drunk that he had almost fallen in the central fireplace and had caught his cloak alight. Whipping it off, he had swept it upwards and a few sparks from the burning fabric had set fire to the roof of the hall. Pandemonium had set in, with the guests fleeing as best they could and the thralls trying to put the fire out with no directions from their drunken master. Aethelfled had been away at the time and was very angry when he had returned home and had found his hall burnt down.

"Where did your god come from and what does he control?" asked Brunne, toying nervously with the silver imitation keys at her waist, a symbol of her rank as housekeeper and a relative of a thane. She felt she had to try and change the subject.

"God has always been and always will be." Birinus explained. "He has no beginning and no end. Moreover he is everywhere and in everything. He has all knowledge and loves all things. This is why it saddens him to see men fighting with one another, keeping up old scores from long ago, instead of forgiving each another as he forgives them, that is, when they ask for forgiveness." He stressed this essential part of the act of contrition.

"I forgive no one!" shouted Aethelfled. "My family have suffered many wrongs, especially in more recent years at the hands of our neighbour Wulfmaer. He has five sons and every one of that family is an enemy to me and mine. I haven't yet been able to prove it, but I am sure they steal my cattle. I have had to employ an oxherd to guard them! If I could only catch their men at it, I'd have them fined!"

"And yet, if we could persuade your family and his to become Christians and follow the true Lord, you would all give up this hatred of one another and be subject to God's laws."

Aethelfled shouted at once in reply: "Wulfmaer would never agree, and neither would I!"

Birinus quickly saw that this was not a wise path to follow and instead, pointed to a small lyre, about twelve inches long and four inches wide, sitting on a shelf that ran high up along the far wall. "What is that? A musical instrument?"

"Yes," Judith informed him further: "my father makes music with it. Its tones are sharp and arresting, especially when he accompanies our poet friends. It isn't all swearing and bragging and revelry here at feast times, you know. Almost all the men can play and the lyre is passed around, each man singing or reciting a verse in turn. They sing long sagas, like *Beowulf*, that tell of the exploits of our forebears as they sit around the crackling fires on dark nights; it's a wonderful way to pass the long winters."

"Then let us hear you play!" Birinus appealed to a side of Aethelfled's nature that he had not realised existed. Perhaps God would lead them this way to the man's soul.

Aethelfled took down the lyre and began to play, smiling at Judith as he did so. "Will you sing for us, my dear?" She nodded her assent and so they began. The body of the lyre was flat and made of wood with tuning pegs and six gut strings. Plucked with a plectrum made from horn, it produced rather weak, almost twanging tones that were not loud and did not carry far, but it had a certain attraction, especially when accompanying the sweet voice of Judith.

Then Aethelfled changed the tune, plucking the strings rapidly, making the plectrum leap joyfully and Judith began to sing again, a song that seemed to tell of the coming of Spring; the word 'cuckoo' came into it time and again. The sound of Judith singing in the light of the central fire and the playing of the lyre, combined to soften the evening and gradually the two visitors saw their host family in quite a new way.

"I didn't realise that music played such a part of Saxon life." Birinus said, remembering to himself the Saxon reputation for barbarism and brutality.

"Oh, yes, indeed. I have always been fond of music and am now learning to play a full harp. I have my own and I've engaged a gleeman to teach me. I have a wound to my arm that prevents me doing heavier work and it is one of the few things I can do, now that I am old. You might almost call it a vanity."

"Let us hear you play the harp, Father." Aethelstaen pleaded. It was the first time that the ten year old had spoken. He was a quiet boy whose mother had died as he was born. His aunt had tried to take the place of his mother and she had been kind, but he was shy and over-protected, speaking almost only when spoken to.

"Very well, but you mustn't expect too much. It is much more difficult than the lyre. Almost any man can play that."

Going over to a dark corner, he took a cloth off a small harp and brought it into the light. "I call it 'the wood of delight'." he said proudly as he sat down to play the larger instrument. It was shaped like the capital letter 'D', and, having its own hollow sounding board down one side, so much fuller was its resonance that it carried all around the long hall. The fact, too, that it had more strings gave a wider range of notes and a warmer tone to the music. From the harp Aethelfled drew a far sweeter sound than from the lyre, one full of wistfulness, as if it spoke of a love known long ago. It was a melodic, mysterious and melancholy piece, plaintive and bitter-sweet, inspiring in its listeners a feeling of sorrow and pain, for something that had been joyful and was now lost for ever. The whole room fell silent. As his father played, even Aethelric, the rough farmer, sat quietly.

The slaves listened with delight, too, for the joy of hearing the harp in silence while they waited at table was rare for them. When the performer had finished the listeners applauded and Judith smiled at her father. "I must confess that I haven't played that melody since I composed it, after the death of my wife, Eadyth. That was ten years ago and yet it came back to my memory in its fullness."

"I hope that one day you will come down to Dorcic and play for us there." invited Birinus.

"Perhaps." Aethelfled was not going to make any promises at this stage.

"Now, you younger ones, it is time you were abed," their aunt admonished. "You have stayed up very late and we shall all be going to our beds soon." Judith would have liked to stay longer and to have heard more about the God of Love, for the idea of a kind and gentle god appealed to her.

"Will you come again?" she asked the guests.

"Yes, if your father will have us. Better still we would like to talk to your people, if you will give us leave to call a meeting. Perhaps on the hill up which we came, where Brother Paulinus met your daughter would be a good place." Birinus suggested.

"We will talk more of it soon." Aethelfled was more receptive now. Turning to his children he ordered: "Off to bed with you! I'll tell you in the morning what has been agreed."

"And I will withdraw, also, Aethelfled, with your permission." Brunne requested. "I will see the children to their beds first."

"I am not a child!" Judith retorted.

"Ah, then, all the more you know the need for your beauty sleep," her aunt said soothingly, as she led the way. Aethelric took the opportunity at this point. "I must be up early to oversee my herdsmen."

"You have many herdsmen? Are they all slaves or are some free men?" Paulinus enquired, interested as ever in farming life.

"We have many men, and women too, working on our land. Some are thralls, as we call our slaves. Others are free, either by birth or we have given them their freedom when they have deserved it, or even allowed them to buy it, though not many of them have ever been able to afford to do that. We pay them in kind and few of them have coins."

"But you treat them well, I think? The workers we saw as we came from Dorcic gave us that impression."

"Yes, I suppose so. My mother was a good woman," Aethelric paused, as if saddened at the memory of his mother. "She always insisted that even the slaves should be cared for, especially in winter, and would often take food and potions to them and their children when they were sick. Aunt Brunne does what she can now, but she is old and cannot get about as she used to.

Also, I should tell you that there are certain accepted rules for the provisioning of thralls. They are each entitled to ten pounds of corn, a sheep for winter food, a *sester* of beans for spring food and all the whey in summer. The amount for women is less than for men, for their work is easier. The serving maids, dairy maids, cheese-makers and so on don't need as much food as the men who work in the fields, of course!" Aethelric laughed.

Birinus said: "You will forgive me, I hope, but although Paulinus taught me the basics of your language before we left Milano and on the long journey, he had little time to tell me anything about the life of your people, especially country life, about which I do not know a great deal, even in my own country, for I am city born. Which men are free and which are thralls?" asked Birinus.

"The ploughmen are slaves," explained Aethelric. "Theirs is a good job in spring, summer and autumn, but in the winter it is hard for them. Our ploughmen are up at daybreak, they drive the oxen to the field, yoke them, fit the ploughshare and the coulter to the plough..."

"...the coulter?" Paulinus enquired for his own sake as well as for that of Birinus.

"It's an iron blade that's fitted to the front of the plough. The land hereabouts is full of flint stones and they soon blunt the ploughshare."

"We don't have that extra piece where I come from," said Paulinus. "Probably our soil is softer and lighter, for we have more sunshine."

"Yes, sunshine, would that we had more of that! However, the climate is warmer than in north Germania, that is why my great grandsire came here." Aethelric seemed suddenly to have forgotten about his early night, now that they were talking of his favourite subject, working the land. "Anyway," he continued. "Whatever the weather, they must complete at least an acre of land a day, even on the shortest days, though each ploughman is helped by a lad who goads the beasts. After ploughing is finished, as my father said, we now have an *oxherd*, and he fodders and waters the cattle and oxen, and mucks out the *shippon*."

"The *shippon*?" asked Birinus this time. "You must forgive us, we are still learning your language and, though it has far fewer and more simple words than ours, many of them are strange to us."

"Sorry, a shippon is a cattle shed. There the oxherd sleeps with the oxen overnight to guard them. In the morning he waters and feeds the cattle and oxen again and brings them out to the ploughmen.

"You say he guards them overnight?"

"Yes, cattle stealing is very bad hereabouts, although when I buy cattle I am obliged to bring them on to the common pasture with the witness of the village, so that all may know which belong to me and which to the churls."

"So the churls have cattle too?"

"Yes, one or two each. They also own bits of land and have a pig or a goat, maybe even a few sheep, but they don't have much time for looking after their own beasts. The women do much of that sort of work, the old women especially, and the children."

"Of course," Paulinus said. "It is the same with us."

"The swineherd attends to the pigs," continued Aethelric, "the shepherd is also a slave and has to take his flock to pasture and back. He stays with the sheep and, with his dogs to help him, guards against wolves and..."

"You are troubled by wolves too then?" Paulinus cut in.

"Yes, they are worse in winter, of course, and when there are lambs. The shepherd must always be on his guard. From time to time he moves the pens, too, and milks the ewes twice a day. My aunt is very fond of ewe's cheese."

"And who are the churls; the free men?"

"Yes. They have certain rights that slaves don't, of course. If the churls have any quarrel, they can air their views at our *tun moot* [court] and we see that justice is done. If any is found guilty of a crime then he has to pay. There are all sorts of rules laid down for punishments, but fortunately our people are mostly law-abiding and we don't get much trouble. In fact, they are all very useful to us and we try to be good to them.

The huntsman, for example, is a churl, and has rather a good life, I fancy. The swift-footed animals he hunts with hounds; he drives some beasts into nets and stabs them; the boar he ambushes and spears, though it is dangerous work. He gives his prey to us and we in turn, feed and clothe him and see that he gets a good horse. Our fish we buy from the fishermen who live by the river. They have small boats called *coracles* and catch trout, salmon, eels and pike.

The blacksmith is a churl too. His is a great skill, labouring amid fire and sparks, with the sound of blowing bellows and the beating of sledge-hammers. I shouldn't want to work amid all that noise. We value him highly, for in his smithy he makes our swords, spearheads, knives, scythe blades, hammer heads, adzes and axes, all sorts of tools. He's very skilful and often makes much smaller items, too, from bronze, like strap ends, buckles, brooches, pendants, keys, locks, even cups and spoons for use here in the house. All the churls give their services free or for very little wage but, in return, they look to Father and me for help in times of bad harvests or sickness."

"That is so in most countries, I think." said Birinus, "though I don't know much about rural life. As I think I said, I was born in a city and have always lived in towns."

"Bah, towns! We Saxons despise towns and townsmen. We see no point in keeping up all those old Roman buildings, either. We prefer village life and although this is the largest on my lands, I would not have it become a town." Aethelfled spat on the floor to empha-sise his disgust.

"I must to bed now." said Aethelric, conscious that the conversa-tion had taken a turn for the worse again. "I will leave you to attend to the needs of our guests, Father."

"Sleep well my son. Don't forget to warn the cattle-herd about our plans to purchase more cows soon."

"Very well, Father. Goodnight sirs, I may see you in the morning." Aethelric said quietly, as he withdrew.

"Our forefathers didn't all come from the same area." Aethelfled explained. "We are Saxons, from the north of Germania, but other parts of this country have been settled by tribes from further north, the Angles, the Jutes and some from further south, the Frisians. They are wonderful with cattle. We always buy our cows from them. They yield the best milk and in great quantity."

Birinus, however, was not so interested in farming and changed the subject once again by asking: "Is that your helmet and sword hanging on the wall over there?"

"No, that belonged to my great-grandsire. He was killed in battle, defending the life of the king, far to the northeast. Nevertheless, we lost the land and it was not possible to rebury his body, otherwise his helmet, his sword and his war horn would have been buried with him. However his personal servant did escape and faithfully brought these to my grandsire. They have been in our family ever since that day."

"The scabbard of the short sword is heavily ornamented, too." observed Birinus.

Aethelfled, proud of his inheritance, took it down to show to the priest, who admired it. "The scabbard is silver I see, and set with semi-precious stones. The design is unusual too, the pattern is of a snake caught between whirling leaves, and there are letters too, of a kind, like the ones on the ring you wear. All fine workmanship, I notice."

"Yes, this ring is of gold, with runic lettering, it's the type used by my ancestors in the north. They are magical words. They form a spell. In fact, the runes are the strongest form of magic, bought for men by the sufferings of our great god, Odin."

"What does the wording mean?"

"It means 'I stop the bleeding'." Aethelfled explained. "When I was injured in battle, my mother gave it to me."

"She obviously loved you dearly. What wonderful kin you have. You are fortunate to have such love and fidelity in your family."

"Indeed, but like all families, we have our problems and I miss having Eadyth to discuss them with. Brunne does her best, but she is far on in years and is not able to see things from the young peoples' point of view. However, it is too late to speak of my troubles now. Perhaps I could talk with you in the morning?"

"Of course." Birinus readily agreed. "Sometimes it is good to confide in a stranger who may see things a little differently. It is late now, but we thank you for your hospitality, which has been of the highest order. Perhaps you will be kind enough to show us to our beds?"

"I will be pleased to do so." Aethelfled concurred. "This way, sirs."

******

At breakfast next morning, Birinus, accepting slices of ham and some coarse bread which he spread thickly with butter, thanked his host for the good night's sleep that he and Paulinus had enjoyed and enquired: "You were going to tell us of your problems?"

"Yes. As you said last evening, it is sometimes worthwhile to confide in strangers. They often see things from a different angle. My most urgent problem concerns my daughter, Judith. She has gone to the river with her Aunt Brunne, so we may talk freely."

"The Lady Brunne is your brother's widow?" asked Paulinus, who had been silent for some time.

"Yes, Aethelclun was killed by Wulfmaer, our neighbour and he has never paid the *wergild* in full. That is the main reason why we hate him and his family so much!" he declared viciously.

"Why do you...," Paulinus was about to enquire when Birinus cut in:

"Forgive my ignorance. What is wergild?"

"Hold hard, sirs! One question at a time! What were you going to ask, Brother Paulinus?"

"Why do you all have similar names? It must be very confusing!" Paulinus smiled as he helped himself to a boiled egg and broke off another piece of the hard dark brown bread.

"It may be for you, but not for us. You see, just part is the same, generally the first part. This is kept so others will know that we are all part of the same great and indeed, proud family, with the same heroic ancestors. Of course, if one of us is disgraced, this then goes against the family name. Many of we Saxons have the same or similar name. Take Wulfmaer for example. He has five sons: Wulfig, Wulfhelm, Denewulf, Wulfcyne and Ceowulf and here lies the gist of my difficulty."

Aethelfled poured himself some more ale from the huge earthen-ware jug. "Judith has been seen by my fowler in the company of Ceowulf, up on the ridge where the wilgias grow."

Seeing the look of doubt again in Paulinus' eyes, he went on to clarify: "The fowler is, like the huntsman, a churl. He takes fledgling hawks in autumn, tames them and flies them over the winter. In spring he sets them free so as to avoid having to keep them through the summer. Some hawkers don't bother to train new birds each year, preferring to keep them from year to year and then they get fond of them. I don't allow ours to do that!"

"But you were telling us about Wulfmaer's failure to pay the wergild in full and you were going to tell us what the word means." Birinus reminded the Saxon overlord.

"No, he did not and we have been bitter enemies ever since that day, seventeen years ago, when he killed my brother!" Aethelfled's voice took on a violent tone once more. "Our laws set a price on the head of every man, according to his wealth, his lands and the good name of his family. If one man should be slain, the slayer's family must pay for that. The fines are all laid down. The amount to be paid is called the *wergild.* It is supposed to keep down the bloodshed. Wulfmaer had a year to pay and didn't pay it all. Ever since then there has been a blood feud between us. We have sworn oaths to keep apart. His family and mine have agreed never to cross the boundary between our lands. That boundary runs the length of the Long Valley. My lands end at the east of the hill and his start on the Wilgia Ridge."

Sighing deeply, he went on: "Judith had no business going there at all, she knows it is beyond our border." Aethelfled offered more cheese and bread to his guests who accepted gratefully.

"So the meeting between Judith and Ceowulf was just accidental, then? Surely this is no great cause for concern?" asked Birinus gently.

"Huh! It was more than a chance meeting, according to my fowler. It seems he saw them embracing one another. I am so fond of Judith and haven't yet found the courage to talk to her about the matter. Strange, yet I could kill an animal or even a man without flinching." he mused, half to himself.

"God will give you the opportunity soon, of that I have no doubt." reassured Birinus, comfortingly.

"Thank you. Now if you have finished breaking your fast, perhaps you would like to see something of the village before you leave?"

"That would, indeed, be a pleasure. We saw part of it as we came through the west gate."

"Then we shall take a walk to the east, down the hill and I shall show you Wilgia Hill on the other side, where my daughter was seen."

Aethelfled led his guests out of the great hall and into the village. For the most part the earth was beaten flat by the comings and goings of the village folk, but there were clumps of grass at the edges of the paths. Here and there they were being nibbled by goats; tethered to stakes. As they passed among the thatched wooden huts and outhouses, Aethelfled explained the functions of the various buildings, telling his visitors about many of his people. It soon became obvious that this landowner cared passionately for his peoples' welfare.

The air on the hill was fresh and the sky had become clear blue, dotted with fluffy white clouds. As the three men descended into the Long Valley, the trees that overhung the narrow track provided a pleasant, dappled shade and they fell silent for a while. Then Aethelfled spoke again: "Ahead of us is Wilgia Hill."

Turning to Paulinus, Birinus said in Latin: "Wilgia? This is the Salix (willow) is it not, from which bows are made?" Paulinus nodded. Aware of his impoliteness, Birinus apologised, saying: "You mention Wilgia, but these trees do not grow on hills where we come from, they thrive beside water, do they not?"

"There is truth in that." Aethelfled agreed. "We do have large ones of that kind down by the streams that feed the great river and it is from those that we make our bows. These are just a small, stunted creeping variety. They flourish where the clay has bedded the bottoms of ponds and the water lies throughout most of the year. The rest of the hill is covered in golden gorse bushes in early summer. The sight of them warms the heart. We used to use it for bedding our cattle but we have access to it no more."

Again, he sighed deeply. "And there is another loss, for the nettle fields lie in Wulfmaer's land, a little to the north of here."

"Nettles?" checked Paulinus. "The plant with the leaves that sting?"

"Yes, the thralls eat the leaves, they make a nourishing soup. I myself have drunk of it and it tastes good. More importantly, though, they make cloth from these plants and now, although a few of them grow on this side of the valley, our slaves can't get enough of them to make their clothes."

"They make clothes from plants that sting!" ejaculated Paulinus, who nearly tripped over a tree root in his astonishment.

"Yes, they cut and beat the plants. Then the green parts fall off and they dry the fibres from the stems and weave them, though the garments are very coarse and rough to the touch. Slaves have thick skins though!" He roared with embarrassed laughter, lest the priests should think he cared little for his slaves and quickly continued: "There is another side to this quarrel between Wulfmaer's family and mine. On Wulfmaer's lands, to the northwest of this spot, is the village of Aewielm [Ewelme] and streams wherein good dark cress grows. It is another good fresh green food and now we can't get to that village either and they may not come here to sell their produce."

"So, through your continued feud with Wulfmaer you and your family and his too, no doubt, have made for yourselves many disadvantages. I say again that you must learn to forgive one another and then blessings will once more fall upon your households."

"Perhaps." Aethelfled admitted, unwillingly. Lifting his head, as if to change the subject, he said: "Now we have reached the bottom of our hill and are in the Long Valley. This is the boundary of my land. As you can see, it is very beautiful, but now we must turn around and go back to the village."

"You said there was another matter you wished to discuss, now that we are alone?" enquired Birinus, gently.

"Yes. It's Aethelstaen. He is now ten years of age and shows no inclination to be a warrior or even a farmer. I should like him to have an education, to learn his letters, but there is no chance here for such training. I have some learning but not really enough to teach him."

"I could arrange for him to enter a monastery at Aebbandun [Abingdon]." offered Birinus. "It is small, but it was established in Celtic times. I am hoping soon to have it enlarged and could ask if there is a place for an *Oblate* in the *Schola* at the present time."

"Now you will have to explain your words to me!" Aethelfled laughed.

"Gladly." Birinus smiled at the landowner.

"As you probably know, monks are some of the few men who can read and write. Some write new books, but most translate or copy the gospels and other religious works from the Latin. Oblates are the boys sent to live in the monasteries when they are quite young. They work and pray with the monks and study in the *Schola.* They practice their letters on tablets of beeswax, incising them with pointed tools. When the tablets are full, they smooth them out and start again."

Finding it quite hard work to mount the steep hill and yet talk rapidly at the same time, Birinus stopped to gain his breath once more. "The boys are supervised by a *Magister* or schoolmaster. They are there to learn, not just intellectual studies but also the virtues of veracity, piety, humility, diligence and, above all things, charity, in all they do. They have few possessions of their own and are discouraged from having an interest in worldly goods."

Aethelfled was not sure he knew exactly what the priest meant by all those virtues, but he could tell that his guest knew what he was talking about and began to think that a monastic life might suit his quiet young son. "A monk, eh? Hmmm... Is this a place where they teach this Christianity you have been speaking about? Perhaps we should sit here a while before we climb the rest of the hill and you could tell me more?" He pointed to a large fallen oak, upon which the older man sat down gratefully and his younger companion joined him, while Aethelfled sat cross-legged upon the ground.

"Yes, it is home to a small number of pious men who have dedicated their lives to God."

"Hmmm. Maybe that is a good thing but he is surely yet too young to leave home?"

"You need have no fear upon that score. The boys are well cared for. They have extra privileges, a nap after *prandium*, the mid-day meal. They are allowed to eat meat, for they are still growing, otherwise they are fed well on fresh fish, eggs, cheese, butter and vegetables, all of which are produced in the monastery grounds. On special days they get ale to drink, but usually it's well water. Our Magister says 'wine is for the old and wise and not for the young and silly!'"

"Yes, but I would not want him to become soft. We Aethels have always been strong, hardy Norsemen!" the landowner declared proudly.

"This is true, but the boys are subject to a stern discipline. They get beaten if they do wrong or play about during prayers. They must learn the merits of obedience and not to act in any way as having a will of one's own or become puffed up with pride. Also they must never do the least thing untoward without the permission of the Abbot. He represents Christ in the community and should they sin they must prostate themselves and ask for his pardon."

Aethelfled looked thoughtful. "I must ponder further on this matter. It is true that I am anxious for the boy to learn his letters, but I am reluctant for him to give up our gods in favour of your one and only God. I think I must go to this monastery and see for myself what sort of life these men lead."

"Indeed, I believe you should," enjoined Birinus, and Paulinus nodded vigorously. Birinus picked out a small stone from his sandal. "I myself have spent most of my life in monasteries. In fact, I passed several years in one in Italy before I started on this missionary work. It is no soft life I can assure you, on the contrary, it is quite a hard one!"

Returning to the life of the oblates, Birinus told his host: "The boys study their letters and numbers but they also have time for relaxation.

Some play board games, others musical instruments and some even invent riddles to test others. One of the monks there, a former thane from the northwest, told me that your people like puzzles. Here is one he asked me, perhaps you already know the answer?"

"Try me!" challenged Aethelfled.

> 'An enemy robbed me of my origin of life. He removed its skin, soaked it in water and then dried it in the sun. With his knife he scraped off the hair and folded the skin. A feather moved over my surface and left wise markings upon it. I swallowed the dye and this left marks on me. Lastly the man put a cover upon me. What am I?'

"I can't guess," confessed the landowner. "Some of our riddles are very difficult and those from the north are harder still."

"It's a book." smiled Birinus

"I have few books and don't read or write more than I have to," admitted Aethelfled. "That's why I want Aethelstaen to have an education. More and more these days it seems necessary that one member of the family should have some learning. I had not thought of a monastery. It sounds a very busy place to me. How do they get their income? Do they farm?"

Birinus explained: "Monasteries produce all their own food and most other requirements. The monks fish in the river from simple rowing boats. Some work in the fields and vegetable gardens, others in the dispensary and the hospital where they care for the poor when they are ill. There is a church at the heart of the community, a kitchen and refectory where everyone eats together. In addition to all this there is a hostel for poor travellers, though the more important people are usually hosted in the Abbey. It's an ideal life, calm, orderly and virtuous, at least, most of the time." Paulinus smiled, remembering that, even in a monastery things sometimes went awry.

"It does sound more austere than I had thought, but that could do the boy no harm. I like the thought that he might learn how to care for the sick. We sometimes have illness here, or accidents, much as I try to prevent them. I really must go to this monastery and see it for myself."

"Of course, my friend." Birinus agreed. "But perhaps now we should continue up the hill. We must be back at Dorcic before sundown."

The three men continued to walk slowly up the steep slope to the stockaded village and upon their return to the hall were grateful for the ale and sweetmeats that a servant hastily brought in response to his master's command. "We thank you for your kind hospitality." ·Birinus said. "Do remember my invitation to come and play your harp at Dorcic. Also I hope you will agree that I may talk to your people about the one true God and His holy son, Jesus Christ."

"Yes, you may do so. I will not take on your Christianity but I will allow you to talk to my people. I suggest you do so on the hill to the west, near the old Roman well. Name your day."

"It would be as well for us to come on their rest day." stated Birinus, who already knew that Saxon thralls and churls enjoyed few days of rest.

"Rest day! They have workless and partly workless days when we have our festivals to honour our gods, but they are not regular events."

Birinus gently reminded the landowner: "We believe that the one and only true God made the earth in six days and on the seventh day he rested. You should allow one day each week for your people to rest, for from relaxation comes renewed strength and health. We take our rest day on a Son-tag, the day you named after the sun. On that day we shall be at the spot you suggest." Birinus mounted his mare and Paulinus held the bridle.

"So shall it be, then." Aethelfled promised. "You may come on Son-tag and talk to them at mid-tag for one hour, while they eat their food, but they must work first and afterwards." So saying, the landowner bade them "Fare well!" and seemed more receptive towards the monks than he had been when they arrived. He wished them a good journey and turned to go indoors, resolving as he did so that he would talk with Judith this very day about her clandestine meeting with Ceowulf.

******

103

The fowler had not been mistaken in his sighting of the Lady Judith with the young Lord Ceowulf. In fact, when he had seen them it was their third clandestine meeting for they knew that to be seen together would anger both their fathers.

It was a few weeks before in early May when Judith had strolled down to the Long Valley to the north east of the stockaded village and noticed on the Wilgia ridge an old woman trying to prevent a swarm of bees from leaving the braided straw *skep,* where they had stayed quietly all winter. Since honey was the only sweetening stuff known to the Saxons and was the main ingredient of mead it was very valuable. These bees fed on the pollen of the yellow gorse that bloomed in profusion on the hill in early summer and the woman was afraid the swarm might go off to a hole in a tree where they would be less accessible.

As they began to mass, the crone threw handfuls of earth over them and recited an age-long spell:

> *"Settle, women of victory, sink into the ground,*
> *Never fly wild to the wood,*
> *Be as mindful of my advantage*
> *As every man is of food and land."*

Whether it was the spell or the fact that the earth broke the speed of the bees' flight and made them settle nearer and sooner, is open to question, but her activities aroused curiosity in Judith and she dared to venture upwards from the Long Valley onto the hill itself. The old woman turned and looked down towards her.

"Why it's the Lady Judith! You be careful, my dear, for if the Lord Aethelfled or the Lord Wulfmaer should see you beyond your boundary, you would be in trouble for sure. Not that old Hella would give you away. Why, I mind when you were born and all the celebration there was, you being the only girl and now so like your mother, too."

"I shall not linger, but I was interested in your spell and its effect on the bees."

"Ah, old Hella knows many a spell, my dear. I know of all sorts of charms, lucky and unlucky, and," she added menacingly, "I am familiar with many of the goblins, sprites and elves that live hereabouts."

"Yes, so I have heard."

"Anyway, I must go now, for I have much to do. If I were you, I'd go back to your own land. It's not safe to linger."

So saying the old woman scurried away around the hill and out of sight. However, before Judith had reached the bottom of the lower slope she heard the whinny of a horse and, looking upwards, saw a young rider on a fine black stallion with colourful trappings. He was accompanied by a servant on a lesser mount. Judith hurried to reach the safety of the valley but the young man had dismounted quickly and run down the hill to catch up with her before she did so.

"Do not flee. I will do you no harm." he assured her, his heart beating faster than the exercise had caused.

"I am Ceowulf and I know you must be the Lady Judith for I have heard you were a maid of great beauty," he said, flushing slightly. Although he was almost eighteen years of age he was the youngest of five brothers and not used to the company of girls.

"I only came to watch old Hella settle the bees. I have heard that she has power over animals and birds and wanted to see for myself. I must go back to my own land now for if my father knew I had even gone down into the Valley he would be angry."

"That is probably true. Also my father, if he knew that I had been talking to you, would have me whipped." He glanced up at his servant, holding the bridles of the two horses. "No need to fear Cuthwyne. He will not tell. He has been my loyal servant since I was very young."

"Do you come riding often in these parts? I understand your father's lands are much larger than ours."

"That is true. Our territory goes out almost to Oxnaford to the west and to our home near Tame to the north but much of it is flat. This hilly area has always attracted me for it is wild and almost all forest. There is good hunting to be had here."

"But you are not hunting today? You have no bow?"

"No, I am exercising my new stallion, Dunhelm. You can see from here, he is a fine beast even though he is a bit frisky."

"Yes, indeed. I do not ride. It is not thought fit for young ladies to ride. If I wish to travel any distance I am taken in a litter. But I must go now. Old Hella might return and I am afraid to be seen with you."

"Will you come another time? I'd like to see you again," he spoke nervously, afraid of losing this beautiful girl for whom he already felt a warmth of spirit.

"Perhaps," she said, shyly. "I could come next week, on the same day for Father is to go to the Witan at Oxnaford."

"Yes. My father will go to the meeting too. So we could meet safely. Do say you will come!"

"I will come," she said modestly. "But our meeting must not be for long."

"Even a few minutes will help me to get to know you better, though what future there is in it I do not know, for we are forbidden to mention the name of Aethel in our hall."

"Fare well until then!" she said softly and, running quickly down the slope and across the valley she reached the foot of her own hill, breathless and excited.

The following week they kept their appointed tryst. The trusted Cuthwyne kept a look-out for old Hella who lived over the hill or anyone else who might be about this lone and wild place but he saw no one and the young couple were free to converse again.

"Did no one ask why you came out alone, with no handmaid?"

"No. I often go out alone. I have a maid but she is old now, past thirty years I think, and she was happy when I said she should stay and work on my new gown"

"A new gown?" He smiled. "This one befits you very well, I think. The soft green becomes you. The band around your head is of braid matches that around your hem, doesn't it?"

"Thank you, sir. I am fond of green. It is the colour all around us and I am much interested in wildflowers, especially the bluebells. You can smell the perfume from here. I think it drifts on the breeze from that end of the valley." She pointed to the south-east, where the stream ran through the Long Valley down to the lower wood. "My mother knew local flowers and herbs well, but she died some ten years ago. My Aunt oversees the house now, but she knows little of these matters. However, I am teaching myself and as each season passes I learn more."

"I too love natural things though I know little of plants or herbs, I must confess. My interest is more in animals, and not only the ones I hunt." he laughed gently. "I only kill the animals we eat. I never kill just for the sake of killing, though my brothers do so, especially Wulfcyne. He can be very violent when he's aroused and to lose a prey makes him angry and all the more keen to get it in the end. He calls it sport. I call it cruel but it is not the Saxon tradition to be kind. As you know, it is thought soft and we nobles especially must be strong."

"There is a strength in being different from the others," Judith reminded him.

"Yes, I suppose there is." And so, comparing their lives and those of their families they passed almost half an hour when suddenly Cuthwyne gave a low whistle. It might have been a bird, but Ceowulf knew the sound and said quickly. "Someone comes. We must part. Come again tomorrow, early in the morning. Your father will not be back until *Thors-tag* [Thursday]."

Before she could counter his suggestion he was gone, leaping up the hill and jumping through the gorse bushes attracting the attention of old Hella away from Judith, who sped quickly through the grass and over the brook at the bottom of the valley to her own land.

The next day she was there again, this time even earlier than before and clad in a gown of pale saffron, edged with a strip of woven cloth in hues of deeper yellow and green. She had not, however, remembered that the Valley was a frosty hollow, and, although her dress had long sleeves, she felt suddenly very cold and afraid. Fortunately she had thought to throw a stole around her neck, which she now wound over her head, laying the ends across her throat. As she waited, thinking perhaps that Ceowulf might not keep the tryst, she began to shiver and wished that she had thought to wear a cloak.

Only a few moments later Ceowulf himself arrived. He hopped down quickly from his steed and leaped down the hill to where the girl was waiting.

"By Thor! It's cold down here and yet it is the month of May. The mist lies late in valleys like these and keeps the cold with it while the sun shines already high upon the hills. Why! You are shivering!" He was glad of the chance to wrap the girl in his heavy, long, grey woollen cloak, fastened at the shoulder with an exquisite brooch, fashioned in the shape of a trefoil.

"Yes, I should have worn my cloak I know but I slipped out before my maid could question my going. What a lovely brooch," she said, fingering it gently. "A trefoil. That is a pretty little plant, it grows along the ground in summer and has a tiny yellow flower, you know"

Again they talked for a long time, glad of the warmth of each other and the great cloak that enveloped them both. This time there was no call from Cuthwyne who kept guard patiently.

However, even Cuthwyne did not notice Aethelfled's fowler, a man used to concealing himself in order to catch and shoot birds. He was still on his master's land but espied the young couple standing, albeit low down on the hill, but beyond the boundary, in the land belonging to Wulfmaer. "It is true," he said to himself, "he appears to be doing the Lady Judith no harm but the master should hear of it for no good will come of a meeting between these two, so sworn are their families in the old blood-feud."

"When can we meet again?" asked Ceowulf after about an hour, which seemed to have gone like the wind in winter.

"I don't know. I must not do this too often or I will be found out."

"I don't know either but I will think of a way for I must meet with you again my sweet love. Can you read a letter if I send one?"

"No." she admitted. "I have no learning. Girls like me are taught spinning, weaving, dying and embroidery and how to control the servants but not reading or writing. Even my father and brothers cannot do that though I know that my father would like my youngest brother, Aethelstaen, to be educated."

"Fear not! I shall find a way. I shall think of you all the time until we come together once more. Trust me. Meantime, fare well!" And so saying they parted, and the fowler, having seen that the Lady Judith was once more safely returned to her own territory made his way through the woods to where he knew a flock of wildfowl would soon be overhead, coming back for the summer.

******

As Birinus had promised, at noon on the following Son-tag he and Paulinus were seated on a fallen log near the old Roman well on the hill that overlooked Aethelfled's lands all the way down to the river. As usual both monks were clad simply in their brown robes but this time Paulinus had no need of his staff for they had journeyed from Dorcic on the brown mare. Birinus however held his Bishop's *crozier*, a rather ornamental form of a shepherd's crook, while Paulinus held one of the very valuable books, a beautiful set of manuscripts of the four Gospels, illumined with bright hand-coloured drawings and enhanced with gold. These Birinus had brought with him from Milan.

Quite a few people were there already when they arrived. Judith and her young brother, Aethelstaen, had watched them for over half an hour as they made their way up the path through the great open fields of wheat and barley, some of which were newly created from land that was formerly wooded and all typical of the Saxon country-side. Other portions of land were given over to grass for hay, so much needed since the Romans brought horses to England.

"Good day to you, Father Birinus. You are very welcome. I am sorry that my father is not here, nor Aethelric either, but as you know, Father is not keen to hear about your God and Aethelric, though he might be, has much work on the farm and does not approve of the thralls having free time like this."

"Pax Vobiscum, [Peace be with you] my children." Birinus touched the heads of the noble girl and her brother in a blessing. "I am glad to see so many of you here."

"And more are coming, from all directions! Look!" said Aethelstaen, unusually excited at the sight. It was very apparent that he liked to learn of new things. And they did come, dozens of them, young and old, many of them carrying the tools of their trade. Most of the men wore only skins, some wolf skins, held on with belts. On these hung knife scabbards and pouches to hold a sharpening stone, while a few of the women still carried a cloth or a flat soft broom, made from straw. It seemed as if they had dared not leave their tools behind.

When Birinus felt that most of his audience was assembled he began to speak. Although he was an educated man and had fluent Latin, Greek and even Gallic, he had found the Saxon language difficult to learn and even harder to pronounce. Therefore he spoke slowly but clearly, sometimes pausing for a more obscure word, with occasional help from Paulinus.

"Good people! You have always known fear. All your gods are harsh and you are full of dread and superstitions. You are told you must sacrifice animals to your gods, especially in the Blood month, but I have come to tell you that these ideas are all mythical. In truth, I bring you good news! There is only one God, and he is the God of Love. He is not vengeful. He is forgiving. He is not awe-inspiring but loves us and wishes us to love him and, just as important, to love one another."

"We mostly do love one another, Father!" shouted a man at the front, who carried a pickaxe. His teeth, like so many of the village people, were blackened and badly worn from biting on grit which came off millstones when wheat was ground into flour. "That is, except them that hate us and then we hate them too, sometimes for many generations!"

"This I know and I am here to persuade you to give up these violent ways. For you this is a new way of thinking and I realise it will take time but believe me, it works!"

"And what if that man shall do evil to me?" enquired another, probably a carpenter, for he held a chisel in his hand.

"Then you must do him no evil in return. Rather you shall try to do good to him. I see you are a carpenter? I come to tell you of our Saviour, Jesus of Nazareth, who followed the same trade as you. He was persecuted for teaching as I do about the Love of God and men put him to death on the cross!" So saying, Birinus fingered the cross around his neck. "But Love overcame death. He rose from the dead and was seen by hundreds of people afterwards, still preaching his message: 'Love the Lord thy God with all thy heart and Love thy Neighbour as thyself.'"

The crowd fell silent at the thought of evil done to a good man. On the whole Saxons had very strong thoughts on fairness. Evil would be returned for evil but good men usually avoided the ill will of others.

"Who are you? And where do you come from? Why do you carry a shepherd's crook? That is no ordinary one, like mine," said a young man who wore a long brown wool cloak, fastened with a simple pin at his shoulder. In one hand he had his crook and in the other, wrapped in the cloak, a newborn lamb.

"I am like you," said Birinus, who had the gift of relating to his audience. "I too, am a shepherd, but of men. Jesus Christ often called himself the Good Shepherd for he too came from a land where sheep grazed on the hills as they do here and he knew a lot about sheep.

He told many stories about them." At this point Birinus related the parable of the lost sheep and told his audience about many of the miracles performed by Jesus only about six hundred years previously.

He sometimes referred to the Gospels, showing his audience the exquisitely lettered work but he did not need to read from them for he knew almost all of them by heart. As he spoke they ate their food and drank the thin ale they had brought in skin bags. After a while the younger children grew tired of the man talking and went off at a distance to play football with a pig's bladder stuffed with wool but their parents listened avidly.

Birinus spent almost an hour talking to the people and answering their questions. "This time next week I shall come again but mainly to speak to the river folk down by the jetty. I hope you will be there. Meantime," he said, standing up slowly, "may the God of Love go with you and bless all those you love and even those you find it difficult to love." He could see that few of them were convinced of this new idea of a God of Love but some talked together as they went back to their work.

Only Judith and her younger brother remained when all the workers had departed to their various tasks. "We shall come again, won't we Aethelstaen? I like the sound of your God. I wish my father would learn to forgive his enemies, especially Wulfmaer, our neighbour." She blushed as she spoke, for she was thinking as she had so often done in recent weeks, about Ceowulf.

"So you could then meet with young Ceowulf without anxiety?" asked Birinus, gently.

"You know about Ceowulf?" she enquired, astonished.

"Yes, my child. Have no fear for God is with you. I think we shall see a reconciliation between your family and his before too long and then you and Ceowulf will be free to meet again."

"How can this be? My father has always said there is a blood feud between us and nothing can break that, I know."

"Have faith, daughter. The king, Cynegils, is to come to Dorcic soon. I have spent many hours with him and I can tell you in confidence that I believe he wishes to become a Christian. I have been instructing him in our faith for some time now. Moreover, Oswald, the saintly King of Northumbria, is planning to marry

Cynegils' daughter, Cyneburga, but he will only do so if the King's family is all baptised. If this all takes place, and Paulinus and I pray constantly that it does, then all the thanes loyal to the King will have to give up these long-standing hostilities and agree to forgive one another."

"Oh, Father, I pray too that it will be so."

"And I!" said Aethelstaen, unexpectedly. "For all this talk of hatred is displeasing to me. My father says he is thinking of sending me to study in a monastery. I think I should like that."

"Then let the four of us pray together that it may all come about for the prayers of children are dear to God." So saying, Birinus and Paulinus knelt down and the two aristocratic children followed suit closing their eyes and clasping they hands together as the monks did.

> *"Our Father, who art in heaven, hallowed be thy name. Thy kingdom come. Thy will be done on earth, as it is in heaven. Give us this day our daily bread and forgive us our trespasses as we forgive those who trespass against us. Lead us not into temptation, but deliver us from evil. For Thine is the kingdom, the power and the glory, for ever and ever. Amen."*

"What a lovely prayer. Will you teach it to me?" Judith begged.

"Yes, my child. Remember the main part though. It is God's will and not ours that shall be done. But as His will is that we should all love one another it seems to me that your wish will come to pass so hold to that thought until we meet again."

Joyfully, Judith and her brother returned to the Long Hall in the stockaded village, for it seemed to them both as if, with the coming of the news of this God of Love that both their wishes, hers for Ceowulf and his for a chance of education, would be met in full.

The following week Birinus and Paulinus were again ready to talk to the people. Even more came this time for they were sitting on a jetty beside the Tamisa, the dark river, and some folk had crossed over in the small coracles from which they caught fish. Once again Birinus showed his gift for empathising with the people in the terms they understood. He told them about Peter, James, John and Andrew, the fishermen, and the story of the time when the disciples had been out all night on the Lake of Galilee and had caught nothing and how Jesus had said "Let down your nets to the right side of your boat and you will have fish in abundance," and how it was so.

Gradually those who had been to his previous sermon began to understand and believe Birinus and to want to learn more about the God who loved and seemed so different from the old harsh Nordic gods that their ancestors had brought with them. Birinus also told them as they ate their mid-day meal about the five loaves and two fish and how with them Jesus had fed five thousand people. "And even then twelve baskets were filled with what was left over!" he announced, in conclusion.

Again, when the crowds had gone about their work the monks were left alone with the two young aristocrats. "I think we can recite the Lord's Prayer now you have said it again." said Aethelstaen, who seemed to have a very quick and retentive memory. At once they all knelt down and prayed together.

"God has heard your prayers," Birinus told them as they stood up again. "Cynegils is to come to Dorcic next month and Oswald is coming down the coast by boat and then up the river. There will be a great meeting and a baptism of all of Cynegils' people. It will be a foolhardy man who stays away."

"Oh, thank you, Father!"

"Thank not me, my child. Thank God and bless His name always, for He has given us many good things. I shall be on the hill again next week and will tell you more then. By that time your father will have heard the word too."

The following Sunday Birinus and Paulinus were again by the well and this time news of Cynegils' coming to Dorcic had spread far and wide and folk flocked to hear the word of God, though some still stayed away not just because of their work but because they did not want to leave their old ways.

Birinus had promised to be on the grassy hill that was later to bear his name, Berin's Hill, and sure enough the following Son-tag, he was there. He told the people about the Ten Commandments of Moses and the newer version that Jesus had given to the world. The poorer folk among his audience understood well the meaning of the Lord's words:

113

'Blessed are the poor in spirit: for theirs is the kingdom of
*   heaven.*
Blessed are they that mourn: for they shall be comforted.
Blessed are the meek: for they shall inherit the earth.
Blessed are they which do hunger and thirst after
*   righteousness: for they shall be filled.*
Blessed are the merciful: for they shall obtain mercy.
Blessed are the pure in heart: for they shall see God.
Blessed are the peacemakers: for they shall be called the
*   children of God.*
Blessed are they which are persecuted for righteousness'
*   sake: for their's is the kingdom of Heaven.*

Love your enemies, do good to those who hate you. Bless
them who curse you and pray for them who despitefully use you.
For if you love only those who do good to you, what thanks have
you from your Father who is in Heaven? Sinners do only that.
Judge not and you shall not be judged. Give and it shall be given
to you in good measure and running over."

At the end of his sermon, Bishop Birinus talked quietly to Judith and Aethelstaen. Even Aethelric had come this time but confessed he could not stay long. "I have been surprised how much harder the thralls have laboured since you have been coming. They have more than made up the time they have not worked." he admitted, "and everyone in the village seems to be more cheerful though some are still for the old gods and omens. If as you say Cynegils is to be baptised then we must all do the same for we thanes, our churls and thralls must do as the king wishes. It is part of our way of life, each is dependent upon the other and loyal in all matters."

"Yes, my Lord Aethelric. I hope and pray that happier times are coming for you and your people though I am not foolish enough to think it will all change at once. Many folk are slow to accept a different way of life. To what extent things will alter we shall have to wait and see. Meantime, may God go with you all."

******

It was the greatest Witan that Wessex had ever experienced. Months before King Cynegils arrived all the area around Dorcic had been alive with the sound of hammering and sawing and the rustle of thatchers at work. A huge Witan Hall was erected for the use of the King and his *ealdormen* during the day, its gables crested with antlers. At night they stayed in the 'castle' at *Baensingtun* [Benson]. In effect this was not much more than a fortified village, which had belonged to the chief of the British Gwissae and where the huge thatched timber 'palace' had been quickly refurbished. A church, almost as large as the Hall, was also constructed at Dorcic beside the river. It could hold a hundred and was made ready for the Bishop to celebrate High Mass on the morning after the great baptismal ceremony.

Many a new house, too, was quickly erected in the usual fashion from wooden poles, roof timbers and thatch. Shelters for animals, small stalls, benches for the onlookers, there was no end to the work, as carts trundled in with more and yet more timber from the wooded uplands and rushes brought in from the marshes near the 'dark river'.

The news about the baptism of the King, his family and his court, to say nothing of the visit of King Oswald and his entourage, had spread like wildfire around all of Wessex and for weeks all manner of men had come to Dorcic for many reasons. It was quickly realised that this would be a great chance to find work and to make sales of every kind. Every free man who could get away from his thane's estate was there, offering his services. Builders, thatchers, carpenters, smiths, people selling baskets, tools, rope, and leather goods; there was no end to them.

To cater for them all sorts of provision merchants came too, butchers, bakers, fishmongers, vegetable sellers, mead and ale brewers and enterprising pedlars selling every sort of trinket you could imagine, especially crosses. There were wooden crosses on strings to be worn by men around their necks and bronze ones on chains for the women. Stalls were set up selling big wooden crosses, gold and silver crosses and candles of all sizes, drinking horns and pottery for every purpose.

Much of the pottery had, like the timber, come from the area around the palisaded village in the hills where there were still very large clay deposits. By Saxon times, sand and horse dung were sometimes added to give the vessels strength. The produce was still very simple, beakers, round pots, some with lips and some big pitchers with spouts and handles. Shallow dishes were often made by rolling the clay into long thin lengths and winding them around and around in a coil before they were baked.

Saxon pots were fired in a very simple oven, just a shallow hole in the ground, about a metre across, with a little basketwork dome over it, covered with clay. At one side of the shallow pit was a deeper one, in which the potters made a bonfire and the heat from this passed along the small horizontal hole connecting the two to enter the kiln and leave through a hole in the top. Each time a batch of pots was made a new oven had to be constructed, but the work was simple and soon done.

At this time the potters were working during every hour of daylight for they were quick to realise that this great festival would be a good place to sell their wares and every day carts full of them creaked down the track from the uplands to Dorcic by the river.

Jugglers and minstrels also came in to entertain the crowds especially in the evening, though the work did not stop until late in the day as there seemed to be so little time before the great week of the Witan, that was due to start on the first of September.

It was a good time to have chosen, for the harvest was in and the people were in a celebratory mood. Cynegils had come to the town two days before his guests, in order to see that everything was prepared to his satisfaction. The chief *ealdorman* of Oxnaford had overseen the work and the king was pleased. The role of an ealdorman varied in different parts of the country. The name gave rise to the word alderman, who was responsible for a burgh, or town, but he could also be in charge of a shire, or indeed later on, over reeves controlling several shires and this has left us with the title of *earl*. Most of these ealdormen, however, were each principally responsible for one shire and lived in its chief town. Later they became *shire reeves* or later, *sheriffs*.

This man might well have been apprehensive, for there was much at stake. The holy and victorious Oswald, King of Northumbria, who was coming to marry Cynegils' daughter, ruled over all the land from the River Mersey to the River Humber, northwards as far as Hadrian's Wall. It was a huge territory, almost a third of England. A liaison between them would result in a very powerful union.

Eventually the great day did arrive and with it bright sunshine as Oswald's galley was rowed up the river *Tamisa* [Thames] which, at that time, was navigable as far as Oxnaford, though boats did have to be hauled up slopes in certain places. This ship had a shallower draught than the one with black sails that had brought him down the east coast to Essex and up as far as the tiding point of the Tamisa, but it was magnificent, nonetheless and bedecked with banners. Cynegils stepped forward to greet his guest and everyone could see that this visit from the Chief of Northumbria was a great honour for the King of Wessex.

From this point, where the river Tamisa was joined by its tributary, the Tame, which flowed through Dorcic, the procession made its way on horseback, with pack animals bringing up the rear, laden with the possessions of Oswald and his court. The Saxons were not a people given to pomp and ceremony, but the train was impressive, nonetheless.

The two men spent the remainder of the day in conference, together with Birinus and the ealdormen who served both kings.

In the morning, soon after sunrise, King Cynegils and all his family with Oswald and his entourage, made the long procession to Dorcic on foot, as a mark of humility. Bishop Birinus was there to receive them and all was prepared for the great baptismal ceremony.

It was of course, King Cynegils who first came to the font and everyone murmured their approval as the Bishop uttered the holy words:

"I baptise you in the name of the Father, the Son and the Holy Ghost."

Oswald, who was standing as sponsor or godfather to the King, immediately stepped forward, took the hand of Cynegils and said: "I am happy to receive you fresh from these regenerating waters as my adopted son."

Then came the turn of Cynegils' daughter, Cyneburga, to whom Oswald was betrothed and with her came her mother and all the ladies of the court, followed by the ealdormen of Oxnaford, Aethelfled, Wulfmaer and all the other ealdormen and their families. It is believed that about one thousand people were baptised that day.

The kings were more than just chieftains, the word *cyning* meant 'man of the family' and royal families were proud of their origins,

117

keeping their genealogies alive in verse that was recited at every great feast. The banquet that night was no exception, save for the fact that, again, there was very little of the boasting and swaggering that usually set the tone at Saxon festivals. But nevertheless, the scene was a joyful one. The King and all his people from the ealdormen down to the slaves seemed to be happy on this great occasion.

At this magnificent dinner, Birinus, on receiving from King Cynegils the gift of the city of Dorchester as his *Episcopal See*, [an area committed to the care of a Bishop] told the monarch: "Before I left Rome, I promised His Holiness, Pope Honorius 'to sow the seeds of our holy faith in the most inland and remote regions of the English, where no teacher has been before me.' I shall continue my work until all Wessex is converted to our faith." At his words there was a great cry of *'Waes-thael!'* and the drinking horns were raised in unison.

The next day the great Witan was held on the opposite bank of the River Tame, tributory of the Thames, where Birinus was later to build a cathedral church and a great abbey. Bishop Birinus with Brother Paulinus and monks from small monasteries scattered all over Wessex who had maintained their Christian status very quietly since Celtic times, celebrated Holy Communion in the new church beside the river that morning.

Again, the weather was fine and sunny and the scene was set for the momentous occasion. A long stretch of grass had been fenced off and at one end of it the Great Hall had been erected for the two kings and their courts. Inside King Oswald and King Cynegils sat side by side on huge wooden thrones etched with patterns of gold and inlaid with semi-precious stones. These had been placed upon a dais and before them, in rows down each side, were the ealdormen. Behind them were their thanes, as many as had been able to make the journey. All the local ones were there, of course, among them Aethelfled and Wulfmaer who still steadfastly refused to speak to one another.

When much of the main business of the Witan was concluded and the meeting was beginning to break up, the chief ealdorman of Oxnaford called Bishop Birinus to him and also sent for his two thanes, Aethelfled and Wulfmaer. "Before the Bishop, and in the presence of Almighty God, I command you both, Aethelfled of Stoc

Rah and Wulfmaer of Tame, that you embrace and forgive one another. From this day hence you are to cease your blood feud!" Reluctantly the two men shook hands, though both looked far from happy as the ealdorman walked away.

This was the first time that the name of *Stoc Rah* had been given to the stockaded settlement in the rough wooded upland. Similar names were later also applied to the palisaded villages nearer to the river, which later became North Stoke, South Stoke and Little Stoke.

Birinus remained and in his ecclesiastical garments seemed more authoritative than he had been at the dinner table or on the hillside. "You are now both baptised as sons of God and the dissension between you must cease, as Christianity requires that you forgive one another. This means more than just a handshake. You must give me your word that you will quarrel no more and that you will allow your children to mix with one another quite freely."

Aethelfled nodded slowly and Wulfmaer said gruffly: "My son, Ceowulf, tells me he wishes to marry your daughter Judith. Has she said aught to you about it?"

"Yes. It seems they love one another. I must say it is touching to see them together. It reminds me of when I was young and courted Eadyth."

"Ah, I remember her well. She was a beautiful woman. You must feel the loss of her deeply. Let me see, it was some ten years ago that she died, was it not?"

"That is so. I am surprised that you remember that."

"Yes, I do and have sometimes regretted our blood feud, especially since we are close neighbours. I never paid the wergild in full because I felt it unfair, but my son shall marry your daughter and I shall provide a home for them on a piece of the best part of my land."

"That is good of you." returned Aethelfled reluctantly. "I shall, of course, provide Judith with a generous dowry."

"So be it, then. I am glad to see peace between you," said Birinus, feeling somehow that the reuniting of these two thanes was at least equal in the sight of God as the baptism of their king the previous day.

The two neighbouring landowners went off to discuss the betrothal terms and to give the good news to Ceowulf and Judith, who were waiting anxiously together outside.

"You will be glad to learn that we have agreed to your being wed," said Aethelfled. "There is no close relationship between our two families and the marriage should suit us all."

"You had better be thinking of what you will give to Judith as her *morngifu*," Wulfmaer later teased his son because this present was given by a husband to his wife after the first night of marriage, if she had pleased him. Also laid down in the marriage agreement was what she would get if he predeceased her, usually half of his possessions, or if they had a child, all of them, unless she remarried.

"I have already promised Judith a necklet of gold beads, with gold and garnet pendants and a solid gold cross." Ceowulf announced proudly and Judith smiled.

Aethelfled said: "We have much to talk about then. Let us get away from these throngs of people and sit by the river to make plans for the wedding. If you will provide them with a house, Wulfmaer then I shall build a church for them to be married in. Let it be as soon as possible!"

Within three months a small church was erected on Aethelfled's land on the hill at Ipsden, near the point where Birinus had preached for the first time. It was, like so many of the churches erected at the time, just built of timber and thatch. Eventually this thane built several other chapels like this at North Stoke, Little Stoke, South Stoke, Newnham, Woodcote and Checkendon, though they were all later reconstructed in stone.

Judith and Ceowulf were married on Christmas Day. Judith, who liked doing embroidery with her maids, using the beautiful cylindrical workbox containing scissors, threads, bronze and bone needles that her aunt Brunne had given to her as a wedding present, made the church vestments, stoles and the altar cloths during subsequent years.

Aethelfled sent Aethelstaen to the monastery at Abingdon where he did well and stayed on. Eventually he helped in the work to enlarge it.

When he died, Aethelfled left in his will a clause that allowed for the freedom of his thralls, as an act of Christian charity, 'to the glory of God and the redemption of my soul.'

******

The Saxons were not an intellectual race but when they took Christianity upon themselves they became pious in their simple way. Theirs was a pure faith unsullied by sophistication. They realised their many gods, even though worshipped and appeased, were fickle and so Christianity, with its love of one's fellow man appealed to them as being more believable. But they still buried grave goods with their dead and many superstitions from the pre-Christian era persisted well into the end of Anglo-Saxon England.

The cathedral church that Birinus built at Dorchester became for a long time the centre of Christianity in the south and west of England. Since the closing of the Roman camp, Dorchester had just become a trading post between the Catuellauni to the north, the Atrebates to the south and the Dubonni to the west.

The building of the cathedral revived the town completely. Birinus exercised his ecclesiastical jurisdiction throughout the whole of the West Saxon kingdom. His zeal, in founding and consecrating churches in his diocese, was especially praised by Bede, who wrote: "many churches were built and dedicated by him."

During his time in Dorchester, Birinus also devised plans for parishes to be created all along the side of the river and in the nearby uplands. Archbishop Honorius, based at Canterbury, began the formation of parishes in England and he probably instructed Birinus to do likewise. Birinus was wise and set up his parishes in long strips rising from the River Thames, so that each parish had a piece of river frontage, water meadows, upland grazing and woodland, high up in the hills.

Many churches were very soon erected throughout Wessex by the liberality of the king, the generosity of the ealdormen and the wealthier thanes. They raised churches on their own manorial estates, for the use of themselves, their dependants and friends.

Thorpe, in his *Ancient Laws and Institutions* explained: 'Each year added a number of these sacred edifices. Worldly, as well as religious motives concurred in their erection, till at last the existence of a church on the lands of a proprietor became the necessary qualification for the elevation to the rank of a thane.'

Birinus enjoyed his bishopric for fourteen years and died at Dorchester, where he was buried in AD 650. Afterwards his body was taken to Winchester where the King instituted a new and larger

Bishopric when Mercia threatened war again. The feast day of Birinus in the *Roman Martyrology* was 3rd December, the day when he was reputed to have died of a snake-bite.

In 644, Penda, King of the neighbouring Mercians, who remained heathen, drove Cenwalh, who was by then King of the West Saxons, out of his kingdom and "carried out his ravages over these and other parts." However, in spite of his victories Christianity revived everywhere; Wessex quietly became Christian again and Penda's son, Wulfhere, received Christian baptism.

After the death of Penda in 654, Wulfhere was chosen King of Mercia and Britain remained Christian and its ecclesiastical life was subject to decrees from the Pope. Penda's daughter, also Cyneburga, became canonised for her religious life.

The peace that Christianity brought about was shattered in the ninth and tenth centuries by the arrival of the Danes and the Vikings. First of all they came only to the eastern shores of England, but gradually they made their way up the Thames and by 870 the Vikings had reached Reading. Luckily for the folk on these hills, King Alfred drove them back, about the year 878. This Christian king did not kill his captives but instead encouraged them to become Christians. Alfred died in 899.

From this time on, under a series of Saxon kings, England was split mainly into seven earldoms and life gradually became more orderly and settled although the Thames Valley and the Chiltern Hills continued to be ravaged by the Vikings, Wallingford being burned to the ground twice.

In fact, it was not until the accession of King Canute in 1017 that England enjoyed peace of a kind that lasted until the Norman Conquest.

******

Today Birinus is keenly remembered in Dorchester and the story of his founding of the Cathedral and the Abbey are shown in the Museum there.

In Stoke Row he is commemorated by the name of Berin's Hill that descends from the Nuffield Road down to Well Place and its farm. It was by the old Roman Well, hidden in private woods halfway down the hill, that he first preached to the Saxon people.

The Old Place

Chapter 6. The Norman Baron and the Saxon Maid: 1068

After the Battle of Hastings in 1066, William the Conqueror tried unsuccessfully to enter London and had to find another place to cross the Thames. He had an old friend in Wallingford and so marched in a westerly direction, along the south side of the river. His ally was the Saxon lord, Wigod, who governed the *burgh* [fortified town] that had been created in the ninth century by King Alfred as part of his defences against the Danes, who actually got as far as Reading in 871. Later on they got further still, when Guthrum reached as far west as Devon in 877.

Wallingford's Saxon walls are still very visible today. The earth banks can be seen in the Kinecroft and Bullcroft to the west of the town that was laid out in a grid system. Its position on the river made it a great centre for a market, and a growing trade led to the need for a *Mint* [where coins are made] started by Athelstan (924-939). Creating money was the right of the King, but the manufacturing was done in provincial centres. Wallingford was one of them and minted between 925 and 940. The Mint is believed to have been at the top of Goldsmith's Lane, although no gold coins were struck here, only silver ones.

Although a Saxon himself, Wigod greeted William warmly, enabled him to cross the river at the ford and enter the gates of the burgh. William stayed a while in the town, which is about ten miles west of Stoke Row, before he took his army on to Berkhamsted further northeast. There he received loyal homage of the surviving English leaders and went on south to London. He entered the city in

123

triumph and was crowned in Westminster Abbey on Christmas Day 1066.

Before that, however, during his stay at Wallingford, William attended the wedding of his favourite leader, Robert D'Oyley of Normandy, to Wigod's only daughter, Ealdgyth. Before leaving this important crossing town William gave orders that D'Oyley should build a castle to defend it. The knight obediently began at once to turn his father-in-law's residence into a strongly fortified castle that was completed in 1071. This, of course, was not the stone castle that was built later and stood for centuries, but just a *motte and bailey*, a moated hill with a wooden keep on the top. For all his loyal work D'Oyley was granted several portions of land in South Oxfordshire and in 1084, his only child, Matilda, married Miles ('Milo') Crispin. In 1090 D'Oyley died and Milo became Lord of the Honor and Castle of Wallingford. In fact, the parish of Newnham was granted as a part of the Honor and the income from it was used for the Castle maintenance.

In time Wallingford became one of the strongest castles in the land. William the Conqueror never forgot the support he had from the town in 1066, and so, in 1069 when he enforced a *curfew* [the hour when all fires had to be put out] at 8.00 pm, he allowed Wallingford an extra hour and its bell did not have to toll until 9.00 pm.

Every acre that the King did not want for himself he granted to his supporters and kinsmen, especially the latter on whom he felt he could usually rely and whom he had often known for longer than the English barons.

Among the many other favours that King William I conferred on his supporters was the granting of the parish of Mongewell [from the Saxon for Monk's Well] to the proud and powerful Count William de Warenne, the Conqueror's son-in-law. He was also given Rotherfield Peppard on the top of the Chiltern Hills. He owned several other towns and lands in England, too, including Lewes in Sussex. A little later part of Newnham was taken to extend Mongewell to allow de Warenne to have one long, narrow piece of land that enabled him to travel freely from Rotherfield Peppard up in the hills, down through Mongewell to Wallingford and the river. This made it possible for him to travel safely to London by water, the roads to the capital from Oxfordshire being so few, of poor quality and dangerous.

Although, according to the Anglo-Saxon Chronicles, Wallingford was almost burned to the ground in 1006 by the Danes, who again came up from the Isle of Wight through Hampshire to Reading, it seems to have made a speedy recovery and by 1066 was a prosperous town of some importance.

A little before the Conquest, all two hundred and seventy-six houses in the town belonged to King Edward the Confessor, but the Doomsday survey in 1086 recorded that there were four hundred and ninety-one houses there, of which only two hundred and sixty-three belonged to the King. In this important book, Wallingford was stated to be the chief town in Berkshire [in which county it stood at the time], outstripping its later rivals, Reading, Windsor and Newbury.

****

In the spring of 1084, a remarkable procession was travelling through the valley to the east of Stoke Row, having come down the hill from Rotherfield Peppard, and entered the parish of Mongewell along the foot of Witheridge Hill. The procession wound its way on, through Englysche Lane [so named by Benet Englysche who later set up English Farm there], on to Tuffield [later Nuffield] and eventually down to Wallingford.

The column was long and slow moving. At its head were a few mounted soldiers and some bowmen on foot but hard on their heels came the great white steed of Count William de Warenne, son-in-law to William the Conqueror, who he had supported loyally at the Battle of Hastings some twenty years before. With his blond hair, shaved at the back and a fringe over his ice-cold blue eyes, de Warenne was every inch a Norman nobleman born of Viking stock. Everyone was terrified of him, and with good reason, for he was very ambitious and let little stand in his way.

He and his *entourage*, consisting of his family, courtiers and servants, had spent several weeks making the journey from his principal abode in Lewes, Sussex, where he had settled when the town was given to him by the Conqueror in recognition of his services at the Battle of Hastings. He encouraged Lewes to grow and prosper and in 1077 founded the Priory of St Pancras there.

Also, like so many Norman Barons he saw to it that the people on his lands began to use a surname, usually taken from their trade, any physical feature they may have had, or where they lived.

As de Warenne, de Torigny and their parties passed over the bridge everyone got out of their way, for it was obvious that these were important visitors to the castle. Robert D'Oyley and his wife were on the drawbridge to greet them.

Count William de Warenne spoke first with the customary greeting: "May peace attend thy gate. Joy within thee wait to bless the soul of every guest!"

Robert D'Oyley replied: "We bid you welcome William and Pierre, too; all is prepared for your visit. As you can see, we are much occupied with arrangements for the wedding on the morrow, but I am sure we shall have some time to *parley* [French, speak together]."

The Lady Ealdgyth, herself half Saxon, waited until her husband had taken his guests inside and then she too, with her ladies, greeted the Lady Gundrada, although they were careful to try and speak the French that the Normans had brought with them.

Her maid, Margaria, however, found it very difficult to understand because French was so very different from her own language. She had only been in the service of Lady Gundrada for a few weeks before their departure from Lewes and she had felt unhappy many times but none more than now. Also she found all the noise and bustle very disturbing for she had grown up in a quiet small Saxon town in Sussex where Gundrada's family were the landowners.

Being Norman nobility, Count William de Warenne and his wife the Lady Gundrada were given a room within the Castle. Gundrada was given a room to herself and she soon set about seeing that Margaria unpacked the very finest of her clothes and laid them out on the bed. At first she was only concerned with those she would wear for the dinner that was to be held that evening. While she was with others this lady put on airs and graces and treated her maid with apparent kindness, but as soon as they were alone she resorted to her natural bullying manner, saying irritably: "For the sake of God, girl, make haste, do! How slow you are!!" Desperately Margaria tried to hurry but she was so upset that she made mistakes that she might not normally have made.

Gundrada did nothing to help her servant but just sat in a high-back chair and watched her constantly, making cutting remarks from time to time. "By the Good Lord, how clumsy you are! Don't put my travelling cloak with my best gown, put it on the peg, over there. By the Holy Saints, how slow you are, why I could run rings around you!" Poor Margaria found herself thinking of her mother, who had always been so kind to her and of her pretty little sister who she loved and who now seemed so far away. As soon as Gundrada had gone down into the Great Hall, leaving her maid to finish the unpacking, Margaria burst into tears. For several days now she had felt like doing so but now the tears came in floods and despite her efforts to do so she could not stop her silent weeping.

In the next room, however, Beric, the page to William de Warenne, was also unpacking but his master had left him to do it by himself. He felt confident that although the lad was only thirteen he had always shown himself to be capable and after a year in his service was to be trusted with all his attire. Once Beric had finished his duties he went across the landing to see how his friend, Gerard, page to Pierre de Torigny, was faring. The two had become friends on the journey from Lewes as they were both Normans. They had much in common even though Gerard was almost a year older and more taciturn than Beric.

"Have you finished yet?" Beric enquired.

"Almost." replied Gerard, in his crisp French tone. "My master said that as soon as I have finished I am free to go out until sundown. Are you free, too?"

Beric nodded and suggested: "I have a notion to go out into the town! I love a market and there is so much happening down there!"

And indeed there was. Once they had crossed the drawbridge and were out in the burgh they could see how even the wooden stronghold towered over the small town serving as a constant reminder of the new political order in England. At the far end of the grid-plan streets was the timber-framed Market Hall, the lower part used as a covered market and the upper rooms for conducting official business.

Most of the main buildings were also timber-framed with wattle and daub walls but it was not these that the boys were looking at.

"See Beric, the entertainers are over there in the Town Square!" Gerard pointed through the crowd.

"Yes", Beric cried, "Come on, I can see jugglers and acrobats and, look, there's even a dancing bear on the end of a chain!"

They made their way through the throng and for some time watched the spectacle, while munching on buns they had bought from a country woman in a plain brown gown, who was *cheaping* [selling] them.

So much were the lads enjoying themselves, watching the dancing bear, that they almost forgot to return to the Castle until suddenly they saw one of the soldiers, also off-duty, and this reminded them that the sun was setting and it was beginning to get dark. "We must get back, it will soon be time for our lords to dress for dinner!" Gerard shouted above the applause that the crowd was giving to the dancing bear and its master.

Luckily, they had not far to go and were soon about their duties again. William de Warenne was not an easy employer to work for but he was fair, and, providing Beric did his bidding he was quite happy about the boy. In any case, the Count had more important things to think about, unlike his snobbish, vain wife, who judged everyone by their clothes and jewellery. Back in her room Gundrada was berating her maid again. "By thunder, girl, what a fool you are! Can you get nothing right!" she snapped as Margaria handed her a blue girdle. "Why would I wear a blue girdle with a green gown, have you no idea of what befits a lady?" As much as her maid tried to please her so the Saxon woman spoke sharply. She never actually hit the young girl but she spoke in such a brutal manner that it seemed to Margaria like a whip across her back.

Eventually, Gundrada was ready, dressed in a tight-fitting, floor-length green wool gown with an embroidered girdle and a matching floor-length cloak with a red lining, trimmed with *ermine* [a costly fur]. On the back of her head was a veil with a small coronet to hold it in place and at her throat she wore a magnificent necklace while her hands, at the ends of long loose sleeves, sparkled with many jewelled rings. Once she was satisfied as to her appearance, she joined her husband and they descended to the Great Hall.

Margaria was just left to her own devices and once again started to weep. Then she thought of what her mother would have said:

"Laugh and the world laughs with you, cry and you cry alone." So she dried her tears and dabbed her red eyes with a damp cloth before she too went down but by the back stairs, to watch the events taking place in the Great Hall. She hid behind a pillar and took in the magnificent and colourful scene.

At the far end of the Hall was a long table where sat Robert D'Oyley and his lady, Ealdgyth. On either side of them were placed Count Pierre de Torigny, Count William de Warenne and the Lady Gundrada. On their table was the rare and valuable saltcellar.

All the other guests sat at tables set at right angles. They were spoken of as being 'below the salt' which meant less than nobility. There were rushes on the floor and on the walls hung tapestries and colourful battle flags. Servants were bringing in the food. The nobility ate from gold plates and their better class guests from silver ones, but the ordinary people had their food on *trenchers,* [slices of thick bread, afterwards given to the poor]. While they ate, a minstrel was singing the long ballad about knightly battles, entitled *The Song of Roland.*

Margaria was too frightened to leave the shadows and was suddenly surprised by Beric and his friend, Gerard who came up behind her. "You're the handmaid of the Lady Gundrada, aren't you?" enquired Gerard kindly. She nodded timidly, lowering her head. "Why, I do believe you've been crying!" exclaimed Beric, continuing: "What for?"

"Oh, it's nothing," whispered Margaria, but Beric was persistent. "Has the Lady Gundrada been unkind to you?"

She nodded nervously. "Does she hit you?" asked Gerard.

"No, it's just as bad though," she sniffed, wiping her eyes with her kerchief, "she speaks so unkindly to me."

Gerard and Beric nodded to one another as they decided to do something for the unfortunate girl. "Come on, let's get out of here!" ordered the older boy, Gerard, as he took the arms of Margaria and Beric. "We'll go into the courtyard where we can talk in a corner." No one noticed as they slipped away from the Hall and made their way down the many steps from the keep into the courtyard. On one side were the stables, huts and tents for the cavalry and on the other side was the archery practice area for the bowmen to hone their skills.

A little beyond that was the *quintain*, [an upright post with a cross bar. Sandbags were balanced on the top of it] on which the knights practised their *jousting* [fighting in full armour, on horseback], with *javelins*, [long spear-like weapons] for the tournaments. It was all now deserted. "This'll do. We'll sit with our backs to the wall, it's still warm enough out here."

Gradually the two lads drew the truth from Margaria, how unhappy she was and how unkind Gundrada had been to her whilst at the same time putting on a show of caring for her handmaiden when others were about. "That's really awful!" sympathised Gerard. "My master is very strict but he is fair."

"So is Count William," stated Beric firmly. "But what can we do about it?"

"Oh, if you please, don't say anything to anyone. I should be in such trouble if the Lady Gundrada were to learn that I had spoken to you." she whispered, timidly.

"Have no fear," said Beric. "I shall mention to my lord that I have overheard the way in which his lady speaks to you. He does not tolerate fools gladly but neither will he allow unfair treatment of those around him and I'll wager he will speak to his wife about this."

Gerard agreed. "It would be wise to speak to him while the Lady Gundrada is not near but I do think it may help poor Margaria." Turning to the girl he explained in a comforting manner: "You may not realise it, but the reason she does this is to make herself more important, by making you seem less so. It is such a pity that my Lord de Torigny does not have a wife and therefore a hand-maiden, otherwise you would have a friend, like I have Beric. But fear not, for something will be done. Just go back quietly and continue to do the best you can."

The following day, Saturday, dawned bright and sunny for the wedding of Milo Crispin to Matilda. Life in the stronghold worked up to a fever pitch and by noon the procession was ready to depart from Wallingford over the wooden bridge and along the road to Dorchester. All the people came from the burgh to watch the nobles in all their costly clothes as they departed the town. Many older children followed at the back and as they all trooped through the countryside, the people left their work in the fields to see the glittering procession go by. It was the greatest event since the Conqueror had come to the town and even at that time it was just the King on horseback with his army. This was much more entertaining because it included ladies wearing fine clothes and jewels and seated in their litters. The people were amazed at the beautiful horses with their rich *caparisons* [horse trappings].

On reaching Dorchester, the procession crossed the wooden bridge there and entered the beautiful Abbey Church that Birinus started some four centuries previously and was now being built in stone. The peasants were not allowed in of course, but they delighted in the richness of the pageantry as the bride, her father, her many handmaidens and all the wealthy tenants-in-chief and their families passed before their eyes. Rarely did they see such finery!

Some of them then went home, but a few waited the two hours that the service took and listened to the chanting of the monks from the Abbey. Among the hymns sung that day was one that had been written by Venantius Fortunatus, in 589. The last verse was sung so loudly and clearly that the poor people in the street outside could hear it:

> *Unto God be praise and glory:*
> *To the Father and the Son,*
> *To the Eternal Spirit, honour*
> *Now and evermore be done;*
> *Praise and glory in the highest,*
> *While timeless ages run.*

Amen

It is hard for us today to realise how great was the faith of the people in the first centuries after Christ. The Church played a very large part in their lives and had tremendous power, mostly for the good, at least in its early days. The peasantry had few pleasures but one of them was the celebration of *Holy Days* [Saints' Days] as they were known. There were sometimes as many as fifty in a year when there was feasting and often some form of entertainment, too.

When the wedding was finally over and the party had returned to the Castle, it was time for another great feast. The cooks and their *scullions* [kitchen servants] raced about, good French wines came up from the cellars and the smell of home-made bread pervaded the air.

Afterwards a serving man came round, with a towel over his shoulder and an *ewer* [jug] of water in one hand and a silver bowl containing scented water in the other. As he used the water to wash his greasy hands, Gerard said, "By St George, I could hardly eat another thing. What a spread it was! Did you see all those swans and peacocks, with their plumage replaced so beautifully? Didn't they look attractive!"

Beric replied: "No meat for me, I detest pork and beef. [The Normans gave these new French names to their dishes, *porc* and *boeuf*, instead of pig and cow]. I prefer fish, anyway, like pike, eels or best of all carp!"

Until it was all over, the poor had to wait outside but later they got that which remained of the fine food. Fortunately for them there was plenty of it

Later in the evening a minstrel played soft music on the lute and a jester came to entertain the wedding party. Soon afterwards, Lady Ealdgyth took the Lady Gundrada up to her *bower* [lady's room] to show off her weaving skills to her guest on her new loom, recently brought over from France. This room was a woman's world, with costly silken hangings and a high bed with curtains enclosing it, to keep out the draughts. In one corner was the padded bed for her much-pampered lap dog; quite unlike her husband's sleek hunting hounds that lived in kennels out of doors.

Luckily this proved an opportunity for the pages to explain Margaria's situation to Count William. They were never told what happened, but from that time onwards Gundrada behaved rather better to her maid who, in turn, began to be less nervous of her mistress and so naturally went on to perform her duties in a more efficient manner.

After a week of rejoicing over the wedding that brought the Saxons and Normans closer together the visitors began preparations for their return to Lewes. The Lady Ealdgyth and the Lady Gundrada spent several afternoons together, embroidering an altar cloth in tiny stitches. It was to be a gift to the Abbey Church at Dorchester, which was completed nearly a hundred years later, in 1170.

As they departed from the castle William de Warenne and Robert D'Oyley embraced each other, a sign that they had become firm friends. "Now that the King has granted me the parish of

Mongewell," de Warenne explained, "I am able to travel easily between Wallingford and my lands at Rotherfield Peppard. I plan to build a *manoir* there, so we shall be seeing more of each other in the future."

******

The following year, 1085, at Easter, King William [known in England as the Conqueror, whereas in France he had been known as the Bastard] again visited Wallingford and so highly did he think of Milo Crispin that, apart from his hosts and the Bishop of Sarum, this son-in-law of Robert D'Oyley was the only other guest permitted to sit at the King's table.

Robert D'Oyley died in 1090 and Milo Crispin became Lord of the Honor and Castle of Wallingford. He proved to be a worthy landowner and gave a great deal to the Church. Eventually, he too died, in 1107, but left no heirs to inherit his estates, so they reverted to the Crown and Matilda kept the Castle and Honor of Wallingford.

She later engaged in a long civil war with her cousin, Stephen, for the throne of England. Wallingford suffered three long sieges in this period but finally a treaty concluding the war was drawn up in 1153.

In 1155 Henry II held a *Great Council* at Wallingford at which he rewarded the town for supporting his mother, Matilda, by granting it a magnificent Charter of Liberties, one of the oldest in England. The town continued as a centre of importance in the thirteenth and fourteenth centuries.

Later, new bridges at Dorchester and Culham took trade away from Wallingford and it slipped quietly into obscurity for several hundreds of years.

******

The map at the front shows how the parishes were split up into long sections.

In his book, The History of Stoke Row, *written in 1872, Mr Edward Anderdon Reade stated: 'Mung Well: Mongewell was granted to Count de Warenne, as he was the Conqueror's son-in-law. Also he had the grant of Rotherfield Peppard on the other side of the Chiltern Hills and*

133

thus Mongewell was elongated at the expense of its neighbour to form a junction.' It is almost certain that this was along the base of Witheridge Hill.

In 2005, the town of Wallingford celebrated the 850th anniversary of the granting of its Charter in grand style. Judy and Stuart Dewey wrote '1155 and All That' in honour of the occasion. It is an excellent little book that tells the story of the document that came to mean so much to this country market town.

Chapter 7. The Robber and the Oak Tree: 1279

During the Middle Ages there was much moral integrity and pious devotion. In the major towns, guilds and wealthy people built churches, chantries, hospitals or schools. Associated with those charities were priests, whose role it was to say Masses. They were either endowed with the cost of maintenance or left to depend on the voluntary gifts of posterity. Nevertheless there was also a great deal of poverty and consequently many miscreants.

In the thirteenth century, towns like Wallingford and Henley, built by the river Thames, began to grow and thrive. Most of the people who lived in the uplands would rarely have gone down to the towns, only perhaps a few representatives for their community would have travelled thus far, just to trade goods and make purchases. Occasionally, however, some people of importance would make a long journey, usually on business, but these were difficult. There were no proper roads through the hilly, wooded terrain.

The woods hereabouts were very thick in parts, though in other areas they had been *assarted* [cleared for cultivation]. The village of Woodcote [a dwelling in a wood] is first recorded in 1109 and everywhere most tenants had to carry out customary duties for their lord. Timber, especially from tall trees, was sometimes sold further afield. In 1231 forty *copulas* [timber beams], were given to the Earl of Chester and Lincoln from a wood in Henley and these were probably conveyed by water for most of the way.

At Whitchurch in 1279, tenants had to carry two cartloads of wood for their lord before Christmas, while in the same year Robert

Luvkyn of Huntercombe had to make four crates from his lord's coppice, either for sheep or chickens, besides carrying wood for one day. Robert, son of Simon, the blacksmith of Ipsden, who held three acres of woodland and perhaps a shaw, had to cut a certain number of *faggots* [bundles of firewood] for his lord. In South Stoke, twenty-three villeins were allowed a cartload of wood for the 'cooking of their meat'. Men at Ipsden had to carry two cartloads and others had to do the same job for two days.

Wood was not only used for timber-framed buildings, wheels, furniture and carts but also for wooden nails for holding wooden structures together, handles for ploughs and other farming implements. Household tools, such as brushes and brooms were also made of wood and other tree parts. Firewood was much in demand especially by blacksmiths and charcoal burners, as well as in houses for cooking and heating in the severe winter weather. Coppiced hazel was used for besom brooms, rakes, thatching spars and split to make wattle sticks for walls.

The name of *Woodward* was one given to those officers who organised the employment of men, cutting of coppices, felling of timber, banking and fencing of fields and sale of the produce. They probably kept their accounts by making notches on measuring sticks. They were freemen who usually sold their services for a retaining fee and traditionally therefore kept a 'cut' of the money from sales to make the job worthwhile.

These were poverty-stricken hills, mainly due to a lack of natural water. Such water as there was, largely accumulated through the winters in deserted clay pits, was quite undrinkable and thin ale mainly took its place. It was often hard to survive the harsh winters. The peasants found it especially difficult and existed largely on such cereals [oats, barley and wheat] and root vegetables as they could keep.

Nettlebed was a poor hamlet that straggled along the Henley to Oxford Road. It owed its name to the growing of *Urtica dioica*, which we know as the common stinging nettle. Strange to relate, this objectionable weed, which now grows profusely throughout Britain and will voraciously colonise any fertile soil, was relatively rare in the country in 1279 and was treated with great respect. Historically, the ancient Egyptians were known to have made a fibre cloth from it and later this skill passed up through Europe to England.

It was also thought to possess many medicinal properties; roots and leaves were boiled and used by monks to relieve pleurisy. Being stung by a nettle was believed to alleviate rheumatism. It was also cooked and eaten as a vegetable with a taste not unlike that of spinach.

Edward Sarney was, like his namesake, Edward I, a tall man, some six feet in stature. When he was born in 1240 his mother named him after King Henry III's son who had been born the year before. Now aged thirty-nine, Edward Sarney had been growing nettles for about twenty years and, since he was a freeman, was able to employ several people. Two of them were his younger brothers, Hugo and Simon.

It was early May, and spring was just asserting itself as the bluebells started to carpet the nearby woods in bright blue. Out in a newly cleared field the three brothers were planting rhizome pieces that were to form the basis for the new crop in the summer. "You get those rootlets down in deep!" Ed'ard, as he was always known, warned his younger brother, Simon. "You'll have to dig your holes deeper than that!" His middle brother, Hugo, remembering how Ed'ard had taught him the same some five or so years before, smiled to himself.

Hugo, who was shorter, more like their mother, liked being out in the fields especially when the weather was warm, but even when it was cold he felt a sense of freedom, a love of the open air. He was fond of nature, the animals, flowers and birds, and especially of the lovely butterflies, Red Admiral, Small Tortoiseshell and Peacock, which depended on the nettle for their food. Simon was not so happy. Aged seventeen, he was the youngest of the three older boys. He had been rather spoiled and had always resented having to work for his living. Up until now he had just lived at home helping his mother in the house and caring for the few animals they had, a goat, the pig, a few chickens and a donkey.

He was never contented and always complaining. Sometimes it was about the goat: "Mother always gets so cross when Gertie eats the nettles, she does love 'em so!" and if it wasn't about the goat, he moaned about the pig: "I hate having to clean out the sty, Porkie's so dirty. And now with the little ones, she makes such a mess!" Even the chickens seemed to displease him: "Feeding chickens is no job for me, now I'm a grown man, I ought to be doing a man's work!" he grumbled.

"Well, you'd best come along with Hugo and me, then," his brother offered. "You can work with us in the fields and see how you like that. Young Ellie's getting old enough to look after the animals, and we need more hands now we're doing better with the nettle crop." Although he jumped at the chance to work away from the house, Simon still wasn't happy.

In the early autumn, soon after he started working with his brothers, when the stems had to be cut and dried, steeped in water and then dried again, he groused about the work. "Why we have to wet 'em and dry 'em again, I don't know!" he complained.

"Because it's not until you wet 'em and dry 'em again that the outer bark begins to rot, then we can get to the inner, woody core." Ed'ard explained. "You wait till next week, then we have to boil the bark so the fibres can be hackled and..."

"Hackled, I've heard you use that word before. What's it mean?" Simon winged.

"You'll see." Ed'ard replied sharply, sensing that his youngest brother was not going to like the next stage of the work.

Sure enough, as they boiled the bark and got the fibres out of the stems, Simon was discontented again. His older brother, Hugo, just got on with the job of *hackling,* combing and oiling the fibres that began to turn grey and then gradually creamy white because they had taken great care during the retting process. The brothers were beginning to be well-known by the local merchant for the quality of their fibres, which were about three feet long.

"You bring me stuff as good as this and I'll always buy it," he had assured Simon some years before.

In the retting shed, Simon was still muttering about the work. "You just do as I show you and you'll be alright." Hugo tried to placate his younger brother. "You're doing a man's job now. It's not for weaklings, this job, you have to be tough to do work like this." Even so, the strands were becoming remarkably soft and when they were finally sold to the weavers they would be woven into sheets and table linen for rich people to use.

The resultant products made enough money for the family to survive the winter. James Sarney, the father of the family, had been a labourer in the local brick and tile works, but he had had an accident in the kiln and suffered very bad burns to his arms and legs. This meant that although he did some light work, he was not able to provide enough to feed his wife and nine children.

The eldest, Ed'ard, was courting Mary, a pretty village girl, but he knew there wasn't much chance of marrying her, at least until the nettle crop was big enough to support his own family first.

In the October of that year, 1279, the bundles of silky strands were finally ready to be taken down to Hanlea [Henley] to the merchant. For once, this was the part of the work that Simon did not moan about although he had had to work on Ed'ard to allow him to go down into the town by the river. "You know I've never been before. Do let me come along with you!" he pleaded.

"Oh, all right, then, I expect Hugo will be happy enough to stay behind. There's many a job still to be done here but you'd better not moan about walking all the way down there and back! It's a long way, you know, it'll be about ten miles all told."

They piled the sacks of fibres on to the back of the donkey and Simon quite happily led it as they walked down the hill, along the track that was beginning to get muddy after the previous week's autumn rain. Down in Hanlea they found the merchant in his store by the river Thames, from whence he dispatched goods down to London or up to Oxford and to many places in between. He paid them a fair price for their wares and soon they were exploring the Market.

"I've never seen the like of this! It's marvellous, there's so much goin' on here!" Simon exclaimed. Soon they regaled themselves with a couple of horn mugs of small beer and muffins, freshly cooked over a brazier in the centre of the town. After that they bought from stall-holders items that could not be made or grown in the village or the neighbouring ones.

However, Simon was not quite so pleased when he looked up to the hill that they had to climb in order to reach their home again. Luckily his older brother allowed him to ride the donkey up the steepest part as the animal had in its panniers only a few items that the men had bought at the market,

As they came nearer to the top of the hill, Ed'ard began to talk about the local gang of robbers who were known to hold up travellers. The brothers were carrying money, it was true, but none of the highwaymen would have stolen from a local person because they were known to everyone in the neighbourhood. "No, my lad, they lay in wait for richer prey than us!" laughed Ed'ard.

"Do you know their names?" enquired the younger man.

"Why, yes, we all do and now that you are a grown man, you'd better know them too. And be wary of them, for they are not men to be trifled with, I'll warrant!"

He described Martin Barnard as the Falcon, the leader of the group. "There's no mistaking him anywhere for he's got red hair and he's blind in one eye. He says it was the work of an infidel bowman when he was out on one of the Crusades. John Backhouse, Robert Cook, Tom Munday, William Hewlett, and Dick Todds, all of them were soldiers in the pay of King Edward when he went out east. Now he's back in England there's no work for them so they've taken to robbery. It's a paying business, they tell me!"

The sound of this way of life made Simon alert to the possibility of making a better living without having to work too hard. "I see that look in your eye, my lad, don't you go thinking you'd be able to join 'em, they're a tough lot. One of these days they'll get caught and they'll be hanged, every man Jack of 'em, you mark my words!"

So Simon said no more but later that evening by the open fire in the middle of their cottage, as he watched the smoke spiralling upwards through a hole in the roof, he casually mentioned the matter to Hugo. The older man was one of few words and in the absence of Ed'ard, who had gone out to bring in more logs; he only let slip that the gang were "sometimes to be found drinking together at Old Mother Okeburn's."

This was enough for Simon and the next evening he stole out for a pint of ale to old Mother Okeburn's. She was a local woman who brewed well and was getting so much custom now that she was said to be thinking of 'putting up the bush'. This meant she was planning to tie the branch of a small tree to a pole outside her home, a sign that she was willing to sell her ale to anyone who passed by. This would effectively make it into what we would today call a public house. He ran all the way through the woods to the little old thatched cottage, which later became a pub named the Rising Sun, deep in the forest, on top of Witheridge Hill. There he found the Falcon and his cronies, drinking strong ale and reminiscing about their lives on the Crusade.

"I mind well the Prince would come..." Will Hewlett started to say.

"...Don't keep calling him Prince, 'e's the King now, King Edward the First, 'e is!" interrupted Tom Munday, scratching his fleas as he did so.

"You wanna rub a bit o' fleabane into yer skin, that do kill them fleas!" advised John Backhouse.

Will snarled back: "Well, 'e's always been the Prince to me, and always will be as long as I live, even if 'e do be the King!"

Tom Munday started to cough. He'd had a terrible cold that winter and this stopped him from arguing further.

Robert Cook, usually called 'Rob', was silent, as always. He had been dumb since birth but was a valued member of the gang because of his skill with a bow and arrow. The thieves usually used the sword as they had done on the Crusade but the more primitive weapons were excellent for use in the forest where the bowman could hide behind a bush or up in a tree and take aim without anyone realising he was there.

"Never mind about the past, what about tomorrow? We need to get something good soon, it's been a hard winter!" moaned Dick Todds, a man who was always grousing about one thing or another.

Will suddenly sat up and then bent over, saying almost in a whisper "I hear there's a coach comin' through later this week. My cousin, Henry, what lives down in Hanlea, told me there's a rich merchant stayin' in the town tonight and he should be goin' on to Oxford soon, maybe even tomorrer."

The Falcon laid a hand on his arm, firmly. "I hope you haven't told anyone else about this, Will?"

"Course not!" affirmed Will almost under his breath. "I knows he could be valuable to us!"

Dark-haired, hook-nosed John Backhouse had said nothing until then, but he was obviously planning something and said, quietly: "What about stoppin' him on Gangsdown Hill?"

"I'll do the deciding', unless you're lookin' for a fight!" snapped the Falcon and then, a bit more slowly he continued: "But you could be right, it's a good spot, they have to slow down, so's the horses don't slip on the gravel goin' down the hill."

"I jus' hope they don't bring none of the Reeve's men with 'em!" Dick looked on the dark side of life as always.

They lived in mortal fear of the Reeve's men and well they might, for the *Shire Reeves* or Sheriffs as they eventually became known, were powerful men and the Reeve of Oxfordshire was well-known for his severity.

At this time people were still operating in the old pre-Conquest ways of self-regulation and acted more or less under ancient Saxon rules that were governed by the idea of victim compensation. However, the Normans were just beginning to introduce collective punishment. This gang were all outlaws, the name given to those who had placed themselves outside the law, having three times failed to attend the Court for trial.

The Reeve at Oxford knew the names of these robbers but catching them was another matter entirely. Outlaws had to be always on the lookout, especially for those who might betray them.

It was at this point that Simon slipped in the door and Old Mother Okeburn gave a loud cough that immediately stopped the gang from speaking another word. Seemingly casually, one by one, they looked up to see who had entered. "Ah, it's young Simon, I see. Ed'ard's brother. What brings you here, lad?" enquired the Falcon, casually.

"Oh, I jus' dropped in for a drink," replied Simon, nonchalantly licking his lips.

Mother Okeburn gave him a pewter mug of her best brew, asking at the same time: "You're a bit out of your way, boy. Does your brother know you're here?"

"No, not exactly and I don' have to answer to him all the time!" Simon said in a defiant tone.

"By St George, 'e's gettin' a bit of life to him, this one," observed the Falcon, with a coarse laugh.

Tom looked up in an interested manner. "You still growin' and cuttin' nettles all day, then? Bit of a dull life, in'it?"

"What else is there to do in this dump, anyway?" Simon grumbled. "My brother keeps me at it all the time from daybreak to sundown!"

"Why not come and join us?" suggested the Falcon, thinking to himself that here was a lad that no one up at Oxford knew anything about. "You might just be the right man to help us on a little job we're thinking of doin' tomorrow." Being called a 'man' flattered Simon and he promptly decided to throw his lot in with the gang, aware that his brothers would not approve but hungry for some form of excitement.

The following morning proved to be misty up in the hills, where low cloud often descended and created a damp and melancholy atmosphere, especially in autumn. Simon's family worried about him when he didn't come home of course, but it was not unknown for him to stay out all night so they just got on with their work, expecting him to come home later in the day, the worse for wear after a night's drinking, as he had sometimes done before.

Out at Mother Okeburn's the outlaws had spent a restless night, thinking about the plans for the morrow. However, they were up early and as it was a raw, cold morning, dressed themselves in several layers of their dirty, dull coloured shifts, which reached down over their hose to their knees. Loose knitted wool hats covered most of their faces, except for a couple of eye-holes, when they pulled them down to their necks. Each carried a quarterstaff. This was often useful for fighting when the need arose. A man could catch his prey out in so many ways if he was adept with one.

Soon they were all fed and ready to set off on foot the three miles through the woods to Gangsdown Hill, near Nettlebed. The Falcon had decided to let Simon do the scouting, since he was young and looked harmless enough. He, too, was clad in dull brown clothes, which provided him with some form of camouflage against the autumn shades but his hat had no eye-holes and his face was fully visible.

The Falcon posted the lad just by the gravely road and gave him a shovel so he could pretend to be digging a ditch. The road was only wide enough for one vehicle. Even though this was the main highway from London to Oxford only a few carts and the occasional carriage passed through each week and the vegetation had grown thick in the previous warm, moist summer months.

Simon was not one to be working when it wasn't really necessary and so for almost an hour he just sat and waited. Soon the sun was higher in the sky and he heard a faint rumbling sound. Immediately he set to work to dig a ditch and was seemingly hard at work as a long, low travelling carriage with a curved brightly-coloured canvas top and a coat of arms painted on its sides hove into view and following it, carrying the owner's goods and chattels, was a large wooden open wagon on rough wheels.

The very moment he spotted this lumbering entourage through the mist, Simon gave a long, low whistle and all at once there was a rustling of dried leaves as the members of the gang positioned themselves ready to attack the convoy. So skilled were they in ambush, using tricks they had learned on the Crusade, that they were soon prepared to attack the party as it got almost halfway down the hill.

The Falcon stood, his sword in his hand, in front of the horses that were nervous as they tried to get their footing on the loose stones. Simon by this time had disappeared and joined Rob up in the tree above where he was poised with his bow and arrow, ready to shoot should anyone try to fight back.

The owners of the long covered carriage jumped out and started to shout in a foreign tongue, similar to the language that the Falcon remembered hearing as he passed through France when he first joined the Black Prince on his famous Crusade.

"Leave him to me, sir!" shouted the driver, as he pulled out his sword and prepared to fight. However, within seconds, Tom, Dick and John, similarly armed, surrounded the group on all sides. The driver looked around him desperately and seeing no other option realised that he had to allow the robbers to take what they would from the merchant and his male companion who reluctantly handed over their bags of gold and all the jewellery they were wearing.

The Falcon and his men were delighted. It was all so easy this time; often there had been more of a fight. But what they had not allowed for was the second escort who came galloping up just as they were putting their booty into their bags. This man's horse had taken a stone into its shoe and he had had to stop on the way up from Hanlea to take it out.

Gilbert D'Arcy, for that was the name of the escort, had been a professional soldier in the pay of Edward I when he was on the Crusade, but had been pensioned off when the King returned to England. He, too, knew all the tricks of sword fighting and as soon as he realised what was happening ahead of him prepared to take on the whole gang. This he did, but just as he drew back to parry he spied Rob Cook, the dumb bowman, up in the tree above him. In that same second Cook let loose his arrow and this went right through D'Arcy's heart.

It was all over in seconds and soon the robbers were running separately, hither and thither, along almost indiscernible paths known only to themselves and to the deer that had been brought here only about a hundred years previously by the Normans. They didn't return immediately to the interior of Old Mother Okeburn's but met as arranged, around the back of the premises on the top of Witheridge Hill, far enough removed from Gangsdown Hill for anyone to know they were there. There they partook of the ale, bread and cheese that they had hidden on their outward journey and lay down to rest, knowing no one would be able to find them in the thick woodland.

As he lay there, Simon watched a red squirrel burying an acorn in the ground and thought to himself: "One day that might grow into an oak tree. Will I see it grow? What'll happen now we've killed a man?"

It was then he realised that he would never again be able to return to the bosom of his family, and that he had joined a band of outlaws for what he saw at the time as an adventurous life, but which was eventually to end, for him and his cronies at the end of a rope on Gallowstree Common, eight miles to the south.

******

Soon after Edward I was crowned in 1274 he began a series of measures aimed at remedying long-standing grievances in England. One of the first of these, the Statute of Winchester in 1285, dealt with the prevalence of highway robbery and violence throughout the country. One of its tenets was the provision of the first Justices of the Peace. It also gave local residents the responsibilities of policing their own communities.

******

In the Bodleian Library is a document, written in the thirteenth century by 'A Florentine traveller, Brunetto Latino'. Writing of his journey from London to Oxford, he stated: "Our journey was with some difficulty and danger, made in two days, for the roads are bad and we had to climb hills of hazardous ascent and which to descend are doubly perilous. We passed through woods which are dangerous places, as they are infested with robbers."

The oak at the top of Witheridge Hill is still there and could tell many a tale. It is said that it takes around 300 years for an oak to grow fully. Then it rests for approximately 300 years, after which it declines gracefully for about 300 years.

The Old Place

Chapter 8. The Black Death: 1348

Rotherfield Greys [usually just known as Greys] is an elongated, wedge-shaped parish, running roughly north-east to south-west, about five miles long and a mile to half a mile wide. It stretches down from the southern slopes of the Chilterns to the outskirts of Henley. Ecclesiastically, until 1860, at Highmore Cross, its highest point, about two hundred and fifty feet, it comprised only a few scattered and humble dwellings.

Greys itself was a tiny hamlet that clustered around the Norman church of St Nicholas, which had probably had its origin in Saxon times. Between the choir stalls, set flush with the floor and now covered with a carpet, is a particularly fine brass plate. Dr Christopher Rawlinson of Oxford (1677-1733) described it as being of 'a fair figure of a man in a complete set of armour, standing, holding his hands up in a devout posture, treading on a lion couchant.' It is, in fact, the figure of Lord Robert de Grey who died in January 1387. This knight fought at Crecy and was given a licence to crenellate his house in 1347. He was a founder Knight of the Garter but was the last of his line to live at Greys Court. Today the house is a National Trust property and still contains the medieval courtyard, the crenellated Great Tower and three smaller towers dating back to the fourteenth century.

Although the Middle Ages is sometimes known as the Missing Ages, the year 1348 is recorded in many places, as it saw the first of the great plagues that beset this country. It is also the best known, although there was another even worse one in 1361 and several more through the centuries until the notorious Great Plague that hit

London in 1665. Fortunately, for us today, modern medicine has been able to keep this disease under control, although it does still break out in many parts of the world from time to time.

A series of wet summers and bad harvests had left the population in a poor state by the year 1348 and there is no doubt that many fell foul of the plague because their resistance was low. It took two forms, the bubonic and the pneumonic. The first was the most common and was transmitted by rats and other animals too. The second was transferred from one human being to another by their breathing and coughing over one another. Increasing trade brought more ships to England and it is believed that it was the black rat on board one of these that carried the flea which then transferred itself to the more common brown rat and thus enabled the dreaded bacteria to travel rapidly northwards and soon it affected the whole country.

******

Adam Blackthorn was a small wiry man, with black hair and a shifty expression on his thin weather-beaten face. A maker of small wagons and carts, he was not renowned for his kindness to others but he did have one weakness, he adored his wife and children. This probably came about because he had been orphaned at an early age and had been brought up by various sets of relatives, each of whom had passed him on to another when he became too difficult. Luckily for him his last home was where he eventually found some security and a measure of happiness.

His uncle, Robin Hewitt, was a kindly man, though his wife, Maryanne, was slightly less so. "The boy needs a home and some guidance in this life." Robin explained, as she brought in his midday meal. This simple fare, bread, cheese and ale, he ate as he worked at his craft in a small workshop by the river where he made small boats. "He could do worse than come and help me and learn a trade. Now I'm getting older, I could do with a pair of young hands."

"You make sure, then, if we share our roof with him, that he does a good day's work. I'm not having any wastrel here!" she announced firmly. "But," she continued, more quietly, "Perhaps if he helps you with the boat building you'd have a bit more time to spend mending the roof!"

In fact, Adam turned out to be anything but a wastrel. He took to his uncle at once, largely because the older man gave him encouragement and kindness, perhaps some of the first he had ever received and at thirteen it became increasingly important to the growing lad. Robin sensed this and soon the pair were firm friends and worked well together. There was as yet not much in the way of formality about being apprenticed to a craftsman. A young man like Adam just worked alongside his master, running errands and doing simple tasks but soon he began to pick up useful tips and, with his willingness to make something of his life, eventually turned into a first class builder of small boats, mostly used for fishing or transporting goods on the Thames.

However, by the time he was twenty-three, Adam had also started to make other kinds of vehicle, small carts and wagons. It had started when a Henley fishmonger had asked Robin Hewitt to make him a hand-cart which he needed to transport fish from his boat to his stall higher up in the town. Hewitt was too busy to do this, so he suggested: "Why not ask young Adam to make you something? It's not in my line but he likes trying new things." The tradesman was so pleased with the result that he began to recommend Adam to other people.

Later on, several others had set up boat building yards and business became harder to get. "Good thing we've got two strings to our bow, lad!" remarked Hewitt one afternoon. "This way we'll never be out of work." And so the business continued until Robin Hewitt died suddenly and his grief-stricken wife decided to move back to London to be with "my own kith and kin", as she put it.

Once again Adam found himself alone but by now he had inherited a sizeable business and a list of satisfied customers. "It's about time I was married", he thought to himself and not long afterwards, much to his surprise, he fell in love with the daughter of a local woodsman from whom he bought the timber with which he made his carts that were sturdy products and lasted their owners for many years.

With such a successful business behind him, Adam had no difficulty in persuading Matthew Woodgett to give him the hand of his daughter, Evie, in marriage. Everyone was pleased about the union, considering it a good omen that their two Christian names should go so well together.

However, Adam decided that he would leave the waterside workshop at Henley and set up another in the woods at Rotherfield Greys. "It makes good sense, " he explained to his new wife, "because the timber's near to hand". His father-in-law kindly let him build a small cottage on his woodland and behind it a tiny workshop.

Every week, Adam would go down to either Henley or Wallingford taking with him one of the carts or sometimes even a small wagon, either of which would have been ordered beforehand, and sell it there. He would then walk back or ride on his pony if he had taken it, bringing back with him such goods as he had bought in the town that could not be grown or made in Greys. More often than not he had received another order or two for more vehicles to be made. Life was looking good for the young married couple.

In time, children came along, "As children will do!" laughed Evie's mother. First, in 1341, came the boy, named after Adam's favourite uncle, Robin, and two years later, a girl, who they named Alice, after Evie's mother. The children had a wonderful life, able to roam free in the woods, although Evie worried about them when they came home wet and she had difficulty drying their clothes. "It rains all the time these days!" she grumbled.

"Never fear, my lovely," Adam reassured her, "I'll light one of my big log fires and we'll soon all be warm and dry." With the repeated bad harvests, food began to be in short supply but the wily Adam always found something when he went down to the towns to sell his carts.

When Robin was about seven years of age, Adam announced his intention to take him down to Wallingford on one of his weekly expeditions. "It's about time the boy saw something of the outside world and learned about life outside these woods." Accordingly, the following Friday, the father and his young son set out along the narrow worn path that led up to Nettlebed where they picked up the Oxford road. By this time it had become rather more of a thoroughfare than it was in the days of the highwaymen. Trees had been cleared from either side and carts, wagons and sometimes carriages, came through every day.

Naturally, Robin was excited about "going down to the big town" with his father and asked questions all the way along. "My goodness, boy, you'll be worn out by the time we get there. Quieten down a while, do!" Adam was unused to constant company and though he loved his son dearly he found his continual chatter to be very wearing. Finally they arrived at Crawmersse Gifford [Crowmarsh Gifford] and crossed the river on the narrow bridge.

The sight of the huge castle ahead of them stunned young Robin into temporary silence as he surveyed the height of the walls and soldiers keeping guard. Quite used to the bustle of the town and castle, Adam just continued on, turned left into the burgh and found his customer without difficulty.

However, he very quickly noticed a different atmosphere about Wallingford from that which had pervaded it only a fortnight before-hand. There was a sombre air about the town, even though it was market day. Finding his customer quickly, Adam asked: "What is it about the town today? It's so quiet. There seem to be few folk around and those there are seem to be hurrying about their affairs. Oh, by the way, this is my lad, Robin, the one I told you about."

Hugh Proudfoot took little notice of the boy, apart from a nod of his head. "You'd best get him back home as soon as you're able. Travellers are telling us of a *murrain* [plague] that's come to Lunnon and everyone fears it may come here!" Dropping his voice, Proudfoot continued: "They say that the folk who get it die within a few days or even a few hours. It's no respecter of persons, either, as I've heard. Lords and ladies have been getting it as well as ordinary folk like us. I myself think they have it up there because of the evil vapours in the city. Hopefully it won't come here in the cleaner air of the country. Anyway, I'm off home! I'm not one to stay out when it's not necessary."

As they were speaking, young Robin had gone up to another boy who was playing with an inflated pig's bladder, using it as a football. "Let me have a go!" he pleaded and was delighted when the other agreed. Soon they were firm friends and Robin begged: "Can my new friend, Joel, come with us, he's nowhere else to go."

Reluctantly, Adam agreed, thinking to himself that perhaps it was a bit lonely for the boy as he himself was engrossed in taking an order for a small handcart from a baker who sold his wares hot from his oven. "I need it to bring the flour from the miller and the eggs from the farmer's wife. My old one is almost broken down and there never was such good quality as yours, Adam." And then, turning to the boys, he shouted: "Mind where you kick that ball, don't you upset my stall!" Returning to his supplier, he said: "My goodness, Adam, you've got your work cut out there! I thought you only had one son?"

"Yes, I do. This one's mine," he explained, pulling Robin towards him. "The other is... what did you say your name was?"

"Joel, sir." replied the boy.

"You don't come from round here?" the baker enquired.

"No, sir, I come off the barge down by the river this mornin' - I come from Lunnon - my mother put me on the boat to get me away from the city. She's afraid I might get the pestilence there."

At this, everyone around them suddenly disappeared from sight. Fear was prevalent throughout the whole of Wallingford; of that there was no doubt. Packing up his stall and hastily closing the doors of his cooling oven, the baker remarked: "He don't look none too good to me, rather dirty and none too well either, I declare!"

In that instant, Adam made the decision to return home at once. "Can't Joel come with us?" Robin begged his father. "He's got no home here." Remembering his own childhood and how lonely he often felt, having no parents from an early age, Adam reluctantly agreed to take the young stranger along with them. Quickly he bought items that he had promised his wife he would purchase in the market, just before the stallholders had begun to dismantle their tables, much earlier than usual.

As they crossed the bridge again and reached Crawmersse, a poor, damp place, where the river often overflowed its banks, Joel fell silent and began to lag behind, despite Robin's efforts to encourage his new friend to walk faster.

"I can't hurry, I'm tired and hot too. I want a drink," he moaned.

Alarmed by this admission from the London boy, Adam immediately turned around to look at him. Certainly he looked flushed and had even dropped his ball some distance back. Adam tried to push the fear to the back of his mind before he had allowed it space there. "Dear Heavenly Father", he prayed. "Let not this boy bring the plague upon us all!"

As they came to the crossing with the track that led to Newnham Murren, he suddenly recalled that there was a leper hospital not far away, founded in 1142, just outside the boundary of Wallingford but under the control of the Burgesses there. Although leprosy had been rampant in the twelfth and thirteenth centuries, it had begun to die out. Now the hospital was divided into two. One part had been set aside for lepers and a newer section was now being developed into a hospital for the sick and especially for those with infectious and contagious diseases. "An isolation hospital, that's what this boy needs!" Adam thought to himself. "It belongs to the church, so they will be good to him there."

Accordingly, though keeping Robin close by him and warning him not to go near Joel again, he eventually managed to get the sick lad to the hospital of St Mary Magdalene and gratefully placed him in the care of the nuns there. He promptly gave them six pence for their funds when they agreed to care for the boy and promised to return later to pay more, should that be necessary.

Giving them food and drink to sustain them on their protracted journey, the Mother Superior asked: "Will you be going back to Greys now?" On receiving a nod from Adam, she continued: "Surely that would be dangerous for your family, since it is obvious the boy has contracted this disease in London and you and your son, having been in contact with him, might pass it on to others. Why not stay here with us until you are sure you are clear of it? I am told it takes two weeks to be sure."

"Thank you, Mother, you are most kind, but my wife will be worried when I do not return."

The wise old nun advised "She will be even more worried if you or your son become ill yourselves. You remind me of the Good Samaritan because you have been kind to a stranger. Our Lord will surely be good to you, but you should not take chances. You can stay apart from everyone else. We have a small outbuilding that you can use as a shelter and we shall give you food, enough for each day."

"Bless you, Mother. I think you are right, this is what we shall do, but tomorrow I will go up to Greys and give my wife the goods that she is waiting for and tell her what has happened. Do not fear, I shall not go near to her or our daughter. To go there and back in one day on foot may be too much for little Robin, though. If I leave him here, will you keep an eye on him?"

"Why, yes, of course, though we must all keep our distance, you understand. I must not allow my Daughters in God to become afflicted if it is not necessary. Already one of them, Sister Martha, has offered to nurse the London boy in isolation and we shall all pray for them both."

Adam fell to his knees and motioned his son to do likewise. "Bless us, holy Mother, before we go to sleep."

"May Our Lady and all the Angels keep you in their care" she said, making the sign of the cross as she did so. "The little shed is over there" she said, pointing to a small wooden building. "We don't use it at the moment, you will be safe there. You can call us by ringing the bell at the gate if you need assistance." Gratefully, Adam led his son over to the shelter that was to become their second home.

Adam slept only fitfully and awoke early the next morning. It was mid-May and a certain amount of daylight filtered through the single dirty window. It had no glass, just a membrane stretched across the small hole that allowed enough light to enable him to find his way about.

He woke Robin with some difficulty, for the seven-year old boy had been exhausted the night before after their long walk down to Wallingford and the extraordinary events which followed. "Listen to me lad", he whispered. "Mother Superior and the other Sisters are going to take care of you while I go up home to your mother and tell her what has happened."

The thought of his father leaving him in a strange place brought Robin to a state of awakenness rapidly. "I want to come with you, Father. I will be good and do as you say."

"No, Robin!" his father put on his stern voice, although he was reluctant to leave his son with even the kindest of strangers. "I shall run all the way there and all the way back. I shan't be long. You just go back to sleep and, when you hear the bell ring, go past the Chapel to the back door of the hospital and there one of the Sisters will give you food to break your fast."

With this Adam picked up his bag, slung it over his shoulder and left before the boy could prevail upon him. True to his word, he ran all the way from Crawmersse, at least until he reached the steepest

154

part of the hill that the local folk had named after Bishop Birinus, in memory of his goodness to them.

Usually he would have stopped at Stoke Rue, to see old friends and perhaps have a horn mug of ale but he feared he might in some way infect them so he just called out to an old man who was sitting by the remains of the gate by the broken-down fencing that had once surrounded the village. "Can't stop now, Wulfrun, the plague has started down in the town. Go and warn your kinfolk not to go down there unless they have to!" He panted because, having reached more level ground, he had started to run again.

Likewise in the tiny hamlet of Highmore he saw old Hugelina, bent and leaning on a stick, carrying the bundle of sticks that she had picked up from the woodland floor. Adam shouted the dreadful news to her with the same warning and hoped that, despite her deafness, she had heard him. Certainly she had nodded and he felt this was enough to enable him to keep running along the tiny track that led over to Rotherfield Pippard [as it was then called], the next tiny settlement. There was no one about, not even on the Common, so he sped on.

Finally, just after he had passed the church and before he would have come to Greys Court, he turned off to the right and continued to make the utmost haste although he was beginning to tire by now. At last he came to the clearing in the wood where lay his beloved cottage and little workshop that he himself had built from wattle fencing, daubed with chalk and mud. A few hundred yards further away stood the similar home of his father and mother-in-law, a tiny simple dwelling, surrounded with cut timber in every shape and form. Out at the back his father-in-law was axing a log, "He's chopping it up for next year's firewood," thought Adam to himself. "He's always so good at keeping the wood dry. It's more important than folk realise."

He was just thinking about his own stocks and how he would have to start on them soon, when his five-year old daughter, Alice, espied him and came running towards him. In that same second he remembered that he wouldn't be chopping firewood just yet and called out to her: "Stay where you are Alice! Go back to Mumma directly and tell her I'm home."

Evie was out at the back, sowing vegetable seedlings and watering them with melted snow from the huge snowballs that Adam and the children had made the previous winter. It was one way of augmenting their precious water supply that they drew from the very deep well on his father-in-law's land. Because these tiny hovels were thatched, the people could not save water from the roof as they were able to do later when tiles and slates became available. Upon hearing her husband's voice she came running round the house to greet him. "Oh, am I glad to see you, where have you been?" And then almost in the same breath: "Robin's lagging behind as usual, I suppose?"

Adam dismissed her greeting with his hand raised in the air. "Don't come any further, wife.   I have bad news." Obediently, struck by the urgency in his tone, she stopped at once and drew the girl to her skirts. "There's a dreadful murrain in London. I heard tell of it in Henley last week but now it's come to Wallingford. They say this plague's a real killer and that people die from it very quickly." He went on to explain about Robin's meeting with the London boy and how he had left him to be nursed at the hospital and that the Sisters were looking after Robin while he came home to tell her what had occurred.

"I'll leave out here these victuals and the tools I bought but don't come and get them until I've gone. If you're careful there's enough flour to make bread for you and Alice and Mother and Father too. But you must be careful and ration it out. Go out into the woods and find what berries you can and cook nettles too. I know Alice doesn't like the taste but she'll eat them when she's hungry. I must go back to Robin now, he's sore afraid alone."

The mere mention of her boy brought Evie to the realisation that this was an emergency, or her husband would never have left him with strangers. "When will you come back?" she shouted back, nervously.

"I'll return every week and bring you what you need." he promised. "Your father never goes far from home now and your mother can hardly walk, what with her arthritis and all, so you'll have company but promise me that none of you will go into the village or near any other human being." Miserably she nodded her assent as he steeled himself to turn and leave her and their little daughter, blowing them a kiss as he did so.

Further on in the wood he stopped for a few moments to get his breath back and to eat a bit of the bread that the nuns had given him. Then he continued to run, which proved easier down Berin's Hill than it had when he came up it. As he ran he had little energy for thinking, but even so it did occur to him that despite the beauty of the May morning, the world suddenly looked very dark. He also realised that he was able to run down the hill, which he had never done before because he had no cart to push and he began to wonder how he would make his living if he did not have access to his workshop and supply of timber. However, he was a simple man and felt instinctively that 'something would turn up, it usually does.' Soon he came out of the woods and into the meadow-land from where he had the town in view and the little hospital beyond.

Soon he had covered the nine miles and reached the sanctuary of the hospital where he made straight for the little wooden shed. Robin was not inside but Adam soon found him round the back playing with a cat that had just given birth to five little kittens. The cat itself was a tortoiseshell, yet all but one of the kittens was black. Robin was delighted to see his father and asked at once: "Can I have the little brown one, Dudda? It's different from the others."

Adam responded thoughtfully: "Yes, perhaps. We'll have to ask one of the Sisters about that but I'm glad you've found something to play with."

He felt uneasy and looked at his son carefully as he spoke, seeking any sign that the boy might have caught the dreaded disease from his playmate of the previous day. "Yesterday!" he thought to himself. "It seems a lifetime away, so much has happened since we set out from home in the morning." Nevertheless, he pulled himself together and took his son over to the Refectory where the nuns were preparing the midday meal.

Having told Robin to go over to a table by the door, he quietly asked one of the Sisters about Joel. "The boy died in the night. He is with Our Lord now." Sister Agnes whispered. "It was the pneumonic form of the plague." At the sight of his uncomprehending face, she continued: "It seems it takes two forms, this one affected the child's lungs but now he is at peace."

Robin crossed himself and at the same time thought of the boy's mother up in London. She would never know about his death. "Maybe that's all the better," he thought to himself grimly.

"We're already getting other patients coming in with the more usual kind, they get boils under their arms and...." Even though she had learned nursing, she could not bring herself to finish her sentence with the words "and in the groin." Instead, she jumped ahead of herself to continue: "We're keeping another part of the hospital for them, a sort of isolation ward but I don't know what we'll do if we get any more. We don't want to put them anywhere near the lepers who have enough troubles of their own." Adam gave an understanding nod and went over to join his son at the table set apart in a corner just for the two of them.

The next morning, he met the Mother Superior as she was emerging from the little Chapel. "Ah, just the man I wish to see," she said. "I believe you said you are a woodworker."

Adam replied: "Yes, Mother, I am. I make small carts and wagons but I have made boats too, in my young days. I can turn my hand to anything in wood."

"Well, my son, you have been sent by God to us, of this I am sure. One of our lepers was a carpenter. He used to make all the things we needed and did all the repairs, too. But last month he died and we have many jobs that need doing. Will you help us?" Suddenly, Adam knew how he could repay these good nuns for their kindness and occupy himself and perhaps young Robin at the same time. He had dreaded the thought of having nothing to do whilst he was away from his home and his beloved workshop.

"But I have no tools here, Mother."

The holy woman replied quietly: "I shall see to it that old John's are made available to you. I will have them sent over from the Leper House. Don't fear, they will not infect you."

And so it was. Gradually, Adam and Robin fell into a sort of pattern governed by the regular life of the community and each Friday Adam ventured into Wallingford to buy food and other goods that he thought his family might need or that his wife had asked him to purchase. At first this was fairly easy, for although the traders came and went quickly and no one went out and about unless it was necessary, life in the town continued basically along the same lines as usual and the market was still held on a Friday, although several funerals were being conducted at the same time in the little church by the Market square.

The following day he ran up the hill to Greys where his wife was already waiting for him at the cottage door, with little Alice holding on to her skirts. Again he left his bundle by the old tree stump and again they shouted greetings, news and instructions to one another before Adam had to run back to his son and the shelter of the hospital.

There he found Robin again playing with the cat and her kittens. "I made a little bed of straw for her and her babbies but when I tried to put them in it, she scratched me!" he whimpered, showing his father a couple of scratches on his hand.

"Ah, lad, you have to learn to respect animals when they have young. They're always on the defensive for they don't know but what you might want to harm them!" He loved this side of his children, especially now they were growing old enough to teach them what he knew. He especially looked forward to this one glimmer of hope in his present dark world, being able to educate his son in the craft of woodwork. "He may even be able to work with me when he's older and be useful when I get infirm." he thought.

"Come on, now, Sister Tabula wants a chair mended and there's a fence to be repaired over the back of the Leper House. You shall come with me and help me. That way you'll learn how to make things for yourself. When we've done those jobs, I'll show you how to make a little box for your kitten but he mustn't leave his mother 'til he's six weeks old." Thus Adam and his son continued to repay their debt to the nuns and the time passed quickly enough, though he was dismayed to learn how many were dying in the town and in the villages around.

"Those that get it in the lungs never survive, but those that get the buboes, sometimes they do, if we nurse them carefully," Sister Tabula whispered as he brought the repaired chair back to her.

By the next week, the situation appeared to have become rapidly worse and Adam had to go to the shops and homes of the tradespeople and shout for what he wanted. An air of complete gloom and desperation overcame the little town and few went into or came out of the castle. Those who were out and about went around anxiously with kerchiefs over their mouths and nostrils while a few gypsy women sat around offering posies of wildflowers, crying out: "Herbs to stop the plague!"

In St Martins Street he ducked in a doorway to avoid a procession, not just of one funeral, but of a cartload of bodies, covered with a white cloth, patchy with bloodstains. "We're having to bury them all in one trench now!" shouted one of the men pushing the cart. "Things is real bad in the town!"

Further on he met another man with a horse drawn wagon piled high with straw. "They all want this now," he called over, "It's for their floors, to soak up the blood!"

Again on the Saturday morning, he climbed Berin's Hill and made his way to his homestead in the upland woods. As before, he exchanged the latest news to his wife at a distance and left the goods he had bought by the stump of an old tree, some way from the cottage. "All seems to be well there, perhaps we shall all pass through this dreadful pestilence," he thought as he ran downhill once more.

The following Friday, Adam could hardly face going over the bridge into Wallingford town especially since he had heard that men were now being paid to bury the dead, several at a time, especially by those who had no relatives or friends fit enough to carry out this gruesome task. However, he was as keen as ever to do the right thing by his little family and to keep them as safe as possible. As he passed through the half-timbered houses and came to the little shops and stalls, he had to call out to the trades-people to come and serve him, for even his old friend the baker shouted out: "Keep away, keep away!"

Adam managed to purchase just enough food and the two blankets that his wife had told him to buy and took them back with him. His money was running out though because the Sisters could not pay him for his work. "Even if I have to steal to get the things Evie and Alice need. I'll always see they're alright." he swore to himself.

The next morning, he rose early as usual and motioned Robin to go back to sleep as he packed up his bundle and started off for his home in the upland woods. Again he left his purchases by the tree stump and was reassured when Evie confirmed that none of them had been away from the clearing. She even smiled when he told her how he and their son were working at repairing and making things

160

in wood together. He briefly shouted the story of how Robin had found playmates in the kittens and how the mother cat had scratched the child in defence of her young. "Do take care, husband, we all depend on you so!" she called out as he waved his hand in parting

He ran on until he reached the open view and thought to himself how lovely it all looked in the morning sun. Usually he was in the enclosed cover of the woodland or down in the town and, more recently, in the confines of the hospital area so he valued highly this wonderful view of the river, the meadowlands and Wallingford, with its castle, spread out below him.

Still he did not stop for more than a moment or two, just enough to get his breath back before setting off once more. "I expect he'll be playing with the cat and her kittens again." he mused, thinking of the little son he was about to rejoin. Sadly, what he did not realise was that this cat was kept by the hospital because she was an expert catcher of mice and rats and consequently became a carrier of the flea that had bitten young Robin the night before.

Returning to the little wooden hut Adam found Robin, not playing with the kittens, but still in bed under the blankets. "What's this, lad, not up and about!" he admonished, but in the same instant saw that all was not well.

"I feel cold, Dudda!" the boy shivered as he spoke. "And the window keeps moving."

At once Adam felt his throat constrict and the muscles of his stomach tighten. "You stay there, Robin," he said, soothingly. "I'm just going over to the hospital for a minute. Here, have my blanket. You'll soon be warm." In petrifying fear, he sought out one of the Sisters who came with him at once to the boy's bedside. Instantly she showed Adam the little red rashes that had appeared under the child's armpits and the buboes that were beginning to show themselves there and in his groin.

"You must stay with your son," the Sister instructed. " I will bring you water and a candle. It is quite dark in here and a draught through the open door would not be good for the child." True to her word, she brought back not only the water and candle but also extra blankets. "You will need these for yourself now. Try not to fear for some do live who get this form of the disease. I shall bring you food regularly and we shall all pray for you both in the Chapel this evening."

Sadly, though, despite all their ministrations to the boy, he vomited constantly and died several days later in great agony with buboes that grew to the size of small apples. Adam wept and wept, until he felt he could weep no more. He prayed too but God did not seem to hear him. He slept little and could hardly eat anything but the Sisters kept urging him to drink at least a little broth. All the time he kept thinking of the plans he had had for the future and the ideas he had enjoyed of the way in which he and his son would be working together making all kinds of things in wood. Now all his life seemed to be of little purpose.

"You must remember your wife and little girl, my son," comforted the Mother Superior. "You will need to look after yourself for their sake." After the lepers had dug the small grave and lowered into the ground the little coffin that Adam hastily made, the priest, who still managed to come each Sunday to the hospital, conducted a brief commital. Then and only then, did the holy woman's words begin to sink into his consciousness.

Gradually it came to him that it was Monday and that his wife would be worrying about his failure to come on the appointed day. At last he was able to make some food stay in his stomach and gather enough strength to make another trek up the hill. This time he had no heavy bundle, just a cloth bag with a couple of loaves from the hospital bakery to take up to his wife, their daughter and his parents-in-law.

When little Alice shouted: "It's Dudda, he's come home again!" Evie ran out to find a man who was just a shadow of his former self, thinner than ever, bowed and almost unkempt.

"Dear Holy Mother of God, what has happened?" she cried, knowing at the same time that something dreadful must have come to pass. Adam could hardly shout the words and some of them got blown away in the wind but she knew, just from the look of him, that their only son was dead and she fell to her knees in despair. "What will become of us if you also should fall ill, and me not there to look after you?" she asked.

"Never fear." he shouted back. "I will always look after you."

Fortunately, even though he had nursed his son through this dreadful disease, Adam did not succumb to it. Why not, no one knows, but some died and some survived. Perhaps he, being a man accustomed to the rigours of an outdoor life, was stronger than his seven-year old son. Certainly the young, the aged and others as vulnerable, died more often than not.

Eventually, after about two months living this way, he gathered together as much food as he could lay his hands on and borrowed a cart from the Sisters to drag it all the way up to his home. It took him all day this time as he was still weak and burdened with his load, but his heart was a little lighter as he knew he was finally returning home for ever, to be able to stay in the wooded area that he loved.

Gradually life regained some of its normality. Sir Robert de Grey, crenallated his house and called it Grey's Court. This provided Adam with work for several years and a regular income.

Indeed, for some time he, like all other workers, was able to ask for much higher wages than he would have been paid before the plague. Fortunately for Lord Grey, who had always commanded great respect from his peasants, most of them stayed faithful to him and eventually life in the hamlet continued much as before. Evie's parents died several years later, but although Adam and his wife had another daughter and three more sons, they never forgot their little Robin, who loved cats and especially kittens.

******

Some villages and towns were almost wiped out by the Black Death, but other areas survived with few losses. In total the nation lost almost a third of its population in 1348. It took a long time to recover so great was the effect on trade, both personal and national. Conditions changed overnight and people spoke of time as 'before the plague' and 'since the plague'.

In fact, this ghastly episode in England's history enabled those who survived to change the whole structure of the old feudal relationship between the lord and his villeins [peasants] and for a while the situation was almost anarchical. People broke their feudal obligations, deserted the cottages that their lords had provided and villeins soon became tenants as landlords tried to ensure that their *demesne* [the lord's own land] was sown and harvested. Changes in work patterns left many fields untilled and every landlord had to pay unprecedented sums to anyone who would do the work.

By 1349, protests began to grow about the high level of wages demanded by the surviving able men and women, so in 1351, King Edward III, who had also lost his daughter, Joan, to the plague, brought in the Statute of Labourers, which regulated wages through the courts and fixed them at pre-Black Death levels. In 1361, after a further series of wet summers and poor harvests, there was another bout of the plague that again killed many people. Once more, it attacked 'the rich man in his castle and the poor man at his gate'. However, most of those who had caught the disease in 1348, which came to be known as The General Mortality, and had survived and those who nursed them, were usually unaffected. Possibly they had been naturally immunised.

******

In his Brittania *(1610) William Camden wrote about the effects of the plague on Wallingford: '1348: This towne was so dispeopled by reason of the continuall mortalitie there, that whereas before time it was passing well Inhabited, and had twelve churches in it, it can shew no more than one or two.'*

Chapter 9. The Englysche Manor: 1495 - 1525

The reign of Henry VII lasted for twenty-four years (1485-1509) and was one marked by considerable domestic achievements in legal and parliamentary reforms. For over one hundred years English, rather than French, had been the official language used in Parliament and the law courts and therefore the word 'English' began to have a significance that it had not had before. J. M. Davenport in his *Oxfordshire Annals* (1869) considered that English Farm at Nuffield was named because it was the 'habitation of the Angles', based on the author's opinion that the nearby Grim's Ditch was a boundary between Wessex and Mercia, and that nearby Newnham meant 'habitation of New Men'.

One of the earliest owners of land hereabouts was Benet Englysche. Although it bears no date, a *demi-figure* [half-figure] brass plate in the floor of Nuffield Church commemorates him. He is depicted as having flowing locks and the dress of the gentry in the reign of Edward III. This was about 1350, since he was known to have bought land at South Stoke in 1348, perhaps fearing death from the plague that was ravaging England at the time. The last document, known to have been signed by him, was written in 1351.

Miss Phyllis Briers, in her *History of Nuffield*, published just before the Second World War, states that the history of the Englysche family thereafter is 'disjointed and tantalising', but we do know they were a family largely engaged in law and taxation. Richard Englysche was appointed assessor and collector of taxes in Oxfordshire in 1432. Although he is described as a knight, whereas his ancestors do not appear to have risen above the rank of esquire, his life has left very little record. His wife, Margery, is mentioned in 1437 and he himself died in February 1460. His son and heir was William Englysche but of him little is known, except that he became father to Thomas, the main figure in our story, though the date of his birth is not recorded.

******

The year was 1497 and on a hill at the west side of the Chilterns about ten miles up from Wallingford, stood a fairly short young man named Thomas Englysche, whose fair hair and blue eyes showed him to be a typical Angle, the tribe from whom he presumed his family had got its name. He had recently married Isabell Langton, sister of the distinguished Doctor of Law, Robert Langton of Queen's College, Oxford.

Thomas held the bridle of his mettlesome palfrey whilst his wife sat on her roan thoroughbred mare. Both were surveying the landscape below them for they were planning to build themselves a house on land that he had recently inherited. True there was an old farmhouse but Thomas was by now a successful lawyer and tax administrator and felt he had enough money to build a home worthy of his station in life. Moreover he was keen that it should reflect not only his wealth but also the very latest fashion in houses.

In his hand he held a little charcoal stick and with this he made notes on a piece of parchment. One of the observations he made was that the estate was also situated near to the ancient Ridgeway that for countless generations had served as a link between the River Thames near Wallingford and towns to the east and the north. In fact the old farmhouse was also adjacent to the even older Grim's Ditch, the dyke that had acted as a barrier and boundary in Iron Age times and was connected at one point to Highmore Trench.

However, the old house was damp, draughty and smoky and although Thomas had grown up there he wanted something far better for his new bride. The marriage was not only a very sound one financially but in it he had also found so much joy. This was so rare in such forms of wedlock that his brother-in-law had stated at the wedding feast: "I do believe he really loves, nay, adores his young wife!"

"We shall have a far better home than the old farmhouse, with its leaking roof." Thomas explained to Isabell. "I plan that we shall have all the latest improvements incorporated in to this new one. I have spoken with Master Giles, the carpenter. He is a real craftsman, a member of the Guild no less. He travels to London and has learned of all the most recent styles."

The reign of Henry VII had been a time of peace and great economic growth in the land and many of the gentry had become rich and were able to indulge themselves in luxurious houses and matching decor. "How much will it all cost?" asked the timid Isabell.

"I reckon about one hundred and twenty five pounds should cover it," he replied.

"Oh dear!" she sighed, "It does seem a great deal. Have you enough money for all that?"

"Enough money?!" expostulated Thomas. "Can you not grasp the extent of the estate that I have now inherited? My lands now consist of a thousand acres of arable, a thousand acres of pasture, a thousand and three hundred acres of wood and a hundred acres of meadow. I also have twenty-four *messuages*, [dwellinghouses with outbuildings and land assigned to their use] as well as an annual yield of rent to the value of thirty shillings!" He took a breath and then continued, more temperately: "In fact, my property extends from the parishes of Mapledurham, where there is a watermill on the River Thames, along to Newnham Murren near to Wallingford. From there it goes through the meadowlands, up into the heaths at Ipsden and right into the woods here at Nuffield and Nettlebed. Just before our wedding I also acquired Hayden Farm, which is about two miles to the north, over there. You must realise that we are now people of great importance, even though this is some twenty miles from your family at Oxford!"

Fearing he had spoken a little too strongly in his pride, he gently lifted Isabell down from her mount and embraced her warmly. "My love, you may have anything you wish! See here, this is what I plan." He then drew a box-shaped frame of wooden timbers with a pitched roof.

"It looks very similar to the old house." Isabell remarked.

"Yes, but there will be differences, great and important differences. Although it may look similar from the outside there will be a porch over the front door so as to protect visitors from the weather while they wait for the door to be opened. The Great Hall will face south with a solar at the side as we have now in the farmhouse but once they get into the Hall there will no longer be the two entrance doors on each side of it with the old screens passage to keep out the draughts."

Proudly he continued: "I want our Hall to be clean and clear of that awful smoke that always makes us cough in the old house. We shall have a stone chimney to take the smoke out from a huge stone fireplace that will be built into the wall on the far side of the front entrance. I have also spoken to Master Pierre, the mason. He served his apprenticeship and so was paid nothing for ten years but he is now a Guildman. He has to pay an annual fee and swear to uphold the rules and standards set up by that great body. It is true he was but a journeyman [French *journee*, a day] up to a year ago. That is to say he was just paid by the day but I am convinced he now has enough skills to build a fireplace and a chimney. You will be amazed what an improvement it will make!"

"Yes, my love, it sounds wonderful, but do not get too excited yet. It will take many months to build, will it not?" Isabell enquired.

"Indeed it will and until then we shall have to continue to live in the old farmhouse which will make it seem all the more wonderful when our new home is complete. Anyway, I have not yet finished my explanations. See here, I am drawing a plan for you to help you to understand it all. There is even to be a bedchamber in an upper room at the far south side of the Hall."

"An upper room? Shall we have a staircase to go up there, as they do in castles?"

"Yes, my dearest, it is called a parlour and will be exclusively for our own use, our private love nest, far away from the servants and the cooking smells."

"Oh good! I do hate the cooking smells." she giggled.

"Ah, there again, there will be improvements on the old house," he continued. "Behind the solar there will be a still room. Outside, at the other end of the house, linked with a *tresaunce* [covered way] there will be a kitchen in which the cooks can practise their culinary arts." It will be . . ."

"Why will the kitchen have to be outside?" Isabell asked.

"It must be away from the house, for fear of fire. The kitchen, too, will have a chimney with a smoke-hole in it, so meat can be smoked there and off the kitchen there will be a pantry for the dry goods such as flour and bread. There will, of course, be a bread oven let into the wall for proving the dough. Next to it will be a buttery for the milk as well as butter and cheese-making and I hope to have a small brewhouse to make ale, too"

His voice again began to rise with excitement as he became enthused with the new ideas that he planned to incorporate into their new dwelling. "There will also be four other bedrooms at the far end of the house. They will be on an upper storey, too."

"What about the windows?" Isabell asked, getting more excited. "Will there be real windows?"

It was little wonder she was hopeful, for in the older buildings there were just openings in the walls with wooden mullions [upright posts inset at two inch intervals] to prevent birds from flying in and out, willy-nilly. There were also interior shutters to close when weather became rough, but they did make the rooms dark.

The new type windows were *fenestral* [lattice frames covered in linen that had been soaked in resin and tallow]. These let in some light whilst keeping out the draughts and could be removed on fine days.

"Of course, my love. We shall have only the very latest type and I have yet another secret but tell no one as yet for I fear they may not think it safe. I am arranging for us to have a special, small private room behind our bedchamber and there we shall have the latest luxury from London. It is called a stoolroom, with copper pots, set into red velvet-covered seats, which will be warm to the touch. Err, err, the pots will, of course, be emptied regularly by the servants", he hastened to add in a low voice. In the old house, as in most castles, there had been a *garderobe,* so named because the strong smell from the urine and faeces had deterred the moths that laid their eggs in the furs and woollen garments but the seats were stone and therefore very cold.

"Shall we also have a garden?" enquired Isabell. She loved flowers and had been taught by her mother which ones were suitable for different types of soil and various situations, bearing in mind they were used for medicines, for sweetening the house and for decorating both the home and the church.

"Yes, of course, all around the house. And there will be stables, too, for our horses. You'll see. I have even planned for a fishpond and, of course, a well will have to be sunk. Believe me, my little turtledove, we shall soon have the finest house for miles around and we shall be able to invite our neighbours in for a great banquet! Also, of course, we shall be able to use the Great Hall for special village feasts, too, such as those after the Harvest and at Christmas. I intend to see that our servants enjoy their holy days."

******

Thomas Englysche was true to his word. He employed the best craftsmen to build his manor house and within the year he and Isabell were installed in their new home. It was constructed in the latest fashion of the day, a box-frame of wooden timbers, with small panels of wattle and daub, since the ability to make larger ones had not yet been discovered. Once the main structure was complete, in accordance with the old Saxon custom, the builder tied the bough of an oak to the chimney stack and poured a little ale on the doorstep to ensure prosperity for the owners.

The oak framework was not treated, it just weathered until it became stone hard, but the wattle and daub was painted with limewash to keep down the infestation of insects. There was a grand double front door, with a pitched roof porch over, and above it was carved a wooden plaque showing the Englysche family's coat of arms, *ermine on a chief or demi-lion issuant vert*. The door had a great iron ring set into it which acted as a knocker and this could also be used to lift the latch on the inside, provided that the great heavy bolts were not drawn for security. This was a job for the servants last thing at night before they went to bed.

"You were quite right, Thomas, about our Great Hall. It is a wonderful room, such light windows and the massive stone fireplace and chimney!" Isabell exclaimed when she first set foot in her new home. "I shall hang the walls with woollen cloths in soft natural colours and everyone who comes to see it shall be impressed by our new home!" In fact the young lawyer and his beautiful bride were so proud of their staircase and parlour that they even showed visitors upstairs in their early days there.

In this room was the large four-poster bed with a *tester*. In effect this was a roof to prevent its occupants suffering the droppings of birds that somehow often seemed to get into the bedchamber. At the head of the bed was a panel of wood carved to look like folded linen. In the centre of that the couple had had carved their coat of arms, as if the sight of it before they retired comforted them. The bed boasted a mattress and four pillows, all filled with goose down. There were also linen sheets and pillowcases and several warm woollen blankets although all of these did tend to harbour fleas! Around the bed were warm woollen curtains that were drawn together at night to keep out the draughts, making the bed a snug and private place.

However, they did not reveal their closest secret, the stoolroom, to anyone. Only the servants saw it when they came to take away the copper pots that they emptied on to the scrap heap away from the house, where their malodorous contents helped to form a very effective compost.

Down in the Great Hall, rushes were always put down on the floor to absorb the damp but Isabell improved the bad smells by scattering dried herbs and flowers amongst them, such as Lavender, Tansy and Ladies' Bedstraw. These not only made strong sweet scents to overcome worse ones but they also deterred fleas. She made sure too, that plenty of flowers were cultivated in the new garden that surrounded the house in season.

There she grew herbs for the kitchen, others for the floors and some for medicines, such as febrifuges, which reduced fevers, as well as blooms with which to decorate the Great Hall and their own bedroom. "Next year I shall make sure we grow enough flowers for decorating our local churches, too." she stated when Thomas admired the flower arrangement in the Hall.

Like all married women, Isabell kept her hair covered in a linen wimple and wore a short-sleeved woollen dress with close-fitting bodice. Under this she wore a linen shift with long sleeves and long woollen stockings with leather garters to keep them up. For Sundays, High Days and holidays she had two beautiful gowns with ornamental sleeves, one lighter for summer and one heavier, with fur cuffs and hem. She always wore a wide leather belt on which hung her *rosary* [prayer beads], a linen purse that served as a pocket and a chatelaine, a chain on which she kept all her keys. On her feet she wore dainty buckled shoes.

Isabell was very accomplished and soon she was painting linen and weaving beautiful tapestries to hang on the walls to keep out draughts. In winter it was often very windy up on the exposed west side of the Chiltern Hills. She was also careful of the household stocks and finances as became any young bride.

It was Isabell's task to oversee all the high days and holy days. Christmas was a favourite time with everyone. Beforehand there was much work to do, bringing in the great Yule Log as well as the holly, ivy and mistletoe. In the kitchen the cooks made bag puddings, boiled in a pot full of water. They also minced up meat, mixed it with spices and put it into oval-shaped pies, with a 'baby' cut from the pastry, to resemble the infant Jesus in his cradle.

On Christmas morning the whole household and all the estate workers went to Mass in the Church of St Mary the Virgin at Ipsden and later in the day came the great celebrations. The main Christmas Feast consisted of sugar-cured ham for the top table, where Master Thomas, Lady Isabell and their family and close friends sat. There were also large pieces of brawn, legs of pork in jelly, game pies with glazed raised crusts, and for those 'below the salt', smoked gammon, beef and salted pork.

The *Lord of Misrule*, some humble person, servant or even a professional clown, governed the Christmas Day feast, and his orders, even the most ridiculous, had to be obeyed. The festivities lasted for twelve whole days, i.e. until Twelfth Night, on 6th January.

Isabell saw to it, too, that any visitors were made welcome. Few people came from outside the area, only perhaps pilgrims passing through to Dorchester, pedlars with their packs or visitors to the landowner. Sometimes travelling merchants too, bringing salt for curing meat or spices from the east came to the house, hopeful of a sale. As they often had news of the outside world they were always received graciously.

Thus Isabell and Thomas lived quietly and contentedly, enjoying the first years of their married life in the great comfort of their splendid new house.

* * * * * *

However, Isabell did become lonely when it was necessary for Thomas to go to London, Oxford or sometimes further, to the west or north-country on legal or taxation matters. It is true there were servants, several of whom became almost friends as the years went by, and she had her dogs and horses, but she longed for more. She desperately wanted a baby.

After two years of marriage she was delighted to find herself with child, but sadly she miscarried after three months and this happened again two years later. Finally she did carry a baby for the full term but to Thomas's disappointment it turned out to be a girl. Like any man in his position he really wanted a boy, an heir to his estates. He had hoped for many years of hunting and showing his son how to manage the lands that he would inherit.

They called their baby daughter Ann. She was a strong-willed child, some said, "just like her father!" However, as the old midwife had predicted, Isabell was not able to bear her husband any more children so he reconciled himself in time and gradually came to love his one and only offspring.

She was not fair of countenance like her mother; instead she had the strong features of her father's family and was not easily repri-manded. As she grew older her mother despaired of ever making a lady out of her for feminine matters did not appear to interest her at all.

When she was ten years old, her parents bought Ann a pony and then all she could think about was riding. It was when they were out riding together one September, that father and daughter began to find a common bond in the management of the Englysche estate. "Tell me what happens here and who does what?" she demanded when she was only twelve years old. This was on a day when Thomas had allowed his daughter to come with him as he rode over to Nettlebed to see about the felling of some trees.

"Well," he began tentatively, "managing an estate is all a matter of handing down work to others, delegating that is. I have men under me, you know some of them and they carry out my orders. The most important man to me is my steward, Henry Slade. His family got their name because, as far back as anyone can recall, they have always lived in one of my cottages by the old *slayed* oak, the one that was blown down in a storm about fifty years ago. I have to pay him well because he is in charge of all the estate accounts. He organises the work and the peasants fear him greatly for he is not a man to be crossed, mark my words!"

Thinking over what he had said about Slade, Thomas fell silent for a while and then added: "Mind you, he can be kind to those who he thinks are badly off through no fault of their own, like Dick Straw who fell off a cart and broke his leg and couldn't work for nearly a year. Slade asked me if we might give him extra produce to see him and his family through that difficult winter. I like that in a man! The Holy Bible stresses that we should be considerate to those less fortunate than ourselves."

Thomas himself tried always to be fair in his judgements for he ran his own manor court. When he was away on legal business his steward, Henry Slade, took his place as judge and tried to make the same balanced decisions that he felt his master would make in the same circumstances. Of course, on his return Thomas wanted to know what had happened, who had been brought before the court, what their misdeeds were and what fines had been imposed.

A few weeks after Ann and her father had taken their first ride together, Isabell and her ladies were helping others to arrange flowers for a wedding at the little Norman church of SS Peter and Paul at Chackenden. Much to the chagrin of her mother, Ann did not enjoy this art at all. Instead she and her father once again found themselves together riding around the Englysche estate. This time they were down at Mapledurham near the River Thames, where there was a small wharf. Thomas enjoyed the benefits of a river frontage and had all his corn ground into flour at the watermill there. "It was mentioned in the Doomsday Book which King William ordered!" Thomas told Ann.

Down there, supervising the loading of surplus flour on to a barge they came upon the bailiff, Edward Allnutt, who wore a long jacket, linen-lined, with pewter buttons, leggings with stirrup straps and leather boots. He removed his pointed black wool cloth cap that had a peak to the front to shade his eyes from the sun. In winter he often reversed it, as the shape allowed the water to run off down his back and not down his neck. He bowed his head in respectful greeting, as he held the bridle of his *skewbald* [brown and white] horse.

"Good morning, my lord, have you come to see the flour loaded?"

"No, Allnutt, I leave that to you. I trust there are no problems with the work?"

"No sir, all is well, I'm glad to say." the bailiff replied, "The watermill is certainly more reliable than the windmills. Those ones up on the hills at Nettlebed and Stoke Row [by now it was usually spelled like this] can't do the same amount of work as a watermill."

"No, indeed but the windmills are nearer and more useful to the serfs. They can't bring their gleanings this far," replied Thomas as he and Ann turned their horses and continued their way.

"Allnutt is another good man, a trusted servant these many years past. He's not a serf of course, but a freeholder, that is to say he owns his bit of land and he is very stable. Henry Slade depends on him a good deal because he can't be everywhere at once. Can you now begin to see the order of things here? You should begin to learn all about the estate because one day it will be yours to govern and it is important that you have a firm sense of what is needed and how to cultivate steady, reliable servants to do your bidding."

"I thought the Reeve was in charge of the work Father. I have seen him directing the peasants as to where and when to do the work in the fields."

"Ah, yes, Roger Godwyne, he works at the direction of Allnutt. They all have their place in the order of things, you see. Godwyne, you may have noticed, carries a white stick. That's his 'badge of office' as you might say. He finds it useful for pointing to things and occasionally for giving a twitch of it to a man who's a bit slow to move!" he laughed. "As we go back through Ipsden you will see him supervising the peasants as they bring in the remainder of the harvest."

Once they reached the top of the hill they reigned in their horses and watched the work. The women laboured on the harvest as well as the men, even the older children had to join in. The wheat was cut with sickles, each clump being grasped firmly so the grains wouldn't shake loose. The corn was then tied into sheaves that were leaned together in groups to form *stooks*, so they could dry.

Later these were loaded on to carts and carried away into barns where they were beaten with a *flail* [a stick with a loose piece of wood attached] to separate the grain from the stalks. The grain was then taken to the mill and the remaining straw used for thatching buildings, for stuffing mattresses or as bedding for animals.

"He makes sure everyone starts and finishes work at the right time of day or a bit longer if needs be and he also ensures that none of the produce is stolen. Each of the serfs is allotted some land in various parts of the estate, you see. It's shared out on the basis that each gets some poor and some good land and each works his own strips or plots and on those they grow what they can. They pay rent for their cottages and strips of course, twice a year at Michaelmas and on Lady Day, sometimes with money but more usually in the form of produce or even part and part. Some days of the week they have to work for us on the *demesne*, on jobs such as ploughing or haymaking and from this work they get some of the produce too."

"What's the *demesne*?" asked Ann, always questioning everything.

"It's an old Norman word. It originates from the Latin, *dominicus,* which means domain or estate." Thomas explained, flattered that his daughter looked up to him with such awe as he aired his knowledge. He and Isabell had ensured their daughter had a governess from whom she learned to read and write but believed that little more was required of a girl in the way of education so she had not studied Latin. He continued: "The harvest is very important. A bad harvest can mean near starvation for us all. Well, that is to say for all of them, for we can always buy food elsewhere for ourselves. A good landowner makes sure his people are fed for only then can they do the work."

That evening Thomas, Isabell and Ann were sitting in the Great Hall by a huge roaring fire. Although it was only September, the nights were already turning cold and as there was plenty of wood readily available in the locality, Isabell ordered a fire on the least pretext in an endeavour to keep the Manor warm.

Apart from a comfortable chair for Thomas, there was a cushioned settle with a high back to keep off the draughts. It was placed near the fire and on it Isabell and Ann sat upright. There was very little other furniture and even that was extremely simple, just a large rectangular table around which there were a few bench seats. There were also wooden chairs at the top of the table for the master of the house, his lady and their guests. The Englysche family had just finished their dinner and the servants were clearing away the pewter plates and mugs and replacing the candles. The housekeeper bobbed a curtsy before she left the family to their quiet conversation.

At the far side there was a board on two supports, known as a *side-board* and a cupboard with carved linenfold panelling on its doors and a lock. In here were kept the master's best wines. A few iron candlesticks had been fixed around the walls and gave a dim light to the large room, making it difficult to discern the images on the tapestries that Isabell and her ladies had created.

Although Isabell chiefly devoted her time and energies to the interior of the Manor and its gardens, she tried to show some interest in the estate, especially since she had noticed how enthusiastic Ann was to learn about the running of it. This evening she was asking her husband about the livestock because it was essential there were enough cows and pigs killed and salted down for the coming winter. Of course, there were always deer in the woods and pigeons in the pigeon-loft for fresh meat but salted meat formed an essential part of the household's diet.

"If the river freezes, we shall have no fish so I'd like Henry Slade's word that the salting will soon be in hand. Remember how difficult it was to come by fish last year, once the stock in the pond had been used up."

"Yes, my little dove," he still spoke to her affectionately, even after so many years of marriage. "Don't you worry, Slade will have all that taken care of. You know how reliable he is."

"And for your part, have you ensured that we have enough onions strung up to dry and that the carrots have been packed into the earth clamps?" enquired Thomas, well aware that very soon the fresh vegetable garden produce, peas, beans and cabbages would be coming to an end.

"Yes, indeed, my love, all is well there. I must say that we are very fortunate in having Martha, she is such a good housekeeper and keeps her eye on all that side of the housekeeping. She has been busy today making the harvest buns for the people working in the fields. She stops them from going dry by adding finely chopped suet. Another secret lies, she tells me, in putting in a pinch of nutmeg and cinnamon, too. The field workers love them.

To tell the truth, I leave much of that side of the house to her. I prefer to busy myself with the flowers, helping to look after our churches and caring for the sick," she laughed. "Lady Knollys has recently shown me how to make an excellent febrifuge from marigold buds, marjoram and lemon balm, steeped in boiling water. Once cooled it is so useful in bringing down fevers."

"You are very kind to our folk, my dear. I'm not sure how many of our neighbours would be as considerate to their people but sometimes I wish that, like Ann," he said, smiling across at his daughter, "you would take more part in the management of the demense."

"Yes, well, perhaps. I leave that mostly to you and your men. But now, concerning another matter. We must soon be making preparations for the Harvest Home. I shall see the priest about the church service tomorrow and start to arrange the feast, probably for the end of next week. What do you think, Thomas, will all be ready by then?"

"It should be, my dear, but..." he was interrupted by Ann who, until then, had patiently waited for a chance to ask a favour of her parents.

"If it pleases you, Mother, may we have a suckling pig? I do so love its meat, so much more soft and tender than the salted pork we have to have in the winter. Can we, just as one last treat?" Her mother nodded her agreement. And treat it was, a succulent delicacy only for the rich, because a young pig had to be fed and nurtured with great care. The poor had only old sows and at the Harvest Feast they had a really large one, skewered on an iron pole over a huge fire in the top field near the big chalk pit.

A peasant's life was hard, very hard. They worked all the hours of daylight, especially in the summer, except on feast days, such as Eastertide, May Day, Midsummer's Eve, Harvest Home and, of course, Christmas. At these times there was great celebrating, with good food and extra amounts of ale if the estate had a good overlord. Life was short too, but there was compensation in the companionship they enjoyed as they worked and the numerous Holy Days to which they all looked forward for weeks beforehand.

The Harvest Home, usually held at the end of September, was a great favourite. The Lord of the manor provided plenty of food and drink for the peasantry and he, his lady and their daughter always came out to the start of the festivities. Thomas took the traditional step of lighting the huge fire with a burning faggot, the fire on which a big old sow or perhaps even a side of beef would be roasted and the people danced around the fire to keep themselves warm as the meat cooked.

Very soon though, as the evening air grew chill, the gentry withdrew to the Great Hall where an even better feast had been prepared for them. The tables were formed in a T-shape, with the 'high' table being the crossbar. This was placed on a platform at one end and at it sat Thomas, Isabell, Ann, the local priests and any other guests who might have been invited or perhaps a merchant, always received graciously, who happened to be passing through that week. It was covered with a huge white linen cloth and a large communal napkin, called the 'long towel' was placed over the knees of the diners once they were seated.

Several long, narrower tables formed the stem of the T and this is where the rest of the household sat, according to their rank. Near the top was the Steward with his son, for he was a widower, the Bailiff and his wife and the Reeve and his wife. After them came the household servants and lesser mortals, still known as 'those below the salt', because that commodity continued to be rare and the salt cellar did not often reach them before they had finished eating.

The feast consisted of three, four or even five courses and for the high table this year it did include young Ann's favourite, suckling pig, but there was also roast swan set about with its feathers to make it look attractive and salmon, caught in the River Thames and dressed with fresh herbs, mint, parsley or sage. The 'low' table had to do with roast beef, pork and trout, but first of all there was *pottage.* Everyone enjoyed this thick broth, with vegetables, but no one started eating before the priest had said the Grace, in Latin, of course. After the meats and fish came sweet and spicy dishes, the best that the kitchen could provide.

The meal was a boisterous affair, with wine for the upper echelons of society and ale for the staff. The dogs roamed freely, gobbling up scraps that fell from the tables or were thrown to them. Servants scurried to and fro with food on large platters and drinks served in large ceramic jugs. The gentry had fine glass goblets from which to drink but those at the low table had to do with leather tankards and, instead of silver dishes which were brought out for the lord and his family on high days and holidays, they had wooden platters. Everyone had their own knife and spoon at this time, the handles of which were engraved with their initials. Forks had not yet been invented. Having their own cutlery prevented the spread of diseases and training in the correct use of it formed an essential part of every wealthy child's education.

"I just can't wait for the acrobats!" exclaimed Ann as the exhausted scullions cleared away the tables and space was made for the entertainment. There were always singers and minstrels, travelling musicians, who made their living from events like this. Often, too, there was a jester whose quaint colourful garb and outrageous jokes made everyone laugh.

And thus the seasons passed. Ann grew older and wiser, taught by her father who grew ever more keen that his daughter should learn the sound ways he had developed of managing his desmesne.

On one of their rides, looking over the water meadows where the cattle grazed, he looked affectionately at her and found himself thinking: "Ann will be fifteen this summer. Isabell and I had better be looking for a suitor for our daughter, one who will be able to help her care for the estate when we are gone."

******

The years that followed passed quickly enough and Ann was more and more at her father's side as he rode about his estate, supervising the work. One day in July they watched as the grass was cut and laid into long rows to dry as hay. This was to be fodder for animals along with wheatstraw and dried beans when the fresh grass died in the winter, though most of the animals were eventually killed and salted.

By now Thomas found Ann to be interested in all aspects of the estate work. "Perhaps even better than a son would have been." he thought to himself but aloud he explained: "You have seen how we rotate the crops. Each year one field lies fallow and is given a rest whilst the other two are given over to wheat, barley or rye. Around the fields we still keep a few of the old oak trees as land markers. I must see that Allnutt gets the women and children on picking up more acorns this autumn; there weren't enough for the pigs last year. There is so much to remember about all this work!" he sighed.

Thomas had other troubles, too. Between 1504 and 1515 he prosecuted a suit against John Wise for refusal to quit the George Inn at Nettlebed, which Thomas had acquired from John Jones in exchange for a property in Cirencester. It was stated that 'Jones was aiding and abetting Wise, doing wilful damage to the Nettlebed property.' Nothing of the outcome of these suits is known but all this litigation over a period of ten years brought added work and worry to the landowner of Englysche and he began to develop heart problems, shortage of breath and palpitations. Some of this could be attributed to his being overweight. He loved his food and wine and rarely walked when he could ride.

But it wasn't all work and worry. Thomas and Isabell also entertained their friends and enjoyed falconry. Indeed they had several favourite birds of prey. One was a great horned owl, two were gyrfalcons and they also had a goshawk. All of these birds were reared from chicks, but most of them died within the first year. If they survived they became valuable and often lived for as much as thirty years. Your social scale was defined partly by what birds of prey you flew, those that were fastest in a *stoop*, or dive, were a tremendous asset in hunting game birds.

Two or three times a year they ran hunts which were considered then to be a noble pursuit. They had a stable of fine horses but Thomas's especial favourite was an old war-horse named Benet, after his ancestor, having borne him reliably for tournaments where two armoured knights cantered towards each other, their lances held before them. These were staged, mock fights between the gentry using old and blunted instruments. In days of relative peace, the idea was that you practised at these mock fights to keep your hand in, the object being to unseat your opponent, not to kill him. A horseman couldn't see the face of his opponent but he knew who he was by his family crest and coat of arms on his tunic and by the colours of his horse's *caparison* [drapes].

Occasionally the Englysche family still went to a 'tourney', as they were popularly called, if one was being held not far from home. However, Thomas was often heard to grumble: "There are fewer and fewer now, partly because the rewards are so poor. Prizes used to be valuable, but since Henry VII came to the throne, with his economical ways, they've become just symbolic. There might be a silver cup for the *Victor Ludorum*, but these days no purses of money at all!"

At one time the bag of gold won in a joust would have bought a contestant a new suit of armour, especially if he had grown too fat or if his old one had become too badly dented. Tournaments sometimes took place at Shirburn Castle in Watlington, a classical medieval fortress, with its crenallated walls, four towers and moat. From time to time Sir Francis Knollys and his wife, Katherine, held one at Greys Court, also partly crenallated, by licence from the King of course.

The ladies loved these events too, since it enabled them to dress up in their finery and to meet with their peers. While the west side of the field was filled with colourful round tents with peaked roofs and banners flying from their tops, the east side was a dangerous place, with knights galloping about on horseback, their squires running to do their bidding and pages constantly racing hither and thither with messages. Those not taking part sat up on a platform overlooking the scene. From this vantage point the host and hostess, several knights and members of the gentry now too aged to fight and their ladies would be keenly watching to see how the contestants fared. There would also be a trumpeter who would sound the signal for 'battle to commence!'

In times of war Thomas Englysche would have had to raise a group of armed men who would fight for the King should he call upon him and his men at any time. Luckily for Thomas this did not become necessary, as he was valued more highly for his legal services than for his fighting ability. Instead, when necessary, he paid the king *scutage* or shield money which could be used to hire mercenaries. As a tax collector Thomas was probably able to ensure that his dues were paid, or at least appeared to be paid, and this gave him an ability to enjoy a quiet life.

It was at one such tourney, in 1513 that Thomas, now too fat to fight, and his wife, Isabell, sat near to a newcomer, recently arrived in the area from York. Although he was not participating, he wore a tunic with his family emblem on it, *sable three covered cups argent*. Thomas was quick to spot this young man, Michael Warcopp, and soon struck up a conversation with him. They were delighted to find that they had much in common, for Isabell's brother, Dr Langton, of Queen's College, Oxford became Treasurer of the York diocese and had interests in the north. In fact, when he died he left £200 to build a school at Appleby in Westmorland.

Ann, who sat unusually quietly whilst this conversation was ensuing, soon discovered that the Warcopp family had a branch in Hertfordshire and relatives in London, too, all quite wealthy by all accounts. Michael Warcopp for his part quickly realised that Ann Englysche was the sole heiress to Englysche Manor and its estates. He decided there and then to pay court to her and in 1514, the two were married. Theirs was not the romantic coupling that her parents' one had been, but they got along well enough and, of course, both Thomas and Isabell were delighted to be linked with such a prosperous family.

A year later Ann bore Michael a son, whom they named Cuthbert. Thomas and Isabell were delighted to have a grandchild and indeed the infant spent much of his early life with them out at Nuffield, because Michael and Ann often went to London. These were joyous days, but they were punctuated by difficult ones, too, as they grew older.

Thomas's health had begun to decline, gradually at first, but later this state of affairs became serious. By 1524 he was having dizzy spells and occasionally had to spend the day in bed in order to recover. Isabell watched her beloved husband with great anxiety and though she brought down well-reputed physicians from Oxford there seemed little they could do apart from bleeding him with leeches, as was the custom.

In an effort to regain his well being, he and Isabell spent more and more time kneeling on their tall-backed prayer stools before the tiny altar they had erected in their bedroom, where they kept a Psalter, written by monks on parchment and richly illustrated. The capital letters that started each page were illumined in colour and adorned with gold leaf.

Thomas and Isabell were both very pious. Like many people of their time, they had great faith in God. This devoted pair supported the church at Nuffield and at Ipsden personally with great regularity and believed the words of the Bible implicitly even if some phrases seemed at odds with others, and they were firmly of the opinion that "the grace of God is the best help in times of danger." Although his ancestor, Benet Englysche, was buried at Nuffield, Thomas and Isabell preferred the mother church at Ipsden and Thomas even took his hawks and hounds in to Mass with him.

When Henry VIII came to the throne in 1509 all churches were still Catholic. It was some ten years before Henry declared his Act of Supremacy in 1534, and so these wealthy landowners regularly made confessions of their sins and were afterwards told by the priest to say the prayers like the *Pater Noster* ['Our Father'] and *Ave Maria* ['Hail Mary'] many times over as a penance. Both had sets of beautiful rosary beads, which enabled them to keep a count of the number of times they repeated these supplications.

It was not surprising, therefore, to learn that they often entertained members of the clergy, especially those in fairly high places. In the spring of 1525, Bartholomew Linstead, Prior of St Mary Overy at Southwark, south of the river in London, came to stay at Englysche Manor for a few days. The connection may well have had to do with the ancestral property or rents held by the Oxfordshire family in that part of the capital.

Up on the Chiltern Hill around Nuffield were beautiful woods for walking in, and they were especially lovely in spring when they were carpeted with bluebells and bright green quaking grass and one could hear the cuckoo as well as many other woodland birds. Thomas took the Prior on one of his rare walks so they could talk privately. However, the overweight host was unused to walking, in fact he was so fat that he waddled rather than walked. He soon began to pant, finding it hard to get his breath. He feared this might be so and had ensured that a servant followed at a discreet distance with a pair of horses, ready saddled.

As soon as they were well away from the house the Prior saw to it that their conversation soon began to deal with Thomas's ill health and the probable shortness of his life expectancy at this time. "You and your good lady wife have always been very devout, I know, but have you yet made your wills?" he enquired.

"Well, no, we haven't Father," Thomas squirmed. "I keep meaning to do so, but I fear somehow that this will bring death closer. Isabell has mentioned it to me on several occasions, but there is yet time, I'm sure."

"Yes, my son but you should think of the salvation of your soul. You never know when the Grim Reaper may strike. Do not delay in this matter. Though I wish you well of course, you really should face up to your obligations to Mother Church, just in case."

At this moment, almost as if it had been pre-ordained, Thomas suddenly stopped in his tracks and began to gasp, put his hand to his chest and then grabbed at his right arm. Looking at him quickly the Prior saw that his face had turned firstly red and then almost blue. The priest immediately shouted to the boy with the horses who had lagged further and further behind. "Come, come, quickly, make haste, lad, your master is not well, help me to get him on his mount!" It was a very difficult task, for Thomas was exceedingly heavy, but in the end they managed it and the boy ran ahead as Prior Bartholomew gently led his host's horse down the hill to the Manor.

When they reached the house, the servants were already at the door, ready to assist their master up the staircase to his bed, but Isabell soon realised that this would be impossible. "Help him to the couch in the Hall. Praise be to God we bought it last year. I had a fear it may be needed for such an occasion!"

Eventually they managed to get Thomas laid down and Isabell then sent one of her most reliable servants to ride as fast as he could the twenty miles to Oxford for the doctor and another for the parish priest to come, lest it be necessary for him to give his benefactor the Last Rites. She then hurried down to the kitchens to make a potion from lungwort and lemon balm that she felt sure would calm her husband's breathing, leaving Prior Bartholomew to watch over the sick man.

"Remember what I said on the hill, Thomas. You should turn your estate over to Mother Church with provision for Isabell during her lifetime. In this way you will be shriven of your sins." The Church at that time made a great deal of money for forgiving people their sins, with the sale of *indulgences*, especially on the deathbed of the sinner. The fear of Hell in the life hereafter was very great in medieval times and wall paintings, like those that still survive in the church at Checkendon, often depicted vivid scenes of terrifying horrors that would be the lot of the unrepentant sinner.

"See here! I will write a simple will for you to sign now, in case the Lord decides to take you to Him tonight." Thomas was too weak to argue and so he waved his hand in the direction of the small side table where there was paper, pen and ink. Speedily the Prior wrote a brief will and by the time Isabell returned with the potion, Thomas had signed it. "I have ensured that there will be provision for you during your lifetime, my lady, but you must realise that your husband is very ill and may not live much longer." It was not until then that Isabell had realised how very serious was her husband's condition and even as she tried to spoon a little of the calming liquid into his throat, Thomas gave a short gasp and quietly died in her arms.

Isabell was stunned. She sat nursing her husband's head and would not be moved, even when the priest came about half an hour afterwards to administer the Last Rites. As soon as he had departed the Prior carefully took the will, together with the deeds and evidences, from the hiding place in the panelling which Thomas had shown him only hours before.

He had no compunction about doing this, telling himself: "The daughter is wealthy in her own right and has no need of further earthly comforts. In any case, Thomas will go straight to heaven, now that I have persuaded him to give his estates to the Mother Church, no hell fires for him, for he has always been a good man."

Later in the evening Isabell would still not be moved and would only drink a little wine. The doctor, who had come over from Oxford had great difficulty in persuading her to go to bed. He gave her a sleeping draught and issued orders to her lady's maid not to leave her side.

Despite the opiate, Isabell awoke near dawn and as soon as she remembered the situation, she became quite distraught, weeping continuously. The Prior had already sent his assistant up to London post-haste to fetch Ann and Michael so they could deal with the details of Thomas's funeral. They arrived next noonday having ridden hard from the capital, leaving their young son, Cuthbert, in the care of his nurse and governess.

Ann tried all she could to comfort her mother but Isabell seemed to be almost unaware of her presence so the daughter and her husband turned instead to arranging Thomas's funeral. In medieval England such affairs were dealt with very quickly especially in the spring when days were already becoming warm.

By the following day the carpenter had made a coffin of the finest beech wood and the body of Thomas was carefully laid in silken sheets within. Fortunately the day was fine and, almost in a daze, Isabell, in her black 'widow's weeds', led the funeral procession across Ipsden Heath and along the narrow road to the Church of St Mary on the top of the hill at Ipsden.

The top of the coffin was not placed in position until everyone had filed past and paid their respects. The local peasantry were all there, of course but as soon as an important personage arrived they all had to stand back. Before sundown Sir Francis Knollys and his wife came from Greys Court. The Camoys from Stonor and even the gentry from Wallingford Castle and those from the crenellated quadrangular moated castle at Shirburn all rode over to say prayers over their long-standing friend and neighbour. Being the landowner Thomas was not buried outside in the graveyard but under the floor of the chancel in front of the altar. The heavy stone that covered the burial chamber was engraved later that week by the local mason.

In the weeks that followed Isabell still appeared to be inconsolable. Michael spoke to Ann as they lay in their bed a few days after the funeral. "I cannot stay much longer. I must return to London. Besides my business interests, Cuthbert will be pining for us. I have arranged for most things here to be kept running and you yourself know quite a lot about the management of the demesne. I suggest you stay here a while longer whilst your mother recovers."

Ann readily agreed but still Isabell did not rally. Lady Katherine Knollys came over from Rotherfield Greys and tried to coax her old friend back to health but Isabell would only talk almost incoherently, over and over again about "the day we stood together and looked over to Wallingford. Thomas showed me how he planned this house and we have been so happy here."

Martha, the former housekeeper who was now living in one of the estate cottages came every day but finally confessed that she could do no more to help her mistress. "She's like a love-sick maid. I really didn't realise how much she adored Master Thomas."

Indeed, no amount of cajoling would lift Isabell's spirits and over the next few months her health, too, slowly declined. When she passed away in the autumn, the Doctor diagnosed: "It is rare case, but I do declare that she died of a broken heart."

Again the daughter and son-in-law were bidden to come down from London. Ann was saddened at the death of her mother but confessed to Michael: "I am really not surprised after Lady Katherine's note of last week." There was no formal postal system but the recipient always paid and this ensured letters reached their destination. Sometimes carried by pedlars or merchants who paid in money or in kind to each other as the missive passed through their hands. Ever practical, she continued: "Now we shall have to get the tomb reopened for though she did not say so, it would be only right for Mother to be buried alongside Father."

"Yes, my dear." replied Michael Warcopp. "May I also suggest that when we return to London I commission a brass-smith, one who I know to have a fine studio in the city to make a brass plate depicting them both. He is very artistic and will make a good one, of that I am sure."

******

And so, in just one year, indeed, within the space of just a few months, Ann lost both her parents. As he grew older, young Cuthbert hardly remembered them. Nevertheless, Michael kept his word and the brass plate was laid in the floor of the church of St Mary the Virgin, Ipsden.

In his book *The Ipsden Country*, Mr John H Baker describes the monument thus: "The brasses are fixed on the floor of the chancel in front of the altar; a male effigy of 17.3/4 inches x 5.1/4 inches and a female effigy of 18 inches x 6 inches. The figures of the knight and his lady are turned away from each other, both with their hands clasped on their breasts... He is bareheaded and dressed in full plate armour with large spurs. The lady wears a kerchief over her head and a long gown reaching down to the floor, concealing her feet."

Above the figures is the Englysche coat of arms and the inscription:

'Here lyeth Master Thomas Englysche and Isabell his wyffe
whyche bothe above namys Discesyd within on yeare.
Interred in the yere of Our Lord God
a thousand fyve hundred and twenty fyve,
on who's soulls thou have mercy.'

It is interesting to note that, according to Miss Briers' book, *The History of Nuffield*:

'between 1529 and 1532, Thomas Englysche's daughter Ann, and her husband Michael Warcopp were suing Bartholomew Linsted, Prior of St Mary Overy, Southwark, on a charge of illegal retention of deeds and evidences about the Manor [here said to include Mongewell and Bix]. Ann claimed that her father had been 'siesed in fee tail, or else some other person siesed to the use of him and his heirs, the certenty whereof ys to your seid orators unknown', as the necessary evidences never came to hand, having been in the Prior's custody ever since the death of Thomas Englysche. The nature and ground of the Prior's case is not made clear in the depleted records which have survived... the Prior (as often happened) may have been claiming that Thomas had, on his deathbed, been persuaded to turn over his estate to the Church, for the salvation of his soul rather than for the comfort of his surviving family... Ann evidently won her suit and delivery of the deeds and records is endorsed on the proceedings in Chancery but she does not seem actually to have occupied the Manor from then until her death.'

In fact, Michael Warcopp later died and Ann then married one Richard Eton, who predeceased her by six years in 1540. He is buried in the church of St Bartholomew at Nettlebed, but it is the future of Cuthbert Warcopp which is of interest to us. According to papers in the Public Record Office: 'soon after this suit, the greater part of the estate was sold for £440 to four persons: Sir Anthony Lee, Richard Greenaway, John Gough and William Slyhurst. They would appear to have been acting as trustees, and subsequent history suggests that they were acting for Cuthbert Warcopp.'

Miss Briers also noted: 'Michael Warcopp's son and heir, Cuthbert, became a merchant stapler, a Freeman of London and one of the London mercers. There is record of his admission to the Mercers Company. He therefore had a town house and this was situated in Budge Row. Although living in London, Cuthbert looked after his Oxfordshire interests. In 1545 he obtained further

Oxfordshire land: Nettlebed Manor and land in Watlington... He died on 8th October 1557, while travelling abroad.'

The Warcopps appear to have continued living at Nuffield until about 1743, when the Dotten family became the landowners. It may have been soon after this that the Manor house was demolished. The outlines of it can still be seen in dry summers. It was probably old and out-moded.

A fine Georgian mansion was subsequently erected to the south. This became English Farm, as we know it today. For some time following the Second World War it had been allowed to deteriorate but the new owner has spent a great deal of time, money and effort on making a complete restoration of this beautiful house.

******

The brasses over the tombs of both Benet Englysche in Nuffield Church and Thomas Englysche and his wife Isabell in Ipsden Church, may still be visited today.

Chapter 10. The Squatters and the Civil War: 1600 - 1660

The second half of the sixteenth and first half of the seventeenth centuries were known as the Great Rebuilding Era. As the price of agricultural goods rose, with it came prosperity. Tenants were largely self sufficient for food but their fixed rents became more onerous to them. The landowners, now more wealthy, were able to improve what had formerly been just hovels and many wattle and daub timber-framed cottages were constructed at this time. The word cottage actually means 'a dwelling built of local materials'. Here in Oxfordshire this was brick, made from the local clay, timber and flint stones.

Unfortunately, the Stonor Estate papers are not available to the general public. However, Miss Georgina Stonor once stated: "the Blackhalls wandered all over our land." In fact, the Stonor lands at one time stretched from Stonor down to the River Thames at Caversham and included Blounts Court at Sonning Common.

******

Along the Henley to Oxford road trundled a windowless goods wagon with thick solid wooden wheels. It travelled at not much more than two miles an hour. The waggoner, Edmund Tyler, walked much of the time, leading his team of oxen, especially up the hills and when the road became badly rutted, muddy and sometimes even boggy. To ride inside this vehicle was extremely uncomfortable largely because it was completely unsprung but sometimes he did take a passenger who was willing to put up with the discomfort in order to make the journey.

On this wet and windy day in the winter of 1601, such a young passenger was Joseph Blackhall. He had walked down to Henley and though quite able and willing to walk back he now had need of help to bring home the many items he had bought down in the town. Most of the villagers who lived in the hamlets off the main road were self-sufficient but from time to time, perhaps twice a year, a man had to make the onerous journey down to the nearest town, usually Wallingford or Henley and occasionally Reading.

Joseph was a woodsman, a tenant of the great landowner at Stonor. Like most peasants at the time his life was a constant struggle. In the dense woods, they had a job to produce enough food in their tiny, very shady clearings to feed their families. Landowners were usually not much interested in their tenants in those days as long as they fulfilled their duties to their lord. This disinterest included housing and for the most part the estate workers existed in tiny 'cotts' that were often home to two or three families.

Joseph and his wife, Ruth, had not been wed long and were already tired of living in her parents' rented cott near Nettlebed, which was only one storey, measuring fifteen feet long by and nine feet wide. Into this were packed four truckle beds, their small wooden wheels making it possible to move them easily. These were one for the parents and one each for two of their three married children, the fourth being for their elder daughter and her baby, her husband having died of a fever the year before, aged just twenty-two. So badly fed and overworked were the peasantry that they rarely measured over five feet in height and were so thin that a husband and wife could sleep together in their narrow beds.

In the daytime these oblong boxes with their straw-filled mattresses and few blankets acted as seats and the family sat on them to eat their food, for there was little space for anything else. There was a stone hearth in the centre of the room and the smoke found its way out through the roof, making the interior dark and smoky, much like the old farmhouse at Englysche, built some one hundred and fifty years before. It was as much as the younger members of the family could do to keep body and soul together and to help to feed their parents who were now too old to work. The women almost dreaded to find themselves 'in the family way' with yet another mouth to feed, before its owner was big enough to earn its living at about nine years of age.

Joseph and Ruth however, were made of sterner stuff than the others and determined to find a way out of this demoralising situation. Joseph confided in Ruth one night as they lay together. "Old Edmund was telling me the other day, when we was walking up from Henley as how, if you can put up four walls and a roof over them on Common land between sunrise and sunset and light a fire in it, the law says it can be yourn! In fact, he says he knows of a couple over at Huntercombe that's done just that and it's been allowed! I've a mind to get a bit of help and do just that this Midsummer's Eve. I reckon that Will, John and Rob would all help me. What's the good of having brothers if they can't give you a hand now and then?"

In the days before the late Georgians and Victorians brought in the Enclosure Acts, certain types of land, often demarcated by earth banks and too poor to be farmed successfully, were owned by the Lord of the Manor 'in common' with the people, hence the name 'Commons Land'. In connection with this land the Commoners had certain rights. These were limited but played a very important part in the village economy.

In the Chilterns, they included the right to graze cattle, horses, sheep and goats. The number allowed for each commoner was specified and there was a penalty for exceeding the limit. They also had the rights to *pannage* [allowing pigs to forage for nuts or other food], *turbary* [the cutting of peat for fuel] *piscary* [where there were streams, the taking of fish] and *estovers* [the collecting of wood for fuel and fencing and bracken for animal bedding] as well as the right to take flint stones, chalk and sand or gravel for building. Some of these privileges remain today.

'Desperate straits demand desperate measures' was a motto much in use at the time and so Joseph and his brothers began to lay their plans for this rather daring step. "I have my eye on a spot at the foot of Witheridge Hill, right on the edge of the Commons. There's a stream down there in the winter, where the water and melted snow flow down from all sides."

"What'll you do in the summer, though?" asked Will, always the practical one.

193

"I dunno," replied his brother "but we'll manage somehow. We must get started on some sort of home for ourselves, we're determined not to get stuck in that cott with my kinfolks."

The couple said nothing to their family but the lads continued to gather together such things as would be useful for the task ahead, flint stones for the base, animal hair and chalk for the daub. During the nights of the previous weeks, they piled up fresh hazel twigs from the coppice in Bear Wood, just yards away from where they planned to erect their building.

Fortunately for them they were blessed with fine weather on Midsummer's Eve which fell that year upon a Sunday, a day when no one worked though all were expected to attend church. Although they were missed, their kinsfolk would not divulge what they were doing. The fact that they had not been told added to their facility to conceal the truth.

At the very first sign from the top of Witheridge Hill of the sun rising to the east, they slipped down to the bottom along one of the many tracks that led hither and thither all over the Commons, until they reached a spot right on the edge of the waste land. The stream at the foot of the hill was still fairly full as it had rained heavily during the previous month. Quickly Joseph and William set about felling small trees whilst Robert and John dug holes for the corner posts and the beams that were to form the cross-braces, as well as a shallow trench that they speedily filled with the flint stones that they had secreted in various places during earlier months.

As they were woodsmen by trade they were skilled at this sort of work and, driven by desperation and fear, laboured at great speed. As soon as the trunks had been cut down and stripped of their branches except for a few at the top which were to prove useful, the two older brothers continued to use their mattocks to cut down stout hazel stems from the coppice. These would act as rods, fixed in the trenches to form the base for the wattled walls. They sweated as the sun rose higher and higher, even though the hill did provide some shade. Joseph was the skilled wattler and he worked as fast as he could, constantly supplied from the piles of slender branches by William.

Meantime John and Robert mixed the daub, chalk, animal hair and water, ready to fill the cracks in the wattle walls, made of woven branches. They all had experience of this sort of work, erecting farm buildings for the Lord of the Manor some five years before and gradually the oblong construction began to take shape.

At midday they stopped briefly to take some nourishment and discuss their main task. This lay in the creating of a stout enough roof structure to take the heavy pieces of turf that they were to dig in the afternoon from the grass alongside the stream. All the time they listened out for the Bailiff. "Let us hope to God in his Heaven that Daniel Bushnell won't come by this day of all days!" muttered William.

"It's my guess he won't, as he was by here yester-eve. You recall we saw him give his nag a drink from the stream when we were just on our way down the hill." John reminded his brothers. "He would have seen this spot clear of any work at all so that'll help our case, if anyone should question what we've done."

"Oh, you're such a worriter, never fear, I vouch it'll be all right!" his older brother, Joseph, reassured him. "Sir Francis in't bothered about this land, it's so chalky and full of flint stones that he can't do nothing with it anyway!"

Soon they were at their labours again and by late in the afternoon the walls were finished.

Now it was time to dig the turfs and place them carefully on the roof structure. Bit by bit, as the sun began to go down they succeeded in their task, leaving a hole in the middle of the roof to let the smoke out. "We won't bother to clay the floor, just quickly make the hearth," stated Joseph, "just as long as we've got the walls and roof up and a fire going, that's all!"

It was almost dark by the time they had finished and they just had time to make their way up to Old Mary's cottage at Highmore for a drink to slake their parched throats. "The good God has been merciful to us, let's drink to our blessings!" proclaimed Joseph. "I thank you my brothers for all your help today. Rest assured I shall not forget your goodness to me and Ruth but I'm off now back to the cott to make up the fire just in case anyone should come by, though there's little chance of that at this time of night."

"I'll call in on Ruth and tell her the good news!" offered William. So saying he gulped down the last of his ale and ran all the way back to Huntercombe to tell his sister-in-law that, at last, she would have a home of her own even if it only had wattle and daub walls with a roof of grass sods.

"Now we'll be able to raise a family of our own, even though it'll be a hard life with not much water around." was her sage comment.

Needless to say, their family were relieved at the thought of having a bit more space to themselves. "As soon as you can, you must come down to see it!" Ruth told them, "but say nothing for a while. It needs for the Bailiff to spot it and tell Sir Francis. We won't be safe until he's given his word, though I doubt he cares. Daniel Bushnell's not a bad fellow; he'll not make trouble for us."

As luck would have it, the Bailiff had need to traverse the track at the bottom of Witheridge Hill again the very next afternoon on his way up to check on some tree felling in Stoke Row and could hardly believe his eyes when he saw the little dwelling that seem to have sprung up overnight. "Well, bless my soul!" he declared. "Who'll have done this then? And what will Sir Francis say? I'll have to tell him when he returns from London on the morrow."

Later on, like the commoners, he too slipped into Old Mary's for a drop of ale to assuage his thirst before he returned to Stonor and she told him the tale. "I must say, they're bold!" she concluded, but Bushnell reassured her: "Sir Francis is not much interested in these poor parts. He's got more of an eye for his richer pastures down at Emmer Green and Caversham, by the river."

And so it was. The pluck of Joseph Blackhall had won him the day and the young couple were soon able to beat clay from higher up the hill into a floor and improve the hearth with larger flintstones. Following their example several other couples also created little homes for themselves on nearby Newnham Hill and other places on the edge of common land.

Of course, these hovels had neither windows nor doors, just an animal skin hung over the low opening and sanitation was non-existent. Why bother about that when the woods were so close at hand? At least they had a home of their own where they could boil a few vegetables in a pot over the fire and maybe cook a rabbit on their little spit. It was a hard life, but they were tough folk and had their freedom, away from the congestion of their previous abode, which counted for a great deal.

******

Joseph and Ruth had a child about a year later and had him baptised Joseph within a few days of his birth, since many children did not even live until they were a year old. At first they just called him 'the baby', but as he grew able to walk he became 'Little Joe' and when he grew taller, 'Young Joe'. Maria came along very soon afterwards and at each Christening the Parish Clerk was a different one. Neither of them stayed long and had not bothered to spell the Blackhall surname properly so each child gained a different spelling in the Baptismal Register, ie Joseph Blackoale and Maria Blackhawle. Finally another male child arrived and he was named William, after his uncle. Fortunately, the latest Clerk had at least a modicum of education and wrote his surname as Blackall. Their father could neither read nor write of course, so he was quite ignorant of these errors.

Ruth acquired a few chickens and was able to barter eggs in season, perhaps for a bit of woven cloth from which she could make their coarse clothes. Like most women, she brewed her own ale made from fermented barley but it was very weak and pints of it could be drunk without anyone becoming too merry. The children drank it too for it was not safe to take water straight from the stream where cattle grazed higher up nor the local pond water which was often stagnant.

In the early part of the seventeenth century, along with many of his fellow landowners, Sir Francis Stonor, Sheriff for Oxfordshire and Justice of the Peace, had grown more prosperous in recent years and decided to improve the lot of his people by replacing the dilapidated old hovels with simple cottages. "Nothing fancy, mind you!" he warned his Steward, James Harwood. "Just four walls but they must be made of brick and flint, set with mortar. The beams must be beech. I can't afford oak; the Navy's well able to pay for that. They'd better have a proper door, too and couple of windows. Now, shall I put in a fireplace and a chimney, perhaps not, that can always come later. Don't want to spoil them, after all!" he laughed heartily.

"And what for the roof, my lord?" enquired Harwood. "Shall it be thatch?" His master bellowed back: "Of course it shall be thatch, but make sure it's thick and properly done."

And so one day early in the summer of 1604, Joseph was surprised to come home and find Ruth in a state of great excitement. "The Steward has been here today and said that Sir Francis is to build us a proper cottage. Look! There, over by the path that goes up to old Mother Jervis's place at Kingwood. His men have laid out pegs to show where, er... um... he called it a word I didn't know, but he said it means we could have a garden where we could grow our own vegetables and perhaps keep a pig and maybe a goat too."

"I expect he said the curtilage," explained Joseph, who had heard the word used before in respect to property. "It's a piece of land attached to a dwelling, but don't you worry your pretty little head about that, I only hope he will build us a sound one, and..." he added thoughtfully, "I trust he won't want too much rent for it!"

Each night when Joseph returned from his work in the woods he found another stage of the work had been done. This time there was no great haste and the work was done well, under the beady eye of the Bailiff who had strict orders from the Steward. The foundations were dug properly, the walls well built, the timbers upright and the thatch good and thick. They were given almost an acre of garden and it was all quite legal, so the fear of eviction was gone, providing, of course, that Joseph was always able to pay the rent.

A month after the first visit from the Steward, the little cottage at the foot of Witheridge Hill was completed. It measured only twenty-four feet by twelve feet but had an upper floor, quite an innovation for the humble cottagers. The bedrooms were reached by a ladder poked through a hole in the corner of the ground floor.

Several years later, Sir Francis added a chimney and an open fireplace, replacing the central hearth. [William Blackall was 'discharged by poverty' from having to pay the Hearth Tax in 1665.] This meant there were now two rooms, one to live in and another for storing vegetables, keeping tools, etc. Upstairs there was another partition, creating two bedrooms, though there were no internal doors, just spaces for the people to pass through. Sanitation was not considered necessary for those who lived in the woods, there being plenty of places where the night soil pot could be emptied, away from the house. Eventually, Joseph dug a pit at the far end of the garden, and laid a plank over it. They called it the 'guzzle hole'.

It was sited many yards away, at the top of the vegetable garden so it would not infect the water in the well that the landowner had provided at the same time as the chimney was inserted. It was one of the most important improvements to the cottage, as water was not easily come by. Prior to the sinking of the well, many was the summer's day when the ale had run out and they thirsted greatly. They then had to go up to Stoke Row or Highmore to beg a drink from their neighbours,

As soon as the children reached five or six years of age they were encouraged to do at least some kind of work especially gathering firewood. It was essential to have enough dry kindling to light the fire and seasoned logs to keep the fire going and it had to be the right kind of wood. Beech or ash burned well and fortunately there was plenty nearby which the family were able to cut up and bring home once a tree had fallen, in a storm, for example.

There was one tree the villagers never burned, swearing: "Elm burns like churchyard mould!" Joseph and Ruth had enough good wood to keep a fire going all winter; usually it was a blazing one. "No smouldering wet logs in my hearth!" Joseph was often heard to boast.

But all this work left little time for any kind of enjoyment, except perhaps for going to church each Sunday, when they loved to sing the hymns. All the peasants of the time were totally illiterate so many of the churches and chapels had biblical stories painted on their walls. These pictures proved an interesting diversion for both parents and children during the long sermons and depictions of the Devil as being clad in red with horns and a forked tail reminded them to be wary of the many temptations and pitfalls of this life.

Unlike their neighbours who were able to go to the nearby churches of Ipsden or Rotherfield Greys, the Blackhalls were all 'hatched, matched and despatched' from the church of St John the Baptist at Mongewell, seven miles to the west. This anomaly was caused by the fact that their cottage was built on a narrow strip of land that had been given to William de Warenne by William the Conqueror.

It was here that Joseph Blackhall was buried, in an unmarked grave, when he died, aged thirty-seven. Even then it was a good age at a time when most working men did not live much past thirty. Ruth kept the family going, assisted by 'Young Joe' as he had now become, his sister Maria and his brother, William, who needed no diminutive as his uncle had died not long after he helped to build the old 'squatter's hovel'.

******

When the Civil War broke out in England in 1642, the nation became divided into two camps, the Royalists and the Parliamentarians. Often families were divided in their loyalties, father fighting against son, brother against brother. Also, on the religious side, the Catholics tended to support the King whilst the Protestants, especially the Puritans, supported Parliament. The portion of the country distinctly loyal to the King included Wales along with Shropshire, Staffordshire, Worcestershire and parts of Cornwall, Devon and Oxfordshire. The remainder, including London, were for Parliament.

In his splendid little book, *Henley and the English Civil War*, written and illustrated for the pupils of Gillotts School in the 1980s, history master R P Phillips explained the situation:

'Up and down the country, in town and village and manor house, people tried to assess what civil war would mean. There was no eagerness to fight. The majority of ordinary folk were neutral and had no fixed preference for either the King's cause or Parliament's. Most men sat still and waited to see what would happen. People gave their support to the King or Parliament for a variety of reasons, some believed the freedom of Parliament was in danger and so they became Roundheads, whilst others feared that Parliament might gain absolute power, so they fought for the King. In many cases, the loyalties of a whole city or district were decided by the energy of one man.

Henley was a typical example of this. The wealthiest landowner in the neighbourhood was Sir Bulstrode Whitelock who owned, among others, the estates of Fawley Court and Phyllis Court. In 1642, acting on orders from Parliament he rode over to Watlington and broke up a Royalist meeting to which the Corporation of Henley had been invited. A number of men were arrested and on his return to Henley Sir Bulstrode made it clear to the leading citizens of the town where their loyalties should lie. Such was Sir Bulstrode's influence in Henley that few would have dreamt of defying him. Consequently, the town seemed to be firmly committed to supporting Parliament when the War began in the late summer of 1642.'

******

It was a dull, grey cloudy day in November, 1642, when Joseph Blackall, the now thirty-five-year old son of Joseph who had squatted at the base of Witheridge Hill in 1601, was about halfway along the Fair Mile on his way back from Henley where he had made some purchases of goods not obtainable in Highmore. His was an old hack of a horse, thin and, like his owner, ill-fed. The heavily laden panniers that hung on his sides made him look more emaciated than ever as he struggled stiffly along the road as his master trudged at his side.

All of a sudden there was a tremendous sound of heavy hooves and into view there appeared a gaily-clad troop of Cavaliers, [from the French *chevalier*, a horseman] resplendent in their flamboyant plumed hats, knee-length 'bucket' boots and fine tunics. The horses they rode looked well fed and, in spite of a certain amount of dust, well-groomed too. Young Prince Rupert had been fighting in Europe for most of his life and his experience of commanding cavalry greatly assisted the King. The speed of his horsemen was said to be incredible.

Joseph immediately pulled his nag to the side of the road as the King's men dashed on down to Henley. In fact, there was very little fighting and the Royalists held Henley for less than three months. During that time a skirmish was fought between the Roundhead troops and Rupert's cavalry on the Mount, which overlooks the Fairmile. After this time it was known as 'Roundhill Clump'.

Standing there by the roadside, amazed at what he had seen, Joseph recalled hearing in the ale-house at Highmore the previous evening that King Charles had unfurled his standard at Nottingham in the August of that year. Like so many working Englishmen he had no interest at all in politics, finding it enough to try and survive the harsh life of his time.

"He's made Oxford his base now," his informant stated. "When he was a boy he had frequently visited Woodstock with his father and I expect he often visited the city. He's certainly got lots of friends there." he continued with that braggartly tone used by 'know-alls' countrywide. "I heard he had gathered support for his army and then set off for London but the Parliamentarians stopped them from reaching the capital long before they got there, somewhere out Brentford way it was, I think the place was called Turnham Green."

Joseph tried hard to remember more of the conversation that

evening. "If they all be Englishmen how do one lot know which is which when they're in a battle, then, it beats me!" he had exclaimed.

"Well the Royalists, that's them for the King, o' course, they wear red sashes or armbands and Cromwell's lot wear orange ones. I expect they would find it difficult to tell one from another, but, of course, their *raiments* [clothes] are quite different. The Puritans are always more plainly dressed, usually they wear sombre black." replied the well-informed outsider, unsure as to which side his listeners might adhere, should they be asked to do so.

"How come you've to know all this? We don't hear about politics much around here." joined in Christopher Biggs, the bulky blacksmith, slaking his thirst after a hard day beating hot irons on his huge anvil. He showed a keen interest in the turn the conversation was taking for he quickly realised that if there was to be fighting, men would need swords and other weapons, not that many Highmore men would have any idea how to wield one.

"Well, I'm a corn-seed merchant," the traveller explained. "I was on my way to Henley when I thought to myself: 'I could do with a drink. I'll turn off the road & go down to Highmore; I'll get a good beer at old Mother Brill's place on the Reading road there.'" Beer had recently come to England from Belgium and was a new, slightly stronger kind of ale, brewed with hops.

In fact, the man was a Puritan spy, not that you would have realised it from his clothes and his manner. He seemed to his audience to be just the sort of man who would ride around selling corn seed, dressed as he was, fairly smartly, in a doublet with winged collar and epaulettes, buttoned from top to bottom, his waist kept in by a leather belt. Below his grey breeches he wore plain grey hose and well-worn leather boots. Like many men of his time, he sported a small moustache and a pointed beard.

He realised when he left the Oxford to Henley road at Nettlebed that he would have to have a plausible story if he was going into an ale-house, as customers in these quiet parts were always as thirsty for news as they were for their drink. Knowing that this was a woodland area and that few would know much about corn, he hoped he was on safe ground. As luck would have it, the blacksmith was more interested in possible forthcoming business than he was in corn. Farmers in the villages that lay nearer to Wallingford would have known more about that.

"Have they got an army up on either side?" Joseph enquired.

"No, I don't think so," replied the stranger. "The King's got his friends, of course, but I don't think, apart from practising for duels with their rapiers, any of them's got much experience. It's my guess that the Puritans'll only have farming tools and maybe a few old-fashioned arms, flintlocks and suchlike."

"Don't know as anyone around here has taken sides just yet." interrupted a dark, swarthy man in the corner, "Except the landowners, that is, they'll be for the King, o' course, 'specially the Catholics, like our Sir Francis Stonor. But if they do," he added thoughtfully, "that'll split families from top to bottom, mark my words. It'll be brother against brother and father against son!"

"Ah, well! We shall have to see, won't we?" was the stranger's evasive reply as he hastily finished his drink and made ready to leave.

"I wish you well, master!" pronounced the blacksmith and the rest joined in similarly, one way or another.

Thinking back to the previous evening Joseph Blackall recalled the blacksmith declaring "He seems a pleasant enough fellow!" and they had all agreed after the traveller had left. They little knew that when he reached Henley he would be discovered for the spy he was and hanged by Prince Rupert and his men from the big old elm tree, since known as Rupert's Elm, in Northfield Road that leads west out of the town on the way to Oxford.

In fact, apart from spies, civilians were rarely treated badly. Neither side took prisoners, largely because they had no place in which to keep them nor means to feed and care for them. Those who were caught were usually kept in a castle or, more often if there was no fortified place available, in the local church, until an exchange of men could be made. Property, however, was quite another matter.

Sir Bulstrode Whitelock, himself a fierce Puritan, was forced to have a number of Rupert's men quartered at Fawley Court. There, it would appear, they did considerable damage to the house and grounds. So angry was Sir Bulstrode that he wrote a letter of complaint in 1642:

'...there being about 1,000 of the King's Horse quartered in and about the house, and none but servants there, there was no insolence and outrage usually committed by common soldiers on a reputed enemy which was omitted by these brutish fellows at my house. They had their women with them; they spent and consumed two loads of corn in the straw.

Divers writings of consequence and books were left in my Study. Some of them were tore to pieces, others they burnt to light their tobacco, and some they carried away with them to my extreme loss and great prejudice in wanting the writings of my estate and losing very many excellent manuscripts of my father's and others and some of my own labours.

They broke down my park pales, killed most of my deer nd let out all the rest, only a tame young stag they carried away and presented to Prince Rupert, and my hounds were extra-ordinary good.

They ate and drank all that the house could afford, broke up all trunks, chests and places and where they found linen or any household stuff they took it away with them and cutting the beds, let out the feathers and took away the ticks [covers].

They likewise carried away my coach and four good horses, and all my saddle horses and did all the mischief and spoil that malice and enmity could provoke barbarous mercenaries to commit, and so they departed.

In January 1643, a Parliamentary army marched from Windsor to Henley. The Royalists had not bothered to fortify the town and they abandoned it without a fight, withdrawing towards Reading. It took the Roundheads some time to cross the river into the town as the bridge had been damaged, probably done by the Royalists before they pulled out.

Shortly afterwards, possibly the same night, Prince Rupert launched a counter-attack from the Reading direction. It was supposed to have been a surprise attack but Parliamentary supporters in Reading got wind of it and sent over an apprentice on horseback to Henley to warn the Roundheads there.

No one could tell the exact approach to the town that Rupert would take so troops were stationed in the four main streets. In addition, cannon loaded with shot were placed by the Bridge, the Market Place and down Duke Street. When Rupert advanced with his cavalry later that night, they charged along the Reading Road, sweeping aside a company of enemy infantry as they did so and entered Duke Street. Here they were met by a hail of shot from one of the cannons. Six Cavaliers were killed and the rest turned tail and fled back to Reading.

In the spring of 1643, the seed was sown in the fields and as it ripened in June and July, the local people began to turn their minds once more to the Harvest and bringing in the sheaves. So great was the work for that short period that all hands were needed and extra men and often women, too, were employed on a temporary basis.

Such people were Jeremiah Blackall, brother of Joseph who had met the spy in the pub. Jeremiah lived in a tiny cottage near the Marlow Road. He had moved there upon his marriage to Dorcas, daughter of a farmer on the land of Sir Bulstrode Whitelock. His Puritan master had seen to it that this joiner soon became sober and disciplined in his ways and dressed in plainer clothes. This had sometimes led to a bit of teasing whenever the brothers met, not that Joseph could afford to wear anything as flamboyant in the way of dress as his superiors.

Every year Jeremiah went out to help bring in the harvest for Sir Bulstrode Whitelock's Home Farm near Fawley Court. Jeremiah and Dorcas, a peace-loving couple tried as best they could to obey their God and the laws of the land. One warm, sunny Monday in August, they returned to the fields after their customary work-free Sabbath. Their baby, Nathaniel, was tied in a cloth suspended from Dorcas's shoulder as they talked over their mid-day meal with their fellow workers. "What think thee of our new 'cleansed church', then?" Dorcas asked her friend, Lydia, as she adjusted her white starched collar.

"For my part, my family, like thine, have been going to our Church for generations, but I was grief-stricken yesterday to see the work that those zealots did to it last week! They've even taken hammers to the wooden rood screen! My grandmother told me that my great-great grandfather carved that over a hundred years ago. He too, like our Holy Lord Jesus, was a carpenter. It's wanton destruction, that's what it is!" Lydia said with feeling.

Obadiah Hayward joined in: "I was there when they came and I think like thee, sister. Those three strangers in their tall black hats and cloaks who came to the church the previous Sunday, now. I reckon it's them who's organised all this wickedness, whitewashing all the lovely wall paintings that've helped our people to remember Bible stories for generations past. I saw no harm in them. All this extremism is giving our people a bad name."

Lydia asked him: "What did thee think to the gentry then, as sat in the wooden boxes? I reckon they came here from the big house, Greenlands; there's a lot of the King's men there. True they behaved themselves well enough, but I could see Sir Bulstrode wasn't very pleased to see them sitting so near to him. Still, it's God's Holy Church, so they couldn't be refused entry, so long as they caused no trouble could they?"

"Pity that more of them aren't like that!" he snapped. "I think they were more interested in seeing what they heard the zealots had done than just coming to worship. Maybe they were out to see who was here and how we behave. After all, they could have gone to Hambleden what's nearer to Greenlands. I never feel safe when the King's friends are about, even the good ones!"

Soon enough the mid-day break was at an end and with it the conversation, but it was typical of how the local people felt. For the most part the War was not so much between the Royalists and the Parliamentarians as between the Parliamentarians and those who wished to be left in peace, especially those involved in the more rural pursuits like farming.

Later on in 1643 Parliament put a permanent garrison of about three hundred and fifty troops into Phyllis Court to keep an eye on the Royalists entrenched at Greenlands and because the town provided a bridging point across the Thames. Cannons on ramps behind a ditch controlled the northern approaches to the town.

Garrisons like this had a weakness however in that they tended to employ riff-raff who were not so keen on fighting as in causing trouble to the local townsfolk. Houses were plundered and goods seized, especially from shops and storehouses without payment being made. The officers also levied illegal heavy taxes on local traders like Jeremiah, who sold his handmade wooden wares, bowls, rolling pins, platters and similar items in the Market Square at Henley every Friday.

By this time most families had taken sides and Joseph, living as he did on land owned by Sir Francis Stonor, soon realised that he and his wife, Patricia, should stay with the Catholic church and therefore with the King. However, each time he came down to Henley, usually once a month, he always found time to have a few words with his brother and in the early days of the War their conversation was amiable enough.

One Friday early in December, however, Joseph was very sharp with Jeremiah: "What's this I hear about a Henley woman being nailed by her tongue to a post alongside the Reading road, just because she complained of the taxes she was forced to pay? They also say a piece of paper was pinned to her back denouncing her offence! That's not Christian, I say!"

Jeremiah immediately looked all around him so as to be sure that no one could hear what he was about to whisper to his brother: "Hush thy voice, for goodness sake. 'Tis not wise to protest in these times, as thou hast heard. I know thou art still a Papist and that thee don't hold with our views but I have to pay up, same as her. Anyway, I just do as I'm told."

"Arms to kill peaceable men!" retorted Joseph, having now lowered his tone. "Your people have also been around whitewashing our beautiful churches and breaking sacred statues and breaking open the reliquaries. What right have you to do this?"

"'Tis not I who have done this work." Jeremiah assured his brother in an undertone. "Master Oliver Cromwell ordered it. He says the churches have become too rich and spend money on ornamentation that should be given to the poor. He feels there's too much betting and gaming. More than that, he hates the theatre and believes that we should be more soberly dressed and behaved, especially on the Lord's Day. 'Tis true, Joseph, and thee knows it!"

"All I know is that we used to be a happy and united family. Now you think in the new way but we shall continue to support the King and Holy Mother Church. I think it better we don't come to you and Dorcas, and don't come to us while you continue to think in this way!" he thundered, as he turned to go.

"The Lord God go with thee!" was Jeremiah's only reply, but in his heart he mourned the state of affairs that had come to pass in his family. The two brothers remained apart and though they might have forgiven each other when the War was over, they never met again because Joseph died soon after this conversation took place.

******

The Royalists continued to hold Greenlands along the Marlow road until it was attacked and destroyed by a Roundhead force in the spring of 1644. No serious attempt was made to dislodge the Roundheads from Henley during the remainder of the Civil War. In comparison to Reading and Wallingford, where there were long and bitter sieges, Henley suffered little real damage.

The Royalist cavalry, under the command of the King's nephew, Prince Rupert, won the cavalry charge at the Battle of Marston Moor, near York in 1644, but was later resoundingly beaten by Cromwell and his army. Rupert respected their superiority and nicknamed them 'Ironsides'. The battle was a turning point as it gave Cromwell a foothold in the North.

In 1645, Cromwell organised his 15,000 strong New Model Army, which adopted a standard uniform: a red tunic, armoured breastplate and a round metal helmet, resulting in his men being given the nickname of 'Roundheads'. They defeated the Royalists at Naseby, thus ending one of the most dramatic periods in the whole of the history of Oxfordshire.

Earlier, in the spring of 1646, Charles I escaped from Oxford, accompanied by two friends. They travelled in the direction of Henley, but on reaching the Fairmile they branched off along the bridle path to Henley Park and rode on to Hambleden Manor where they stayed the night. A few days later the King surrendered himself to the Scots, who promptly handed him over to Parliament. Oxford surrendered in June 1646, but Wallingford held out against Parliament for another month, thus earning the honourable reputation of being the last English town of any size to fly its flag for the

King. During these last weeks of the War many of the Roundhead troops were detached from the garrison at Henley to take part in the siege of Wallingford. In August 1646, Sir Bulstrode Whitelock was given permission to dismantle the fortifications at Phyllis Court. No one was sorry to see the last of the soldiers leave.

After much debate and intrigue and the outbreak of the second Civil War in 1648, Parliament finally had Charles I executed in January 1649, thus bringing the monarchy to an end. In effect, England became a military dictatorship for the next eleven years with Parliament taking a subsidiary role. In 1653 Cromwell styled himself 'Lord Protector' which position he held until his death in 1658.

Two years later Charles II returned to the English throne and this led to a much quieter period in the history of England and, of course, south-east Oxfordshire. When the monarchy was restored in 1660, Sir Bulstrode Whitelock was heavily fined for his activities in the 1640s and 1650s. He was forced to sell off several of his estates but the King allowed him to be reunited with his wife and sixteen children and he passed the remainder of his life in peaceful retirement.

******

The original cottage at the foot of Witheridge Hill appears on a Stonor map of 1600.

Highmoor Hall is still privately owned. The 1661 indenture hangs on a wall there and the Coat of Arms is still over the fireplace.

The Diaries of Sir Bulstrode Whitelock, *Dr Plot's* The Natural History of Oxfordshire *and R P Phillips' excellent little book,* Henley and the English Civil War *may all be found in the reference section of the Henley Library.*

Chapter 11. The Wren Mansion and the Dissenters: 1661 - 1699

With the restoration of the monarchy and the crowning of Charles II in 1661 came a much happier period for most of the people of England, though a few remaining die-hard Puritans still did not keep Christmas Day and deplored the extravagant ways of the 'Merry Monarch' as he became known. Charles was a tall, handsome man and as fond of the ladies as they were of him but he was also a great patron of the arts and also, though this is little known, of yachting.

There was also a serious side to his nature as he was greatly interested in the sciences and founded the Royal Society soon after his accession. He had a passion for architecture as well and this was to make a great impression on English buildings throughout his reign.

******

On 28th March, 1661, John Pearce 'a sieve maker' and his wife, Eleanor, had two children, Lucinda (always known as 'Lucy') and James, who were aged seven and six respectively when the family finally moved into their new home, Hymer Hall, at the northern end of the hamlet of Highmore. John had signed an indenture between himself and 'John Harbert, alias Bowyer, Yeoman of Reading . . . ' '. . . for the purchase price of £6.13.8d and for 999 years at a pepper-corn rent to be paid at the Feast of St Michael the Archangel.'

The house had been several years in the building, but even when it was finished they had had to wait until the festivities of the King's enthronement in London were, at last, at an end, since they were people of quality and expected to attend every royal function.

It had been a very long and tiring journey, for although coaches now had some form of suspension using leather straps, they creaked and squeaked all the way and the many holes in the roads were only filled with stones bound in with ground chalk. "Oh, my aching bones!" exclaimed Eleanor. "How this carriage lurches on these rough roads!"

Her husband made quick to soothe her: "Well, my dear, just give thanks to Almighty God that we have mostly had good weather during these past three days of travel. In wet weather out here in the country coaches sometimes get bogged down in the mud and if that had happened and there were no inn nearby we might have had to spend the night in the vehicle, like my cousin did in a snowstorm last December! In any case, my love, we're almost there, so you'll soon be settled and comfortable," he continued, as the coach turned down from the Henley to Oxford road and started on the half mile or so down to their new house.

This had been built in the new 'classical' style, on plain lines and with diamond-paned windows made of glass. "They say the bricks were made in the kiln which we saw ahead of us in Nettlebed and are some of the most durable to be found. The brickmaster told me that they just shoot them out of the carts and yet none of them are broken. He said that the tiles are also made not far from here in a village that is so proud of its products that it has adopted the name of Tilehurst. It's near Reading, some ten miles to the south of here, so I'm glad to say that the building materials are all good and locally made."

At last the coach turned into the driveway and as Eleanor leaned out she could see the house ahead of her. "Oh, John, you are right, it is beautiful, really beautiful, it's better than it looks in the drawings!" she exclaimed, "I really do think we shall be happy here!"

Within minutes they had drawn up to the front door and immediately the children scrambled out and ran as fast as they could, scampering all around the lawns, so glad to be free at last from the confines of the coach which could only travel a distance of ten miles in a day. Already the Red Lion Hotel at Henley, six miles to the east, seemed to be a lifetime away. As soon as the coach came into sight the staff assembled outside to greet their new master and mistress and their children to welcome them to their new home.

A day or so later after they were all safely settled, the carrier's cart, laden with all their possessions trundled in to the rear entrance. It was the very latest thing in this type of conveyance and had spoked wheels but its progress was painfully slow. Nevertheless, it had arrived safely without mishap and the servants promptly began to unload the many boxes and bundles from the soft-topped vehicle with its cream canvas 'tilt hood' stretched over an arched frame.

The furniture had already been delivered several days before having largely been made in the workshops of Henley joiners and cabinet-makers, who were skilled in making the fashionable high-backed chairs and tables with bulbous legs. The furniture was finely carved, the softness of walnut lending itself to this form of ornamentation. Some family portraits and looking-glasses with a candle sconce on each side, had already been put up to decorate the walls.

The staircase had beautiful banisters, hand-carved into twisted barley-sugar shapes with a ball on the top of each pillar at the bottom and the top. For the bedrooms there had been delivered two large four-poster beds with elaborate hangings and two smaller ones for the children. In addition there were several chests for clothes. These had two drawers fitted to the base and became known as a 'chest of drawers'.

"I think we should engage a painter to paint the ceiling in the saloon" remarked Eleanor, several weeks after their arrival. "The plaster ceiling in the Library is fine, but I feel the saloon needs something prettier! Also, he could paint a set of the Stations of the Cross in our little chapel."

"As you wish, my love. I shall enquire about a suitable fellow when I return to London." John replied, keen that his wife should be happy in their new abode. "You shall have whatever you wish to make the house as comfortable as our London home. I am only so glad that you seem to be otherwise content here and that the children can at last breathe the fresh air of the countryside and now we shall not have to endure the stench of those awful crowded streets any longer!"

For their part Lucy and James loved the new house and its pretty garden. The servants here seemed kinder too and they often found their way through to the kitchen at the rear of the house. In London this area had been forbidden to them because their parents feared they might catch smallpox or other diseases from the low life that swarmed around the back streets.

One Thursday in May the cook had asked whether Master James and Miss Lucy might come down to the staff quarters to see what the Chapman had brought. This travelling salesman came about four times a year on his round of the south-east Oxfordshire villages, leading his two pack ponies, urging them all the time to "go on, go on, make haste, make haste, do!" but they still plodded steadily up the steep slopes of the Chiltern Hills although they sometimes found themselves slithering down on the other side.

The visit of the *Chapman* [from cheap, old French *ceap*, market] was an exciting day in the hamlet of Highmore and when word arrived from the neighbouring village of Chackenden that the salesman was on his way, a message was sent to the farms and cottages all around so the womenfolk could come and buy what little they could afford. Even those who had little money for anything other than the bare necessities of life enjoyed a good gossip over a mug of weak ale and, if they were lucky, a piece of gingerbread or some other sweetmeat made by the cook that morning.

Finally the ponies came through the gates, up to the house and around to the rear. There, in the kitchen the cook had put down new plaited rush mats, throwing out the ones which had already soaked up their own fair share of fat and other spillages. She had also cleared the huge scrubbed wooden table and on to it Amos Bowden unrolled his bundles. Everyone crowded around as he revealed his haberdashery, ribbons, cottons, embroidery silks, needles and pins.

Eleanor had decided it would be wise to accompany her children. Lucy was anxious to purchase a piece of fine canvas and some embroidery silks to make a start on a new sampler for which she had designed a picture of their new home, with the date and her name beneath. The one she had already done hung on her bedroom wall, but, as she explained to the cook, "that was only just my alphabet and numbers one to nine!"

Soon she found what she wanted and then it was the turn of James but he could see nothing he fancied until Amos brought out the stationery. James had only recently become literate and had now started on his Latin and Greek. He wanted to write to his friends in London about his progress. "Father is not happy for me to use his quill and ink, so please can I have my own?" he begged his mother.

"Yes, my dear," she continued, "but you will also need a pen-knife with which to sharpen the quill and a sandbox with which to dust your finished letter. I would fain give you some sealing-wax, too, with which to seal your missive." In the end, James had quite a lot on his tray when he bore it triumphantly up the broad staircase to his room, closely followed by Lucy, with her embroidery materials.

Eleanor, however, remained in the kitchen, listening to the quaint accents of the local women as they bought pieces of material like Holland cloth, stiff white fabric that could be washed and starched, or broadcloth with which to make trousers for their menfolk. Some purchased scarves, kerchiefs and perhaps a comb, a brush or even a hand-held mirror if they could afford such a luxury.

The mistress of the house herself decided to make one or two purchases, having seen the good quality of the white clay pipes carried by Amos. Some of them were the long-stemmed type that eventually became known as churchwardens, but Eleanor knew her husband would not care for those. However, she did buy a couple of pipes and half a pound of best Spanish Indies tobacco at nine shillings a pound for him, leaving the local women to buy just a few scraps of the cheaper Virginia type at only two and six pence per pound for their husbands.

"Do you know how our menfolk keep their pipes clean, mistress?" enquired one of the bolder village women, despite a frown from the cook who felt the old hag was speaking out of turn, without being first spoken to by her mistress.

However, Eleanor was intrigued and so overlooked the transgression of the countrywoman. "No, I do not know. Tell me, please because I always buy new ones for my husband when they go black and it may not be so easy to do so down here in the country."

"Well, ma'am," continued the old woman, more respectfully this time. Our blacksmith do make a rack for pipes to stand in the embers of the kitchen fire and then they get burned off and come up white again, good as new!"

"That sounds a good idea. I shall go to see him tomorrow. Where is his workshop?"

The woman replied readily: "The forge is up at Stoke Row, ma'am. You goes down Witheridge Hill, through the woods, along the bottom by the little old thatched cottage where me and my husband lives. He's a woodman for the Stonor estate. You goes on a piece and then the track turns left up the hill. If you takes the groom, ma'am, he'll show you."

"Yes I will. It should prove interesting. I shall go first thing in the morning. It may be that one or two of the horses need new shoes, too." And so saying, Eleanor left the old women to their gossiping.

The next morning dawned sunny and bright, a typical English May morning. Soon the family were up and having breakfast from a side-board laden with cold meats, home-made cheese and pasties, washed down with thin ale. Lucy and John begged their mother to let them go with her to the blacksmith's forge and reluctantly she agreed, although she feared that they might come to some harm in such a rough and probably very hot working place.

She need not have worried however, for the forge was a small one unlike those in the back streets of London and, having heard that the lady of the 'big house' was coming, together with her children, Hosea Blagrave had tidied up his workshop and made all safe.

It is true the little forge was very hot from the fire, improved from time to time with the huge bellows at the side but Hosea had put all the bigger pieces of agricultural equipment in one corner and placed a chain around the spades, digging forks, scythes and sickles that were usually stood all over the place waiting to be repaired.

He also set out the pots and pans waiting to be mended on a long shelf but hoped he would not have to do these petty jobs himself since the travelling tinker should be in the district soon. This well-known itinerant character not only repaired cooking utensils but also sold a few. He sharpened knives and scissors on his portable pedal-operated grindstone, his arrival always announced from afar by the clanking of his wares that were hung all around his old donkey.

The children found the forge to be a fascinating place especially since they had rarely been allowed out of their London house with its small garden. Most of all their gazes were riveted by the work of the smith as he shod the two horses which Ezekiel, the groom, had brought with them. Eleanor had ridden the half-mile on her mare but the groom had led the other horse and the children had scampered alongside accompanied by their King Charles spaniel, Russet, thrilled to be able to run freely along the narrow lane that led from Hymer Hall down to the turn for Witheridge Hill. They marvelled at the pretty pink and white blossom on the cherry trees and felt they couldn't wait for the fruit which Ezekiel had told them "burdens the trees in the summertime." At first they found it difficult to understand his quaint Oxfordshire speech but gradually they grew used to it.

On their way home, a pleasant walk in the spring, the family listened to the distant cuckoo and heard a strange cackling sound from another bird. "I think that must be the *yaffle* of the *yaffingale*, [green woodpecker], the big green bird I saw in the garden yesterday. He has a red head. Martha told me his name, it is surely a strange one." Lucy said.

She then asked if she could pick bluebells from the sides of the path and was thrilled when her mother agreed. "They would look well in the Library and your father would enjoy the perfume."

And so the summer passed and the children grew used to the country, revelling in their newfound freedom and making friends all over the hamlet with those whom they met. Their mother particularly enjoyed her new garden where, at her behest, Zebediah Horsefield had planted roses, snapdragons, yellow daisies, delphiniums, Canterbury bells, poppies and cornflowers and as many of her beloved Sweet Williams as could be squeezed in. Many of these plants were already in bloom.

The most important aspect of the garden lay beyond the pleasure garden with its pretty flowerbeds. This was the *potager,* or vegetable garden, where peas, beans, lettuce, spinach and carrots were all growing fast. Old Zebediah was proud of his ability to supply fresh vegetables to the cook throughout the summer, but he also planted some herbs as well as sweet smelling lavender and rosemary around the functional beds.

In the fourth day of October in that year, however, life was to change for John for it was his eighth birthday and the long-awaited day dawned when he was to be *breeched*. This custom which had taken place in well-to-do families for many years, involved the cutting off of the long curls that small boys customarily wore until they were eight years old. This ceremony marked his entry into manhood at a time when the average length of life for a man was often not much more than thirty-five.

It was also a day of great celebration for all the family and the parents invited all the local gentry to a grand dinner. "Come along, Master James," coaxed his Nanny. "You'll be wanting to get up early, it's your birthday!" she announced as she drew aside the curtains in his bedroom.

As soon as he had surfaced from his deep and dreamless sleep he realised what she meant. "You mean today is my Big Day?" he asked excitedly.

"Yes, indeed, Master James,. May I be the first to wish you Happy Birthday! Indeed, it is not only your birthday but also your Breeching Day." In a trice he was out of his bed and doffing his nightgown.

"And is it today that the tailor comes?" he enquired, as he put on for the last time the long feminine type skirted frock-coat.

"Yes, Master James," she replied. "There'll be no Latin or Greek for you today. The tailor will be here at ten of the clock with your new doublet and breeches. And the bootmaker will be coming with him from Henley with your new *buskins* [calf-length leather boots]. You remember he measured you for them a month since."

She sighed at the thought of his beautiful curls being cut off and determined to retain one as a keepsake of her little charge. She also smiled to herself at the thought that, although his curls were to be cut off now, when he was a grown man he would no doubt take to wearing a curled periwig, like all the quality did these days.

The dinner proved to be a wonderful affair. James, feeling very proud and grown-up in his new clothes, made larger than necessary so that he could grow into them, and with his new shorter haircut, found himself the guest of honour. Even his little sister, Lucy, looked upon him with admiration. The local gentlemen with their ladies, all most elegantly dressed, had made their *obediences*, bowing and curtsying low to their hosts. The food was served hot from the kitchen where the cook and assistants had all worked the whole day.

As soon as the Parson had said a lengthy 'Grace', asking for God's blessing on the "new young man", the two footmen brought in the spit-roasted meats, legs of mutton, a great ham and a pair of tender capons, as well as a large selection of fresh vegetables, all grown in the kitchen garden to the rear of the house.

Later there were varied cheeses with home-cooked cottage shaped loaves and dairy-churned butter, followed by rich desserts, flummeries, trifles and cakes of every description. A toast was proposed by one of the guests and everyone joined in a hearty response. John's father then made a great fuss of writing up the event in the huge family Bible, bound in black leather.

"Have another glass of wine, sir, if your stomach wills." urged John of his guests, proud of his son and glad that the evening had gone well.

"Thank you, sir, I will," most of them replied and so the evening continued amiably, several of the guests making remarks, such as "I vow your boy will do well, his manners and deportment are excellent." Up until this time James and Lucy had been tutored at home by a schoolmaster from Henley. Others asked when he would be going to school and where.

To all of this his doting mother would only reply: "There is time enough for that, but when he does, we plan for it to be to St Edwards in Oxford." By the end of the evening they were all as relaxed as a slackened bowstring and when the coaches arrived to bear the guests home, all agreed that it had been 'a most convivial evening!'

Not only was James's breeching celebrated in the big house, but John had also sent money to the landlady of The Blue Man, down in the village, so that the local men could have a couple of free mugs of beer. The room had now become more like a public house than just the living room of a local woman who brewed good beer.

There were stools around the room and in one corner a set of wooden ninepins with a ball, so the men could enjoy themselves at the end of the day. On prickets nailed to the wall, the guttering mutton-fat candles gave out a sparse light; the smell from them being something that working people had become accustomed to. But the serving wench, full-bellied with child, felt sickened by their strong odour, especially when it was mixed with the smell of the tobacco now smoked by most of the men.

For men who earned only nine or ten pence a day, a rate fixed by the local magistrates, this was an unusual treat. "Let's drink to the health of the young master!" proposed Hosea Blagrave, the blacksmith, with gusto and all joined in with a hearty cheer.

From there the conversation turned, as it often did on an autumn evening, to the subject of ghosts, witches and witchcraft. One elderly woman, known as 'Old Mother Redcap' from the felt hat she always wore, had a fund of stories and though few of the local women came to the beerhouse she was there every night of the week, ready to put the fear of God into anyone who would listen.

"I hear that the spectre of the Grey Lady's been seen at the bottom of Greyhone Wood again!" she muttered, hoping to catch the ear of the gullible Samuel Bowier, who was already in his cups.

But this time he would have none of it. "Get you gone, Mother Redcap, you rotten old hag! I care not a jot for your stories. Heaven defend us if we were all to listen to you!" This saying, he rose from his stool a little unsteadily and left the beerhouse with the rolling gait of the drunkard, feeling safe in the knowledge that he only had a few steps to take before he reached his cottage and his bed. Nevertheless, he made his way quickly in the dark, with only the waning moon for light. He found himself remembering the old woman's tale which, despite his bravado, had struck a certain amount of terror into his heart.

The next day was Sunday and everyone went to church; those who did not risked the disapproval of the landowner and in any case, it was a reason for the village folk to wash and dress as best as they could and to meet their friends and neighbours. Up at Hymer Hall Lucy was dressing herself in her undergarments, and her mother Eleanor was tying the strings of her daughter's new corsets, the first she had ever had. On top of that was a full white petticoat and a blue kirtle [skirt] made of wool from the Suffolk village of Kersey. "When may I wear a full dress like you, Mother?" she asked.

"Not until you are fully grown, my love." her mother replied. "Dresses are for ladies, young girls who need to be more free, wear kirtles and blouses." So saying, she left Lucy to put on the remainder of her clothes by herself and to brush out her ringlets which had been in paper curlers all night, over which she would place her cotton mob cap, with its lace edging, in an effort to keep her hair in good order.

It was as she did this that Lucy remembered that today at the church across in Rotherfield Peppard, James was to be blessed by Parson Browne, following the boy's breeching the previous day and she hoped he would not be too tired after the excitement of the previous evening's dinner party. Also, in the afternoon, she recalled, there was to be a tea party for James and his friends, although she had been allowed to invite her friend, Mary, as a special favour on this manly day.

She soon slipped downstairs into the kitchen for her collation of warm milk and a few *manchets*, simple scone-like sweetbreads. Lucy preferred this form of breakfast to eating with her family upstairs where a great spread was always put out on the side-board, although her mother did not wholly approve of her mixing so much with the kitchen staff.

Down below stairs, Martha Betteridge, the cook, and her young assistants were busy making not only *manchets* from butter, eggs and milk, but also gingerbread. "Make haste with that coal, I can't afford for the oven fire to go out today!" the cook urged of one of the younger girls, who promptly dashed out to the back for another scuttle of *seacoal,* recently brought down from the north of England by ship and thence by barge to Henley. Near the oven stood the four copper warming-pans with which the beds were warmed for the family every night.

Martha then started to blend the breadcrumbs, honey, almonds and cherries to make *marchpane*, a special treat for the tea party that afternoon. In the sink nearby, another girl was washing a basketful of watercress that had just been delivered from nearby Ewelme, famous for this delectable green vegetable, with its fiery taste. "Master James and his friends are to have tea to drink and you, too, Miss, I dare say. At twenty-five shillings a pound, that will be a rare treat, though I'm not sure if you'll like it. I myself had a taste of it this morning, just to judge how strong to make it, you understand, but I didn't care for it at all. Just give me a tankard of my own rhubarb or elderberry wine!" she laughed.

The Pearce family were fortunate in having obtained the services of Martha Bettridge, who was not only an excellent cook but ran a good stillroom as well. There her speciality was the production of an excellent *metheglyn*, distilled from mead [made from honey] to which she added spices, until it became quite a potent brew. "You'd best be off Miss!" she warned Lucy. "Or you'll be late for church. Parson Browne don't like for people to walk in after he's come over from the Parsonage!"

The church at Peppard was dedicated to All Saints and was a

lovely old stone building, with a Norman porch and beautiful stained glass windows, commemorating some of the great families in the area in days gone by. By the time the Pearce family arrived there were many people already assembled, but their boxed pew was, as always, reserved for them. The Parish Quire had already started to play, though at this stage it was more of a rehearsal for the fiddle, flute, bass viol, clarinet and serpent. James and Lucy were always fascinated by these quaint instruments, which provided music in country churches long before the organ became commonplace. They especially loved the serpent, a great black twisted pipe that emitted deep tones.

Soon Parson Browne entered, wearing a snowy white surplice and conducted the service. One of the hymns they sang was a favourite with John and Eleanor, as it had been played at their wedding, having been based on the 100th Psalm when it was composed some one hundred and fifty years previously by William Kethe:

> All people that on earth do dwell,
> Sing to the Lord with cheerful voice;
> Him serve with mirth, His praise foretell;
> Come ye before Him and rejoice.

Eleanor and John looked at one another when the fourth verse had finally been sung, and smiled before they sat back and started to listen to the Parson's sermon. On the pulpit stood an hourglass, filled with sand. When the sand had flowed entirely through from the top to the bottom, the Parson usually ended his address, but today he finished earlier as he wanted to make a special event of the blessing of young James Pearce.

The next morning, Joshua Norcroft, the Post-man, blowing his horn as he entered the gates, cantered up to the back door on his horse, the satchel on his back full of letters. These were now regularly priced at a fixed rate, 2d for a single page and 4d for a double. There was no envelope, the paper was just folded into four and sealed with red wax to prevent anyone from opening it.

The groom ran out to greet him in the yard. "I'll send it up to the master at once." he promised. A maid took it to the Library where John Pearce stood admiring the family coat of arms which he had recently had carved and placed over the fireplace. Not surprisingly, the letter to John contained information about the forthcoming schooling of his newly breeched young son, James.

******

Seven years later, one pleasant sunny afternoon in early September, Eleanor Pearce took her thirteen-year old daughter up to Watlington, to see the fine new brick Town Hall that had been erected just three years before. It was not a large building, but the brick arches made it look elegant. Beneath it were market stalls and, on the floor above, a small grammar school. During the previous year a clock had been inserted on one wall and a sundial on the other. Eleanor had long since promised Lucy to take her up to the little market town so that she may see the new features on this attractive little building which had been built at the expense of the local landowner, Thomas Stonor.

Also Lucy was keen to buy some new ribbons for her pretty auburn curly locks and as soon as the coach had set them down in a quieter nearby street, mother and daughter made their way to the small square in which the Town Hall was set, between Couching Street and Shirburn Street, High Street and the little narrow Hill Road. They admired the clock and sundial, all shining with their gold-leafed adornments, but were soon looking at the stalls.

All around local people were selling their produce, mostly vegetables and some fruits. On other tables, covered with crisp white cloths, women were offering homemade cakes and fancies. Also there was a cobbler, mending shoes on the spot and a knife-grinder who sharpened knives of all types on his little grindstone, driven by a treadle lathe.

Soon, however, they came to the stall where the travelling haberdasher had set out his wares, lace collars, ribbons, pins, needles and other useful items. He was rather like the *chapman* who travelled around the villages, but this man sold a better class of goods and preferred to take up a position in the markets, going from one town to another through the week. After some indecisive moments, Lucy finally chose some fine silk ribbons in bright colours and her mother decided to purchase a lace collar with matching cuffs, having been told by the vendor that they were 'hand-made in nearby Buckinghamshire.'

They continued their tour of the stalls, enjoying the hustle and bustle of it all. Eleanor bought some sweet-meats and some locally produced honey in a pottery jar before they wandered further down the High Street, looking at its old buildings, some half-timbered, [built entirely of timber, wattle and daub], past the Granary, where men were carrying sacks of corn in from a cart outside.

Finally they came to Gorewell. The origins of this street name had been lost in time, but Eleanor noted that the old public house on the corner had been renamed 'The Royal Oak' in honour of the tree in which King Charles II had hidden from Cromwell's men.

"We haven't time now to go out and look at the church." Eleanor said to her daughter. "It is named for St Leonard and is very old. I believe it goes back to Anglo-Saxon times, but it is a little way away from the town, out in the fields. The Vicar remained true to the old religion and a Royalist throughout the War and the Parliamentarians of this town hounded him out to Oxford. Now, with the restoration of the king, he has been able to return. Perhaps if we go there another day, we shall be able to meet him." And so saying, she led Lucy round to Brook Street where their coach awaited them.

******

One very warm Wednesday afternoon in the July of 1677, John Pearce was seated in his library poring over a very large leather-bound tome when his wife entered the room. "What are you so busy studying, my love?" she enquired. "It is so hot, why do you not come outside and sit under one of the trees? You could bring your book with you."

"No, no, my dearest." he answered. "This book is far too heavy and, indeed, valuable, to take out into the garden!"

"Yes, it does seem rather large, what is it that consumes your interest so, is it the book you brought back from Henley last week?"

"Yes, my dear, it is by the famous Dr Robert Plot, a Fellow of the Royal Society and the first Keeper of the Ashmolean Museum at Oxford. This is his latest work that he has called *The Natural History of Oxfordshire* and he is planning to write one for every county in

England. He is particularly fond of trees and has tried to find an explanation for a number of various types that were found at the bottom of a pond near Blounts Court at Sonning Common when it was being cleaned out two years ago. Let me read you the relevant piece:

"These 'subterraneous oaks' were 'very firm and sound, but quite through to the heart as black as ebony . . .' 'The owner, the worthy Mr Thomas Stonor of Watlington . . . employed a great number of men to sink a pit about twenty yards across and fifty or sixty feet deep. There they found many whole oaks, whereof one stood upright perpendicular to the horizon, the others lay obliquely and one of them was inverted . . .' 'These trees were a foot to fourteen inches in diameter and near the bottom of the pit was a large Stag's head, complete with brow antlers and two Roman urns which were broken by the incurious workmen."

John said: "It is strange. I spoke to him when he signed this copy for me but although he put forward several explanations he seemed entirely satisfied by none of them."

* * * * * *

By 1683 John Pearce had already begun to show distinct signs of ageing. His son, James however, had grown into a handsome man of some thirty years. Both still had a strong interest in building, especially as James had recently founded his own construction concern and this was thriving in the years that followed the Great Fire of London in 1666.

It is true that this catastrophe had had the benefit of killing many of the rats that had brought the Great Plague to London the previous year, but over thirteen thousand homes of both rich and poor were burned to the ground and eighty-four churches in the city were destroyed, including the beautiful old Cathedral of St Paul's. It was therefore decreed that in future houses and shops should be built of brick and stone rather than just timber, wattle and daub with thatched roofs that were so very likely to catch fire.

After many years of designing and supervising the erection of more than fifty of the damaged churches, including the new Cathedral of St Paul's in the City, as well as many houses for the gentry, Sir Christopher Wren had at last found time to create a magnificent new home at Fawley, near Henley-on-Thames for Colonel William Freeman. Sir Christopher and his assistants stayed at the Red Lion Hotel in Henley when they came down from London to supervise this work.

One cold but dry day in March, 1683, while Catherine and her daughter, Lucy, were away in London assisting James's fiancee, Henrietta Maria, (named in memory of the wife of King Charles I), to choose her wedding gown and trousseau, John and James decided to visit the site of the new building, on the Marlow road.

There they found the revered Sir Christopher Wren in person, dressed in his tall-crowned hat with its wide brim; neck-cloth tied into a bow; a knee-length coat with embroidered cuffs over a long waistcoat, which helped to keep him warm, and breeches gathered at the knee with garters. On his feet were shoes with red heels, high tongues and wide bows. Out here in the country this city gentleman and his similarly dressed assistants looked rather out of place. All around them men were scurrying hither and thither, sticking pegs into the ground, to mark the layout of the grand new house, which was to be called 'Fawley Court'.

Neither John nor James dared to approach the famous, now ageing architect but instead enquired of one of his assistants, all of who were very well dressed. "Tell me sire, is this house to be built of brick and stone, like those in London?" asked James.

"Of course, sire!" replied the younger man. "Sir Christopher would not consider anything else." His tone was somewhat haughty but as soon as James explained who he was, Jacob Pococke, for that was his name, became rather more respectful. "Would you care to see the plans, sire?" he offered, and upon James's nod he speedily found a copy of the main drawing and was only too happy to explain to the strangers the layout of the new house. He was also gratified to see how well they were able to relate to it.

"Not only will it be a magnificent red brick house with stone dressings," he pointed out, "but there is a glorious prospect from the rear, all along the River Thames. Mr Lancelot Brown himself has been engaged to design a park and pleasure gardens that will run down to the waterside. I expect you have heard of Mr Brown? They call him 'Capability' because of his favourite phrase. Indeed I myself heard him use it only last week. 'This place has great capabilities!' he said."

The two gentlemen from Highmore smiled on hearing this and then Jacob Pococke enquired as to whether they knew of the work of Mr Grinling Gibbons. "Of course!" James replied: "I myself have had some small pieces of his carvings put into several houses which I have designed, though most of them have been more modest than this."

"Well, sire," declared Pococke proudly, "he has been asked to carve the ceiling of the *withdrawingroom* in this mansion. Naturally he will not be able to do that for some years yet. It will have to wait until the house is almost finished and in any case, I understand he is very busy."

******

Despite all this wealth and opulence and the thriving of the Catholic Royalists, the non-conformist Dissenters, formed from the opposing side in the Civil War, were very active in the Chiltern Hills as in many other areas. In 1661, the year the monarchy was restored, the *Corporation Act* was passed. This excluded nonconformists from holding municipal offices and a year later the *Act of Uniformity* compelled Puritans to accept all the doctrines of the Church of England or leave it. This led to a massive purge of the clergy, one fifth of whom were deprived of their livings. The *Five Mile Act* of 1665 also prohibited dispossessed Ministers from even visiting their former congregations and all Dissenters had to be registered.

By this time James II had taken the throne after the death of his father, Charles II, but he was deposed in 1668, after fears that he might restore Catholicism. In June of that year, seven leading statesmen went to the Netherlands and invited the Protestant, William of Orange, and his wife, Mary, eldest daughter of James II, to come and take the throne of England. It all happened so speedily and peaceably that this period became known as 'The Bloodless Revolution.'

In 1689, The *Toleration Act* granted freedom of worship to Protestant Non-conformists but they still had to be registered. In 1691, it was noted that 'the dwelling of Richard Blackhall of Stoke

Row is recorded as a Meeting House for Congregational Protestant Dissenters.'

One Sunday Morning in June, 1692, the Congregationalists were met in the Old Farm House, the home of Richard Blackhall and his wife, Mercy, in Cox's Lane, Stoke Row, where non-conformists had gathered each Sabbath for a meeting in the drawingroom for several years past. They had come to hear the word of Isaiah Matyngley, a preacher who had been brought over from Wallingford. This Richard Blackhall, a yeoman farmer, was a much wealthier and far distant relative of the poverty-stricken Blackalls who lived in the tiny cottage at the foot of Witheridge Hill. Greeting his guest at the door of the Old Farm House, Richard said: "God's blessing upon you, sir. I trust my servant brought you here without mishap?"

"Indeed he did, sir and I am obliged to you for sending your conveyance to collect me, for I have none of mine own. Living in the town as I do, I have no need of one." The preacher explained. As he divested himself of his outer garments, he ventured: "This is a beautiful house, sir. Has your family always owned it?"

"No," replied Blackhall. "One of my ancestors bought it from the Stonor family who had to pay many fines on their *recusancy* [refusal to attend the Church of England]. They are a very strong Catholic family, you know."

The preacher nodded and then enquired: "Are there many gathered here today?"

"About twenty," Richard informed him. "We are all from the village or from the neighbouring ones of Highmore or Chackenden. Few house owners feel safe in conducting worship in their homes these days. We are registered and so are tolerated, but only just!"

Isaiah Matyngley entered the large drawingroom that overlooked a beautiful garden and addressed the assembled company. "I bring you greetings from your brothers and sisters in Wallingford, dear friends." As they responded with equal warmth, Richard and Mercy took him around the worshippers, introducing each in turn.

There was one person in particular who Richard felt should be made known to the visiting preacher. "This is Arthur Spiers, our new Parish Constable. At the recent Oxford Quarter Sessions, he was nominated by no less a person than Mr Jethro Tull of Crowmarsh Gifford. I am sure you must be acquainted with him."

"Yes, indeed," the preacher replied. "I know him well. Have you read his book on good husbandry? He has some remarkable ideas and has invented some revolutionary farming machinery, too, though I fear it may bring about unemployment among our local agricultural labourers. However, it was not until quite recently that I was made aware of his being Chief Constable of the Langtree Hundred."

He blew his nose on a large white handkerchief and continued: "Congratulations on your appointment, Mr Spiers. Remember what our Lord instructed in his *Sermon on the Mount*: 'Blessed are the peacemakers for they shall see God.'"

Finally, when all the introductions were at an end, Isaiah Matyngley invited the congregation to participate in the morning worship with the words: "Come, let us kneel and pray to our Lord God and thank him for all his goodness to us."

The Congregationalists continued to meet at The Old Farm House until the middle of the eighteenth century, after which their numbers grew to such an extent that they began instead to use an old barn on the north side of the top of Stoke Row Hill.

******

Fawley Court on the Marlow Road, Henley is open to the public from time to time and Greenlands is now Henley Management College.

Arthur Spiers was elected Parish Constable of Stoke Row at the Oxford Quarter Sessions in 1692 and Dissenters did meet in the Old Farm House at Stoke Row. This house is still in private ownership.

Chapter 12. The Hostelries, the News-sheet and the Surveyor: 1700 - 1799

The eighteenth century saw a long period of domestic peace and steady economic growth in England, though some counties, like Dorset, hardly advanced at all. Communications by road and water were improved and, prompted by the work of Jethro Tull of Crowmarsh near Wallingford, agricultural methods and better breeding of animals produced more prosperous country estates and private farms. This led in turn to a growing demand for better buildings, almost always constructed of brick and stone. The symmetrical style grew in popularity and there was an increasing demand for furniture and domestic luxuries of a high standard. Many of these were made in small towns, like Reading that finally shook off the poverty that followed the Civil War siege.

The last of the Stuart monarchs, Queen Anne, succeeded her brother-in-law, William of Orange in 1702. She had married George, Prince of Denmark, in 1683, but thirteen of their eighteen children were stillborn. In fact, her five surviving children died young and so by the time she died in 1714, after thirty-one years of marriage to a man she adored, she had not actually produced an heir. Not surprisingly, Anne was worn out by these many pregnancies and many periods of grief.

She also had dropsy and suffered from severe attacks of painful gout. Little wonder she preferred a quiet life and on every possible occasion fled London for the peace of the castle at Windsor, far out in the country. In order to try and alleviate her symptoms, she also took to visiting Bath where she revived the fashion for 'taking the waters'.

This resulted in the main road from London to Bath being used much more, especially by the gentry. Consequently road surfaces and services had to be vastly improved. Very soon the Bath Road that ran through Reading saw considerably increased traffic. Not only royalty; all the nobility of the day flocked to the elegant town in the west. These wealthy travellers demanded better food, accommodation and attention for themselves and their horses, so Reading's old-established inns, like the appropriately named 'Crown' and also the 'Bear' and the 'George' became the favoured hostelries of the gentry. For those not quite so well-to-do there were at least another dozen almost as good. Much of Reading's prosperity spilled out into the countryside beyond, especially to the farms that supplied the townspeople and their guests with food.

******

Abraham Merrifield (known to his friends as 'Abe') and Job May were itinerant agricultural labourers who had come up from Dorset, where there was much unemployment, to try and find work in Oxfordshire. They made the long journey in just four days, by a method known as 'ride and tie'. Many country people travelled in pairs great distances in this way. One took the horse and rode ahead. He then dismounted, tied up the horse and walked on. When the second one reached the horse, he mounted and caught up with the first one. This way they could cover far more ground than they could by just walking and the horse carried panniers full of their belongings or wares, too. It was very rare for the horse to be stolen as there were so few people on the quiet country roads.

They only passed by two towns on the way, Salisbury and Newbury, and managed to steer clear of both. They stayed the summer of 1715 in Stoke Row with Job's cousin, Benjamin Slaughter and his wife, Jane, in their tiny cottage on Newnham Hill. They worked hard that summer for Mr John Wells, whose father (with the same name), had bought Newnham Hill Farm from its founder, Mr Matthias Chessall. When the harvest season was over however, the two men found themselves out of work again.

"I've a mind to go down to Reading!" announced Abe as he came back from his last day's work. "They say there's more jobs to be had down there, now that the road is so busy, taking the quality from London down to Bath. I know Queen Anne died last year but the fashion she set for taking the waters there seems to be going on."

"Yes, I've heard that said, too," rejoined his friend Job. "Maybe we could get work in one of the inns and hostelries in Reading. It's said there are dozens of them and they all need hands at times!"

"That's it, then! We'll leave the nag with you. You have been so good to us and, by your leave we'll be going there first thing in the morning Ben. We've been most grateful to you and Jane, but we don't want to outstay our welcome, otherwise you might Slaughter us!"

"Now, now, that's enough of your puns, Job!" reproved Jane with a smile. "I've told you before, Ben's family name doesn't mean 'kill', it's a Saxon word for 'a muddy place'. His folk came from a village called Slaughter up in Gloucestershire, that's how they got their name, so let's have no more of your cheek!"

So at first light the two men set off to walk the nine miles to Reading. As they made their way along the muddy lanes, more often just tracks through the woods than proper roads, Job started to talk, taking the lead as he always did. "My cousin's wife is a real one, she is. Talk about 'Plain Jane', she's as sharp as a needle and so strong willed, too, I wonder Ben puts up with her the way he does!"

"Oh, I don't know, she's often good to those less fortunate than herself. Look how kind she's been to let us stay all summer." Abe recalled. "And anyway, she don't lack a sense of humour herself. Remember how, when you asked her: 'Can we stay another week?' and she said: 'You can, but whether you may, Mr May, is another matter!' That was one in the eye for you!"

Job preferred to be the one to make the puns, so he kept quiet for a while. However, he could not be silent for long. In a few minutes he was speculating on what kind of work they might get down in Reading. "I think we'll try The George, Alf was telling me that it's in King Street, both of them are recently named after the new king. We'll ask the way as soon as we get to Caversham. That's this side of the river, you have to cross the bridge there to get into Reading itself."

"What river is that then?" asked Abe.

"The Thames, you idiot, don't you remember, we crossed it at Goring on our way up," his friend berated. "It goes from high up in Oxfordshire all the way down to London and then out to sea. It's another thing that's made Reading rich. Trouble is, the people can only send their goods to Abingdon or Oxford, not anywhere else. There's another little river called the Kennet, we crossed that near Newbury, too but it's not big enough to transport goods on to go the west. That's the reason this road's become so important, the one to the city of Bath I mean, that's why they call it the Bath Road. Now there's a subject for a jest, I shall have a good time there, I'm sure!"

Finally, around midday they came to Caversham and sure enough there was the bridge as they had been warned and they had to pay the toll. They found Reading to be very confusing at first. For one thing there were so many people and the roads were full of carts and the occasional carriage. As they drew near to the centre of the town, the number of coaches and carriages increased. Soon they found their way to King Street and to the George Hotel, recently renamed in honour of the new king, George I. They decided to go inside first, to see what it was like.

"By Heaven, look at this!" exclaimed Job as they entered the Great Room, where there was a huge oval table and around it comfortable cane-seated dining chairs. In the corners of the room there were other tables, long ones, but these just had benches alongside them, covered with long cushions. On one wall was an enormous fireplace with overmantle, fronted by a brass fender. In the hearth were several long-handled iron fire tools, tongs and poker as well as a brush and shovel. Over the fireplace hung a large mirror and beside it were several bell pulls to summon servants. Around the walls were oil paintings, mainly of hunting scenes or hostelry interiors. At the windows hung heavy deep blue velvet curtains, tied back with silken ropes.

"Let's get away from here, I feel we're out of place." whispered Abe, always cautious. "Look, down here, there's a passage." This led to two parlours, handsomely furnished and comfortable. Finally this corridor led down to the kitchen where many people in long aprons were busily bustling about.

The two strangers stood in the doorway, trying to take it all in. "Holy Mary, Mother of God!" swore Job, under his breath. Little wonder he was surprised for neither of them had ever seen anything like it. At one side was a great open hearth, with an ox roasting on a spit. A young boy, his clothes spattered with fat, was turning it by means of a large wheel. Around the base of this fire stood *trivets* on which there were giant black kettles keeping hot and leaning against the walls were warming pans, toasting forks and many other implements that the countrymen were unable to identify.

"What do you want?" shouted a man dressed fairly smartly and all in black. "You looking for work?"

"Yes, if it pleases you, sir." Job spoke up, remembering his manners.

"I think the Head Ostler needs a couple of hired hands. He's over there, by the barn." said the smarter man. Within seconds the two men found themselves hustled out of the kitchen into the yard at the back. They quickly made their way across the yard, another hive of activity.

At one side was a granary where sacks of corn for the horses were kept. Some sacks were being winched up to an opening in the front of the roof. Ostlers were constantly taking horses in and out of the stables and beyond those buildings was the barn. It stood by the wash-house over which was the ostlery, where the horse handlers slept.

In the doorway of the barn, shouting to men left and right, stood the Head Ostler. He was a big man who, on hearing that the strangers were looking for work stopped shouting for a few minutes and ordered them into the barn where it was a little quieter. He barked out: "My name is Adam Appleton and I am just in need of a couple of hands, so you can start work straight away." On hearing the man pronounce his name, Job nearly laughed at the thought of the puns he could make on that, but he quickly straightened his face as the man glared at him, saying: "Well, first things first. Have you eaten yet?"

On hearing that they had not, Mr Appleton sent them back to the kitchen with instructions to tell the cook he had sent them to be fed before they started work. As soon as they had finished their quick meal they both returned to the barn where the senior man was again yelling his orders out to all and sundry, trying to keep order in the yard as coaches continually came and went.

"Now then, you two, I want you to clear up this barn a bit. Make it tidy because we hear King George is coming through the town next week and you never know, he might want to come here. If he does, we have to impress him as to how well-run this place is and the barn's got in a bit of a mess lately!"

On entering the gloomy barn again, Job and Abe saw what he meant. All around were large quantities of things used in connection with the coaching trade, saddles, halters, horse-cloths, bridles, ropes, all sorts of leather straps and even horse brasses. Not only that but there were old *lanthorns* [lamps], ladders of every size, saws and woodworking tools, empty casks, wheelbarrows and even a couple of wheels waiting for repair.

More used to simpler tasks like haymaking or corn-cutting, Job and Abe glanced at each other in despair. However they were well fed by then and the thought of good meals and a straw mattress in the loft above soon appeased them and in no time they were hard at work. By the time Mr Appleton looked in an hour later he could already see a difference and remarked to himself that these two Dorset men could prove very useful.

******

The farms in Stoke Row and Highmore [as it was still being spelled then] were by the national standards of the time very small, a hundred acres or less. It was almost impossible ground for arable farming, being heavy clay or flinty soil. The steep wooded banks of this hilly area added to the problems of cultivation. Most farmers had a little arable, some corn or wheat, along with some beef and dairy cattle and half a dozen sows. Farmers' wives usually made themselves responsible for a few chickens and from these they got their pin money.

There were seven farms in Stoke Row and two in Highmore in this period. The two in Highmore were Satwell Farm and Highmore Farm. Others in the village came later. Highmore Farm was probably built in 1725, as there is a date mark of 1740 on one of the barns. Fields belonging to the farm went by identifying names such as Red

Hangings, [steep hillside], Stubble Close, Home Field and Holly Grove Field. Although we do not know who began it, Satwell Farm was purchased in 1777 by Thomas Mower Keats and later became the property of local landowner Thomas Ovey.

In neighbouring Stoke Row, English Farm had continued to thrive since the days of Thomas Englysche, but it was still quite small at this stage. Church Farm, in Cox's Lane, was formerly known as Atkins Farm but owed its later name to the fact that it had once belonged to the church. Long before the parish church of St John the Evangelist was built in 1846, Church of England villagers met in the drawing-room at Church Farm, much as the Dissenters did just a few hundred yards away in the original farmhouse of Stoke Row Farm. This saved them having to walk all the way to St Mary's at Ipsden and sometimes the Vicar came to preach and to celebrate Communion. Otherwise they usually studied the bible and sang hymns.

The Home Farm belonging to the wealthy Lydalls of Uxmore House, together with Stag Farm in Newlands Lane were doing quite well, but it was Newnham Hill Farm, started by Matthias Chessall in 1680, which generated most of the produce that found its way to the Reading markets and on to the inns. He had erected a comfortable house on the top of the hill and named it The Manor House. Later he sold the farm to a Mr John Wells and built another, grander house about a hundred metres to the north. However, perhaps because of all this extravagance, in the early 1700s, Mr Chessall appears to have got into financial difficulties and so had to sell the larger house, building close by a small one that he named The Little Manor. Two similarly named properties were established on neighbouring Witheridge Hill later in the twentieth century.

******

In the eighteenth century most of the villagers were agricultural labourers in some form or other. Typical of them were Benjamin Slaughter and his wife, Jane, who continued to work at Newnham Hill Farm, long after Ben's cousin, Job, and his friend, Abe, had left for the prosperity and better prospects of Reading.

The owner of The Little Manor and Newnham Hill Farm, John Wells, was a gentleman farmer, that is to say, he had independent means, unlike his neighbour, Richard Blackhall, a yeoman farmer whose income depended solely on the farm he owned. Most yeoman farmers and their servants were Nonconformists, whereas gentlemen farmers usually attended the Church of England and expected their workers to do the same. John Wells was a man of great faith and he tried to practise his Christian beliefs in whatever way he could. He was good to his labourers and saw to it that they had reasonable cottages and were paid the full and approved wage of 11p a day.

His wife, Virginia, made herself responsible for the sick not only among their own employees but any who lived in the village. She and her friends made and gave basic clothing to local children and there was always help for mothers at the time of childbirth and confinement. Both husband and wife treated their workers with kindness although neither stood for any nonsense.

John Wells had bought out the hereditary strips from his labourers and now his land was made up of small fields worked on a rotation system; winter-sown crop one year, spring-sown crop the next and fallow the third. This gentleman farmer spent much time reading about the latest ideas on improvement of the land and left the supervision of the day-to-day work to his overseer.

Almost eight years after Abe and Job had left, Ben and Jane once again found themselves harvesting the corn in the fields on the top of Newnham Hill, above the trees of Bush Wood and Bear Wood. When threshed and winnowed, the corn would be taken up to the 'new' windmill that had been built some fifty years before on top of Stoke Row hill, in the middle of the village.

This day, Tuesday 9th July 1723, was warm and sunny. The men were stripped down to their shirtsleeves and wore straps around the calf of their trousers in order to stop mice and rats, disturbed by the sickles, from running up their trouser legs. The women were dressed in full-length cotton gingham frocks and wore white cotton bonnets that had a wide brim at the front and a deep protective frill at the back.

At noonday the overseer called for break time and all came gratefully to the shade of a large old beech that had been left as a marker when the fields had been cleared of trees many years previously. As they quenched their thirst with flagons of weak ale they were not surprised to see the master come cantering up on his big brown mare. However, instead of the Bible, which he often brought to read aloud to them on such occasions, he had clutched in his hand what appeared to be several sheets of paper. Few agricultural labourers could read or write, of course, but this benevolent gentleman farmer saw fit to come and read to his employees occasionally.

"Seeing that you are taking your well-earned mid-day rest," John Wells announced, as he alighted from his steed, "I thought I would come and show you this. It's a newspaper, not a London one, but one printed and sold yesterday in Reading!" He felt so excited about this event that he sensed a need to tell them about it, for recent news of the outside world was difficult to come by and the publication of a local news-sheet was a happening of great import.

"This is a great novelty," he explained. "It has been published for the people of Reading and surrounding areas and I purchased a copy yesterday morning when I went down to the town. It cost three half pence. Printing has now spread so far and wide that the printers think it fit for Reading to have a newspaper of its own since the town is prospering so."

The farm workers were astonished. Few of them had even seen a London newspaper and certainly could not have read it, had they done so. However, the philanthropic John Wells was keen that his people should be informed, even if he did leave out those matters that he thought they ought not to know.

"It is called the *Reading Mercury, or Weekly Entertainer*," he explained, pointing out the name across the top of the page. "There are twelve pages and, as you can see, here on the front is a picture of the town." The women particularly crowded around and tried to see if they could recognise the view for few of them went into the town more than once or twice a year.

"Inside this newspaper is a letter from the printers to the Mayor. There is also a short account of Berkshire, and Reading in particular." He read this section out loud and they all nodded vigorously when he came to the next extract which stated: 'Reading market is reputed to be one of the best in England for all sorts of grain and provisions and the meadows within the borough are noted for their fertility.'

Farmer Wells continued: "There are advertisements too; of course they will help to pay for the printing, but there are also scraps of news from other lands. He read out one of the headlines: 'A Dutch ship was attacked recently by pirates in the West Indies and Last week a Murder took place in Shrewsbury.' They were all fascinated to hear this account for no murder had ever been heard of in their own village.

He continued: 'A few days ago an underground fire broke out in Kent; a man was robbed in Berkshire by footpads and a Reading person was killed in a cart accident.' All these events were either in places unknown to them or of such regular occurrence that they raised but little comment. However, when the farmer read out: 'One London man has won £10,000 in a lottery!' they all gasped, for it was an unimaginable sum!

Soon enough it was time for them all to go back to work and John Wells returned to his home, The Little Manor, at the top of Newnham Hill, to read other articles more fully. One that interested him particularly was about the need for a better drainage system and water supply in Reading and another that was an account of the town's long and fascinating history.

There was also information about the latest stage in the joining of the Kennet channel between Reading and Newbury, so that a waterway was created some eighteen and a half miles long, controlled by twenty locks and deep enough to carry barges of one hundred and ten tons burden, all of which had cost £85,000.

Later in the day John Wells rode over to his friend at Church Farm to lend him this novel communication and to discuss plans for the coming month's Church services to be held in the drawing-room there.

******

In medieval times ale was a term generally in use in country districts and everyone, including children drank it, since the water was unsafe. There were no formal public houses, just favoured homes where the ale made by the woman of the house was thought to be superior to that of her neighbours and for this reason the local men tended to gather there to take their refreshment. Quite often the only notice to catch the eye of a passing traveller in the country districts was a bush tied to a pole outside the house but from the reign of Richard II in the fourteenth century, publicans had been

238

singled out from other trades and compelled by law to exhibit a proper sign.

By this time small ale had been largely superseded by beer, which was a malt liquor introduced from the Low Countries, chiefly Belgium, in the fifteenth century and became popular, mainly in towns. Its great advantage was that it kept for months whereas ale brewed by a woman in her own home would deteriorate after about a fortnight. However, by the early eighteenth century all beer was hopped and mainly brewed by the publican or 'brewing victualler'. Many country publicans did not understand the delicate art of brewing hopped beer and so gradually they found it more convenient to buy their supplies from a 'common brewer' in the locality.

From the mid-eighteenth century, records known as the *Licensed Victuallers' Recognizances* were made. Richard Gill and Robert Messenger were the first men in Stoke Row to appear as 'Landlords of the Parish of Ipsden and of Mongewell' respectively, though their houses were not named.

By the late eighteenth century beer was being consumed in large quantities, and it soon became obvious that it was making the locals more and more inebriated, often causing great hardship in their homes, partly because they spent more and more of their income this way, but also because once drunk they often became aggressive towards their wives and families, in fact drunkenness became the dominant vice of the eighteenth century.

By 1774 public houses in this wooded area had become such 'dens of vice and bad behaviour' that 'even the constables were afraid to risk their persons' and from then onwards, in order to obtain a licence, a publican had, among other conditions, to provide two respectable householders willing to stand surety in the sum of £10 each for the orderly conduct of his house during the ensuing year. It was quite a considerable sum in those days and so, not surprisingly, they often stood surety for one another or the local brewer did it for them in the hope of becoming their regular supplier. Thereafter the names of these houses were also provided in the county's records.

Richard Gill was named as landlord of the Crooked Billet and Robert Messenger of the Black Horse, [now in the parish of Checkendon, but at that time in Stoke Row]. Among others named in the *Recognizances* was Ann Brown of the Plough and Key, which later

239

became The Jockey, at Dogmore End, Stoke Row, [now a private house]. She held the licence for this public house from 1775 to 1796.

In 1775 Robert Brakspear came up from Faringdon and joined one such small brewery in Henley, owned by his uncle, Richard Hayward. Two years later he became a partner in the firm and thereafter the Brakspear family were continually connected with the brewery that eventually came to bear its name.

Over in Highmore in 1776, Catherine Harris was listed as publican of the Blue Man, a name probably inspired by the practice of the Ancient Britons to paint themselves with blue woad to increase their ferocious appearance.

In 1785 Francis Basdon took over this inn and renamed it more passively as the Green Man, after the old fertility symbol made from grass at harvest time. This public house changed from the one name to the other several times in the ensuing years but it finally stayed as the Green Man.

By 1786 another inn had appeared in Highmore built just opposite the Green Man and this was named the Dog and Duck, from the 'sport' of tying a duck with a rope fastened to a post in the middle of the nearby pond [which is still there] and setting dogs off to catch the unfortunate bird. Bets would be taken as to whose dog caught the duck first.

Robert Brakspear provided surety for the licensee at this pub that he was later to own. This increasing practice led to this local brewer owning 'tied houses', though some were still 'free'.

All the other public houses in Stoke Row and Highmore came about later on, in the nineteenth century.

******

On 20th June in the year of our Lord, seventeen hundred and sixty-five, a surveyor named Edward Robinson was engaged in mapping Oxfordshire for his employer, Thomas Jefferys. He had surveyed the land around Witheridge Hill and had measured the length of the road along the bottom, where there was just one little thatched cottage. Under a big oak on top of the hill, he and his apprentice, Peter Smith, a lad of about sixteen years of age, had eaten their lunch, bread and cheese wrapped in a red spotted kerchief. They had then continued on to Stoke Row and out to Nuffield.

Finally they came to the Oxford Road and turned right for Nettlebed, where Robinson hoped to find a bed for the night at the White Hart. He had been advised down in Henley that he would find a comfortable room there and good service. To his dismay, he was told at the Nettlebed inn that they had no spare rooms at all but that he might be able to find lodgings at a small public house about two miles to the south, in the village of Highmore on the road to Reading.

It was Peter who first noticed the small sign outside a cottage at the side of the road. It bore a badly painted picture of a half-naked man, his skin daubed in blue patterns. "It is a pity the White Hart was full, lad. I'm afraid this will probably have to do. Inns in these parts are few and far between. Let's hope the landlord will be able to provide us with a clean bed." he remarked, looking down from his horse to the boy who was plodding wearily beside him. "At least we shall be in the village itself and ready to start work in the morning."

As they rode up to the little building, Edward noticed a group of village men sitting on benches in the garden, drinking and laughing. A shapely young woman was just closing the small shop that, like the wives of many publicans, she ran at the side of the building. She only sold the basic foodstuffs and a few ironmongery items but the villagers found it useful. She smiled at the newcomer. "Good evening, sir." she said respectfully. "Are you looking for a jug of our good ale and perhaps some dinner for you and your son?"

"Yes, my good woman, though he is not my son, he is my apprentice. I am teaching him the profession of land surveying." It became immediately obvious to him from the blank expression on her face that the phrase meant nothing to her. "I work for a London gentleman who publishes maps," he quickly explained and at this her face brightened a little.

"My husband, Titus his name is, he'll understand more about that than I do, sir. I'll get him to look to your horse directly."

"Make sure my panniers are safely locked away, they contain all my measuring instruments, charts and books." directed Robinson.

Catherine Harris was quick to reply: "Of course, sir. Come you both inside and you shall have a drink of his best ale. I have a dinner ready to prepare and it won't take long." Taking the lead into the

241

house, she continued: "You're not from these parts I can tell. Will you be wanting a bed for the night? The sun will be going down before too long, even though it is Midsummer's Eve."

"If you have such available, we shall be most grateful." said the traveller, hoping that it would be reasonably clean and comfortable.

"Yes, indeed, sir," she replied. "I have a good room upstairs and the boy can sleep in the attic."

"Oh, I'm quite used to having him in with me," the cartographer reassured her, for it was customary at the time for even strangers to sleep together in one bed.

"No, no, sir. We must make you comfortable," she insisted, as she wiped the table with a fairly clean cloth, giving him a warm smile as she did so.

At that moment her husband came in. His manner was cheerful and welcoming. In fact, as soon as he was inside, Robinson could see that, judged by the standards of some of the country inns at which they had recently stayed, this one was not too bad. Robinson was born and bred in London, a member of a professional family and liked his creature comforts.

A few moments later the husband came forward, bringing a jug of his best ale. "I make my own beer, sir. It's true it's not hopped, but I think you'll find it refreshing. It's been a warm day!" Setting the jug and tankards down on the table, he continued: "My wife tells me you are a map-maker, sir. We are indeed happy to have you stay under our roof. You must be the first map-maker we've had in these parts as far as I know. Do you also sell these maps?"

"No indeed not. I am just a land surveyor," replied the cartographer. "My employer is Mr Thomas Jefferys of London. He plans to publish a map of Oxfordshire in four quarto sheets to a two-inch scale. It will be a topographical map, that is, as far as is possible."

"With respect, sir, I don't know what you mean by that. It's a word I've never heard before and a long one at that!"

Robinson paused for a moment in an effort to provide a simple explanation. "Oh, it just means that we try to show the hilly areas as well as the principal houses, villages, hamlets, churches, farms, woods, heaths and commons. In fact, I am pleased to tell you that Mr Jefferys is already famous in the field of cartography, that is to say, map-making. Some fifteen years ago he published *A Small English*

Atlas, a book of 50 maps, in conjunction with another cartographer, Thomas Kitchin. It has sold very well among the landowners and the clergy."

"Well, well, fancy that! It's not often we get a London gentleman here, sir, but we'll do our best to make you comfortable," pronounced the innkeeper. Indeed it did appear to be quite acceptable for a country inn, the dinner was tasty and young Peter partook of it heartily.

Later they took a short walk, "to settle our stomachs," Robinson explained to the boy. As they strolled along, Robinson passed on to his apprentice some information that he had just learned. "The landlord tells me that we are still in Stonor land, Peter. You will recall that when we met the present owner, Mr Charles Stonor up at Stonor House last week he told us that his family have held land from their house right down to the River Thames at Reading ever since the time of William the First. You may recall he also said that this part of the country comes into the Binfield Hundred."

"Yes, Mr Robinson, sir" Peter replied. "I do remember him saying that. But mostly I enjoyed him playing music that evening for us and wasn't his wife the daughter of the landowner at Mapledurham? You said we still had yet to go there to survey that part of the country, down by the river." He was, as ever, interested in the work they were doing but the boy's voice was slow and tired. His master then remembered that it was Midsummer's Eve and, even though the sun was setting, he had not quite realised how late it was.

When they returned to the Blue Man they found Esther Harris, the landlady, awaiting them in the parlour. "I have made the bed ready for your lad, sir. Up the ladder over there," she said, pointing to the corner. Peter was only too glad to get to bed. He had probably walked about ten miles that day and even though he was used to it the weather had been warm and he was very tired. "And when you are ready, sir, you will find yours at the top of the staircase," she concluded in a hospitable manner.

Robinson was pleased to find that although the room was simply furnished, it had all the necessities. The bed was clean and smelled of fresh straw. A candle on a small table beside the bed was already lit. Immediately the tall, slim man divested himself of his fitted knee-length coat with its fashionable flared skirt, hanging it carefully on the back of the chair by the open window. He was ever mindful of his clothes and was particularly pleased with this garment that he had had tailored for himself in London and which was trimmed with gold braid. Before donning his nightshirt, he removed his elegant wig, dressed into formal side curls and tied at the back with a large silk bow. He rather regretted having to wear these head-pieces that were so 'a la mode', as he had a good head of hair himself.

He extinguished the candle and very soon he was fast asleep, but a short while afterwards he heard the wooden latch lift quietly. Robinson was always fearful of being robbed in these country inns, "You never know what's going to happen when you're far from a town." he had often remarked and was instantly sorry he had allowed young Peter to be bedded in another room.

He need not have worried about theft though, for his visitor was none other than the comely Catherine, who carried a stump of a candle that she put down on the little table, alongside his own. "I just came to see as you were comfortable sir?" she smiled. "I thought as how you might be glad of a little company?"

Robinson was too astonished to reply. Many was the time in his younger days that he had himself tempted a chambermaid or serving wench to come and share his bed but never before had a publican's wife offered her services in such a way. "What will your husband say to this?" he asked, at the same time felt his member stiffening at the touch of her warm skin in the cool of the night.

"Oh, he's fast asleep and snoring enough to wake the devil!" she laughed quietly. "I don't come to the bed of every visitor we have, but I rather fancied you when I saw you come through the garden gate. You're so handsome and I see now that you have a fine head of hair to go with it."

Since he had not demurred at the prospect, she quickly lifted the blanket and was soon enfolded in his arms. "What is your Christian name?" she asked. I can't call you Mr Robinson if we're going to enjoy ourselves, can I now?"

Robinson was again taken aback. He was rather a shy man, and not used to the company of forward women like this one. However, he managed to whisper: "Edward is my name. But you must not call me that before my apprentice."

"No, 'course not. Nor shall my husband come to hear of it

neither!" she giggled quietly as she snuggled up even closer to her new-found lover. For his part he was so content in feeling the softness of her breasts that he was unable to make any further remark.

They enjoyed their love-making most wonderfully and finally fell fast asleep in each other's arms. When Robinson awoke in the early hours of the morning he discovered gratefully that she had silently slipped away and, judging from sounds coming up from below, was already preparing breakfast.

Edward Robinson lay there for some time, listening to the singing of the birds and thinking to himself what a rare treat he had found at this inn and how careful he must be not to give any hint of it to young Peter and certainly not to Titus Harris, the husband of the woman whose company those few hours before had given him so much pleasure.

******

It seemed to start off as just another jovial Saturday night early in December 1781 at the Crooked Billet, down a narrow lane in Stoke Row. Richard Gill, Jnr. knew his public house got this name from a piece of wood that was crooked in shape and unsuitable for any purpose except it was thick enough to be cut to length for burning on a fire. This winter being particularly bitter he was glad he had ensured his wood stocks were plentiful. He always cut them several years ahead of their use so they were thoroughly dry and quick to catch light. The cosiness of his pub was legendary in these parts, and Richard often quoted an old rhyme:

> *Beechwood fires burn bright and clear*
> *If the logs are kept a year*
> *Store your beech for Christmastide,*
> *With new-cut Holly laid beside.*

Another of his favourites ran:

> *Pear logs and apple logs*
> *They will scent your room,*
> *But cherry logs across the dogs*
> *Smell like flowers in bloom.*

245

Both beech and holly were everywhere to be found around 'The Billet', as it came to be affectionately called, and cherry trees, both wild and cultivated. Richard Gill was never short of wood for his huge open fire and cherry logs were indeed often laid across the dog-irons, creating an attractive perfume.

The door of the pub was never locked as either Richard or his wife, Rose, were always on hand to serve anyone who found their way to their home. That evening they knew that soon enough, when the daylight had completely faded, several of the local labourers would be calling in to warm themselves by the fire and partake of a tankard or two of Richard's home-brewed beer.

The first was always Aaron West. He was, as ever, accompanied by his younger neighbour, Henry Sarney.

"Rarely beaten to our customary seat each side of the fire!" Aaron proclaimed as he had done so many times before. "Let's have a tankard of your best beer, Richard. I've got a hole in my belly big enough to drown ten of 'em! What you got on here this time? Smells like cherry to me."

"You're right, there, Aaron!" agreed the publican, as he went down the few steps to the cellar to draw a tankard for his first customer of the evening. He drew an identical one for the silent Henry Sarney, for he knew only too well that they both always had the same. "Now there's a good frothy white head!" he pronounced as he returned with the two tankards.

By this time more men had begun to arrive, grumbling about the snow and the bitter wind outside. Quickly Richard Gill filled several large jugs full of his famous beer and soon enough a dozen or so labourers were seated on benches or standing around the fire, thawing themselves out and talking about the day's work.

After half an hour or so two older men arrived, their hobnailed boots clanking as they dragged their tired feet across the cobblestone floor. Preference for the seats in the fireplace was always given to the eldest amongst the men, out of respect for their years and by this time Aaron and Henry were happy to relinquish their seats each side of the fire. In fact they had warmed themselves through and through and had begun to find the heat rather too much for their comfort.

At that moment a big man, a recent newcomer to the village,

suddenly entered and pushed his way to the front, saying brusquely: "Move out of the way you old uns, make way for them what's been working all day!"

"Here, steady on!" snapped Aaron, always a bit of a hot-head. "We always lets Old Jack and Luke sit in the fireplace when they come, being as they've lived here all their lives."

"And their fathers and grandfathers afore 'em," added another man.

The big man took little notice of this piece of information. He had come from the east end of London and, not surprisingly, bore the name of Jake Lunnon. It was rare for an outsider to settle in these parts and there were already several rumours going around as to why this strange man had come out to the west of the capital, so far from the City. He had just told them he was a blacksmith and came in answer to an advertisement in a London paper, inserted by 'a local farmer'. None of the local farmers would admit to knowing anything about this but they were so glad that someone had suddenly shown up to take the place of the old blacksmith who had recently died that little more was said.

Stephen Wyse, who was thought by the locals to have been well named, quickly glanced around his companions. His look told them not to interfere and they could soon tell that he was thinking up one of his plans. Stephen was known as a 'long-headed man', renowned for his fertile brain. This was a rare thing for a rural man who spent most of his time felling trees but his ideas had often been good ones in the past so they allowed the newcomer to come to the front and bided their time.

"Well now!" pronounced Stephen. "It's rare that we have a stranger come to live amongst us, so I think we ought to buy him a drink. How about that, my mates?"

Astonished as they were, his friends knew better than to question his word. James Blackall, who lived in a little cottage at the bottom of Witheridge Hill, spoke up at once: "What'll you have?"

The stranger was somewhat taken aback at this generous reaction. However, the offer of a drink was not one to be turned down, so he quickly said: "Make mine a porter!" This was a much stronger drink than hopped beer and rather more expensive so Richard Gill was not often asked for it. Nevertheless, since the arrival of Jake in the village, he always kept a *firkin* [56 pints] in stock, since it seemed to be the blacksmith's favourite tipple.

Gradually, as each man offered to buy Jake Lunnon a drink, he consumed far more than they did. By the end of the evening he was almost dead drunk. Richard Gill had watched all these proceedings with interest. Glad of the bit of extra income provided by the local men, he too gave the outsider a mug of porter. Lunnon had probably drunk about nine tankards of this thick blackish liquid and finally, around ten o'clock in the evening, he fell off his stool on to the floor.

This was the signal for Stephen Wyse with a broad smile to say: "Right, lads, let's help him outside!"

Richard Gill was profoundly relieved to hear this, as he wanted no trouble with the law in his beerhouse. The Crooked Billet had so far managed to avoid the lawlessness of other local public houses and he was proud of the fact that he had no thieves or ruffians among his customers.

Once they had carried the inebriated blacksmith outside, and it took six of the men to do it, Stephen finally revealed his plan. "Now it would be impossible for us to carry him up to the forge, wouldn't it, my boys? I suggest we leave him here to sleep it off!"

"But it's so cold out here in the snow, he might die!" wailed Robert Weatherall, at which his companions guffawed loudly.

"He'll be alright." Stephen Wyse reassured them. "I tell you what, I'll drop in on the Constable on my way home and tell him that the blacksmith was so drunk he fell down outside the Billet and we were not strong enough to lift him up. Constable Frewin has been in this job for nigh on forty years and he'll see to it that he comes to no real harm!"

"And I bet he'll be a bit more respectful in future!" chuckled Aaron and even his neighbour, Henry, laughed.

"Ah yes," said Stephen Wyse, sagely, "As I've often said, there's more than one way of killing a cat!"

******

248

The Bear Inn closed soon after the railway came to Reading in 1844, but The George in King Street is still in business today.

The Reading Mercury *was published in 1723 and continued to be popular until it closed in 1952.*

The Map of Oxfordshire *referred to here was finally published on 12th April 1769 by Thomas Jefferys in the Strand, London 'According to an Act of Parliament'. Copies may be found in the Centre for Oxfordshire Studies at Westgate, Oxford.*

The Crooked Billet is still active today in Stoke Row and is a well-known and fashionable restaurant.

Chapter 13. The Wraith, the Bishop and the Funeral: 1800 – 1850

The East India Company, founded for the purposes of trading with India and the East Indies, was first given its charter by Queen Elizabeth I in 1600. During the seventeenth century it began to spread and gain territory, building fortresses, raising troops and gaining general recognition. During the eighteenth century despite much competition with other countries, the Company rose to the position of a ruling power. Pitt's India Bill, passed in 1784, created a board of control and gave the political, financial and military control into the hands of the government. Gradually the monopolies of the Company were taken away and it became largely an administrative body.

To carry out all the administration of this huge country, many English people went out to India. Eventually these came to include several members of the same family. One such were the Reades who held land, not only in Ipsden and Stoke Row, but also further afield.

******

John Thurlow Reade was the eldest of eleven children born to John and Anna-Maria Reade. He was probably the cleverest of the family and became Head Boy of Rugby School when he was only fifteen. Rather than live in idleness as he might have done, being heir to the estate, he chose to go into the service of the East India Company so there might be money to educate his many younger brothers and sisters. He was trained in the Company's College in England, where he gained considerable merit and sailed for India in 1817.

In those days mails from India were rare and irregular and when one was reported, John's mother was in the habit of going out to the Wallingford road to meet the mail coach. She had not received a letter for some time and one evening in 1827, whilst walking down the road, Mrs Reade saw the wraith of her son coming towards her and exhibiting signs of utmost distress. She was convinced that he had died and not received a Christian burial.

The following day she arranged with the Vicar of Ipsden to hold a burial service in the church. Both she and the Vicar were strong Protestants and quite unlikely to give way to morbid superstitions, but they were completely convinced of the significance of the vision.

The next mail brought news that John Thurlow Reade had died of dysentery whilst on a journey through the jungle near Sehaarunpore and had been buried by his servants there and then.

His youngest brother, Charles Reade, wrote to his elder brother, Edward Anderdon Reade, who was also in the service of the Company, elsewhere in India: 'The house is like a great mirror cracked across since the news of John's death arrived.'

Charles Reade, DCL (1814 - 1884) eventually became famous as a novelist as well as a lawyer. He wrote nearly twenty books, amongst which was *A Woman-Hater* and *"It's Never Too Late to Mend"*. A bas-relief commemorating his life as 'an author, dramatist and journalist' and mentioning his most famous book, *The Cloister and the Hearth*, is set in a wall in the crypt of St Paul's Cathedral, London.

Edward Anderdon Reade retired from the East India Company in 1860 while his mother was still alive and decided to erect a monument to his eldest brother. He chose the site nearest to the point where the wraith had appeared and had the stone engraved:

JOHN THURLOW READE ESQUIRE
SEHAARUNPORE
NOVEMBER 25TH A.D. 1827
'ALAS MY BROTHER'

This memorial, Edward Anderdon believed, would lay to rest the spirit of his revered brother. It did seem to do so as there were no more sightings of him.

* * * * * *

Before Queen Victoria came to the throne in 1837, the industrial revolution was well under way, Britain traded worldwide and prospered greatly. Even so, life in the country districts, including the Chiltern Hills, was dire. Although now easily accessible to all, this area was thought at that time to be very remote. There were few schools, no regular supply of clean water and the labouring poor lived in cottages so badly maintained they were not much better than hovels. However, a few among the upper classes, often known as 'the great and the good', were trying to alleviate the poverty.

As far back as March 1580, St John's College, Oxford had acquired land at Stoke Row when property was purchased from Sir John Arundell, Knight, of Lanherne in Cornwall.

In June 1738, Reverend William Thomas, Vicar of Ipsden and North Stoke, sent his answers to the *Bishop's Visitation* [a set of questions about the parish] to the Bishop of Oxford, with reference to the Parish of Ipsden, which included the village of Stoke Row. In this report he stated:

> 'The Parish is about three miles in length and half a mile in breadth . . . There are no Papists, Independents, Baptists or Quakers and only four Prestbyterians . . . I know of none who openly profess to disregard Religion or who commonly absent themselves on that Principle from all Publick Worship on the Lord's Day. There are some who absent themselves too often; but it shall be my endeavour to lessen ye number of them . . . There is no Free School, Hospital or Almshouses in this Parish...
>
> There is three pounds per annum left in land by Emery to ye Poorest Inhabitants of ye Parish and a Hundred Pounds left by ye Revd Mr Headlam to buy coats for such Poor People as frequent ye Church... I dispose of the Money at ye Offertory to the Poor Communicants.'

The latter statement is of great interest because it relates to the finding of a 'buried hoard' by William Emery of Newnham, probably about 1660. He farmed a parcel of land below Berin's Hill and, according to tradition this is where he found the treasure. In acknowledgement, in 1691, he bequeathed the rents of lands in

Crowmarsh to the church at Ipsden in trust for the supply of garments to the aged poor.

Later, in his will of 1729, Reverend Richard Headlam, Vicar of North Stoke and Ipsden (1698-1730), added to this amount the sum of one hundred pounds. This money was used to create a row of tenements locally called 'Great Coat Cottages' or, more properly, 'Headlams'.

Mr Dodds of Hailey also founded a blanket charity. He bequeathed the sum of four hundred and fifty pounds, the interest from which was to provide blankets, half for the poor of Ipsden and half for the poor of Stoke Row.

On 30th September 1846 a deed was drawn up which allowed for the Vicar and Churchwardens of Ipsden to administer these trusts. The foregoing shows not only the desperate need of the poor, especially the elderly poor, of blankets and clothes as well as food, but also the kindness of some of the clergy in the eighteenth and nineteenth centuries.

There was also great concern about the village of Stoke Row in the uplands of the parish. It was realised early in the nineteenth century that the church of Ipsden was too far for the villagers to go to church each Sunday. In his replies to the *Bishop's Visitation* of 1811, Revd William Henry Wright, stated that the Parish of Ipsden, which included Stoke Row, consisted of 'one hundred and seven families, about three hundred and seventy souls' and that the church was 'situated at one extremity of the Parish'. The fact that there were only 'about twelve communicants' and that the place was 'overrun by Dissenters' led the local Church of England clergy and gentry to believe it was time to erect a church in Stoke Row for the inhabitants of that end of the parish.

Above all, it worried them to know that an Independent Chapel had been erected by subscription and labour from amongst the Dissenters in Stoke Row in 1815. It was thriving as it was just beyond the limit set by the Five Mile Act of 1665 that prohibited dispossessed Ministers, like those in Henley, from even visiting their former congregations. Up until the building of the Chapel these nonconformists had met firstly in the drawing-room of the farmhouse in Cox's Lane and more latterly in a very large old barn at the top of Stoke Row Hill.

However, it was not until about 1843 that Revd Richard Twopenny and the Bishop of Oxford managed to collect enough private subscriptions and make the necessary arrangements with St John's College, Oxford, for a church to be erected in Stoke Row.

******

Tim Brownjohn, a reporter for the Oxford Chronicle, found the atmosphere pleasantly cooler up on the Chilterns Hills, away from the stifling heat down in Oxford and was glad to be away from the city. It was Thursday 27th June 1844 and he was there to report on the laying of the foundation stone for the new Church of England at Stoke Row, to be dedicated to St John the Evangelist.

Despite the heat, in view of the formality of the occasion, he had dressed himself in his brown top hat, short brown tweed coat, with flared skirt and velvet collar, striped waistcoat with shawl type collar and tight breeches, buttoning at the knee. However, in the very warm weather, it was the long leather gaiters, worn over his short brown boots that he regretted having put on and wondered to himself whether he could hide somewhere to take them off. Unfortunately, no such opportunity offered itself, surrounded as he was by the large crowd. "In any case," he thought. "I would have to carry them and my horse is tethered yonder in the field. I'll just have to put up with the discomfort."

People had come from near and far for the event. Miss Ellinor Hastings Reade of Ipsden House, a winsome lady who by that time had reached middle-age, had promised to come and lay the foundation stone. The footings for the church had already been put in and the plans for the building, designed by Mr Richard Charles Hussey, were laid out on a table for all to see. Moreover, a decorated silver trowel, eleven and a half inches by four inches, with solid ivory handle had been purchased for this grand ceremony.

Several Constables, supervised by Superintendent Moran were around to ensure that order was kept, especially when quiet was demanded as Reverend Hopkins of Nuffield gave an address to the congregation gathered around the site. A green carpet had been put down to ensure that the shoes and boots of the gentry were not dirtied by the soil that had been disturbed by the construction work.

Finally the moment came for Miss Reade to lay the foundation stone. All the ladies in the crowd murmured their approval of her beautiful bonnet, trimmed with embroidered ribbon, posy of flowers and lace frill. She wore a tiered skirt of pleated green taffeta and wrapped around her shoulders was a very large cream cashmere shawl. It really was a lovely thing, with its wide decorative border, embroidered with wool and fringed with tassels.

As he was taking notes for his report in the next edition of the Oxford Chronicle, Tim Brownjohn heard one of the local ladies murmur: "I expect that came from India. Her brother, Edward Anderdon Reade, is out there you know."

Once the Rector had finished his address, Miss Reade stepped forward and was handed the trowel by Mr Clarke, the builder, who looked a little uncomfortable, dressed in his Sunday best. Miss Reade just said a few appropriate words as she touched the stone with the trowel upon which a small blob of mortar had been placed, but was nevertheless warmly applauded by the crowd.

Brownjohn continued to take notes and when he returned to his office in Oxford the next day he wrote a long piece about the joyous event. However, his editor thought this bucolic place to be of little importance and shortened it to just a couple of paragraphs:

'On Thursday last, the 27th instant, the ceremony of laying the foundation stone of the new church at Stoke Row, in the parish of Ipsden, Oxon, was performed by Miss Reade of Ipsden House. A very large company attended and the address to the congregation, by the Revd Hopkins of Nuffield, was highly impressive and made its way with great force to the understanding of every class of his hearers.

A cold lunch was afterwards provided by John Reade, Esquire of Ipsden House and wines, etc., etc. by Mr Meyers of the Lamb Inn at Wallingford in a tent erected by Mr Clarke, the builder, where a large party enjoyed themselves and expressed their satisfaction at the various arrangements.'

The construction work resumed the next day. Aaron Clarke was not one to waste time! Gradually the villagers watched the walls go up and finally the bell tower rose above the roof of the main building.

It took two years to complete the church on land given by the College of St John the Baptist, Oxford. There was not only enough money donated for the church but also sufficient for a Vicarage and a School to be erected at a later date. The cost of constructing the church was put at £2,500. In August of 1846, a little before the final touches were put to the church, Revd John Cole was inducted as Vicar of St John's, where he stayed for three years.

By the September, the church was finally finished and arrangements were made for its dedication. The day chosen for the consecration service was an auspicious one, Tuesday, 19th October 1846. It was the day on which the twelfth century Oxford princess, St Frideswide, was remembered.

Again this was a very grand occasion, for no less a person than Bishop Samuel Wilberforce, well known for his oratory and affectionately known as 'Soapy Sam' [son of William Wilberforce, famous for his work on the abolition of slavery] was coming to perform the ceremony of consecration. This gentleman had been Curate of Checkendon some twenty years previously and was a friend of the Reade family. The event was recorded in a long letter written by Mr Charles Reade to his brother Edward, who was out in India at the time:

Dear Edward

I have long promised myself the pleasure of relating to you the events of which our house and neighbourhood have lately been the scene - events interesting to all right-thinking persons, but to none more than yourself, who are acquainted with the natural beauties of our wood-girded hamlets, and the moral degradation which, alas! has hitherto disfigured them.

You are aware what difficulties have been encountered. First, a considerable sum was to be raised for the building of a church; and this, through the kindness and zeal of Christian friends, was our least impediment.

Next, the endowment was to be obtained partly from the College of St. John's. Cambridge, holding the great tithes of the parish, and partly from surplus subscriptions, aided by a liberal provision, for which our excellent vicar, the Rev. R. Twopenny, is to be thanked; and I am sorry to say we encountered in the college a wearisome obstacle.

All this arranged, our Bishop declined to consecrate the new church until a curate should be found ready at once to undertake its service.

I fear we did not at first appreciate our diocesan's wisdom in making the stipulation; but now we humbly confess our error. This last hindrance was not so easily removed as we hoped, as you yourself might have anticipated.

The secluded situation of Stoke Row - the circumstance of there being no house for the clergyman - and no water fit for use within a distance of several miles.

These disadvantages, added to the smallness of the stipend, no doubt deterred many of those whose zeal languishes without the allurements of what is called society, and is incapable of dispensing with earthly luxuries.

At last, however, one was found willing to labour in this new vineyard, upon such terms as it offered, a gentleman and scholar, indifferent to society of rich or poor, and content to divide his time between the doctors and the Church and its services. His name is Cole.

This was duly notified to the Bishop of Oxford, and after some few changes the consecration was finally fixed for Tuesday, the 19th October 1846.

As the Bishop, the Archdeacons of Berks and Oxford, and other personages were to be entertained and sleep, on Monday, at Ipsden considerable preparation, you may suppose, was necessary. My gun was put in requisition, nor was Covent Garden neglected. My father alone remained discontented with our efforts, on the ground of a falling off of our butter, which used to be excellent, nor could he be brought to believe that a Bishop could put up with butter so inferior to what he, by his position, must be accustomed to.

The solicitude after all was superfluous. The Bishop does not eat butter.

257

Our guests were all assembled on the Monday evening, when the Bishop arrived in exact time. He made a hasty toilet, and immediately reappeared.

He had not brushed his hair. We understand it is not his custom.

We were at opposite ends of the dinner table - the Bishop and I. It was my fate to lead out Lady Catherine Berens. At the Bishop's end of the table the conversation was as lively as it was dull where I was.

Dr. Wilberforce's high and earnest tone in the pulpit, and his deep fervour, whenever a religious subject, always welcome, is started, would hardly prepare a common observer for his ordinary conversation, the characteristic of which is decidedly humorous. I wish my situation had permitted me to bring away some of those sprightly sallies with which he entertained the ladies at his end of the table.

Tuesday, a quarter-past eleven a.m., our cavalcade started for the new church. The Bishop, some time after the rest, led by me and Mr. Pearson in my pony gig, arrived on Stoke Row Common. We saw a very pretty sight, all the country people collected in their gayest colours round the edifice. The church, which is small, was entirely filled with visitors, after which a form was introduced, capable of accommodating a dozen more of the inhabitants. They, however, preferred watching the vehicles outside.

The musical part of the service was provided by Mr. Benfield, of Reading, his daughters and dependants, and was done in a pure and simple style. The Bishop preached an excellent discourse. I wish I could give you some idea of his eloquence and impressive delivery of sacred truths, uttered in their full breadth without any mincing of the matter. My memory contains rhetorical flowers, when the root was better bringing away.

He illustrated the difference between professing and true Christians is the difference between dead things and living.

"These people," said he, "go through religious appearances from custom, because it is the fashion, because respectable people in

their line of life all do it - dead things go with the stream, but living things go by a course of their own, now with, now against, the stream." Then he compared the former characters to stones, on whom, perhaps, the gospel sun shines for a while, the warmth dies away, and they are colder than the very ground which surrounds them. How unlike those living things, the fruits and flowers, which absorb these beams, and give them back in beauty and perfume!

Then he depicted a certain empty religion, of which, after describing its pretensions, he pronounced "it shrinks at singularity, faints under a laugh, and dies under the cross."

In short, to make a singular observation, the sermon ended too soon.

On the termination of the service, I went to make sure the musicians were being taken care of. I found them very hungry, sitting round a table, gazing on vacancy. I left them with the cheerless horizon broken by a fillet of veal, a gigantic ham, and a cake, on which the table might have been set, instead of it on the table. These provisions were kept in abeyance for the clergy, on whose charity I knew I could presume.

I need not describe our return; it was conducted in the same order we came.

The Bishop dined with Mr. Twopenny, returning thence to our house to sleep. Unfortunately, his coachman, to save himself trouble, prevailed on ours (James Hutt) to go for his lordship to the Vicarage. When the carriage was announced, the Bishop was engaged in interesting conversation, and did not move. So after a few minutes, Mr. Twopenny's dolt of a man-servant came again to him.

Dolt - " Mr. Reade's horses are waiting, sir."
Bishop - "I think you must be mistaken, doubtless my horses are waiting."

Dolt - "No! no! I tell 'ee, it's Mr. Reade's carriage and horses as be waiting."

So the prelate was actually bundled off, against his will, and, having arrived, told us the tale in his dramatic way.

Of course we were shocked that he should have thought of deferring so much to our horses.

Whereupon he reminded my mother that he had been admonished twenty years ago, when curate of Checkendon, that he was not to keep the Ipsden horses waiting!

Thus the grave events of the period were diversified by incidents of a lighter character.

Your affectionate,

Charles

Thus was the Church of St John the Evangelist opened for the parishioners of Stoke Row, at the upper end of the large parish of Ipsden.

* * * * * *

By the time that the eighteenth century had turned into the nineteenth, generations of the Blackhall family had lived in the little thatched cottage at the foot of Witheridge Hill for almost two hundred years, ever since Sir Francis Stonor had rebuilt the original squatter's hovel which Joseph Blackhall and his brothers so stealthily constructed in 1601. During these two centuries the names of the Blackhalls had appeared in the parish registers of Mongewell, Rotherfield Peppard and Rotherfield Greys under various spellings, so widespread was this family. Some of them were quite well-to-do, but most were very poor and none poorer than the family who lived in the aforementioned cottage.

Working for the Stonor estate, all the menfolk in the family had been woodsmen of one kind or another and had eked out a very meagre existence, especially when the summers were particularly long and hot. At these times there had been little or no water, just that saved in the clay dewponds throughout the winter, even though this often produced *goitres* [large swellings on the neck, due to iodine deficiency, more usually in women than men]. In winter large snowballs, as big as anyone in the family could push, were rolled into a shady area and these were melted down in the spring to water seedlings.

Their one compensation was the availability of firewood from the nearby Bear Wood and from the Commons land on Witheridge Hill. Just outside the cottage there was a coppice, where wood could be cut every fifteen to twenty years, whereas mature timber took a hundred years to grow. The product from this belonged to the estate, of course, but the left-overs and off-cuts were soon gathered up by the cottagers. Branches that came down in the winter storms or the very tops of the trees that had been felled by the estate and were considered as unsaleable timber were what most of the poorer families mainly used for fuel.

On their small piece of land, about half an acre, they grew a few vegetables and on the grass that grew at the side of the tracks that came down Witheridge Hill almost every family kept a pig that was killed just before the onset of winter. The meat was dried and salted, the skin was made into clothes, especially shoes, and the fat went to make candles. The bones were added to vegetables to make a nourishing broth. Nothing was ever wasted. Each local family killed its pig in turn, so that parts of the fresh meat could be exchanged for surplus goods that a neighbour had to offer.

Usually the family had a goat as well and from this they had milk, especially for the children. The wife usually kept some chickens, too and sometimes she was able to barter a few eggs, extra to the family's needs, for some excess food that neighbours had grown. Down in the valley, far from the village, it was easy to snare a rabbit and sometimes this meant the difference between life and death for the cottage dwellers.

The Enclosure Acts, passed between 1750 and 1850 were traumatic for country folk, enclosing any land that could be possibly used for farming, thus depriving the peasantry of the strips of land on which they had subsisted for so long. However, the Free Trade Act of 1846 did alleviate their condition somewhat, making bread and other foods a little cheaper.

Not surprisingly, these labouring people, especially the very young and elderly, were prone to die of disease, often brought about or exacerbated by malnutrition. There was also the very great risk of agricultural and domestic accidents. On Wednesday 28 July 1813, Sarah Blackall 'of Witheridge Hill' was killed 'by a fall from a cherry tree'. The verdict by the Coroner, Mr G P Cooke was that 'she fell from a ladder'. He charged a fee of twenty shillings and this was paid, plus seven shillings and six pence expenses by the Court, probably because her family were too poor to do so.

The surname of the Witheridge Hill branch of the family was by now spelled Blackall on a more standardised basis and it is believed that they lived in the one and only thatched cottage at the foot of the hill.

There was a further tragedy on Saturday 13th September 1817, when John Blackall, aged 14, was 'killed by a threshing machine'. He was buried in Mongewell Churchyard. Again, the Coroner's fee was twenty shillings with only six shillings expenses. The total amount was paid by the Quarterly Assizes.

Ten years later, on Friday 7th December 1827, another woman by the name of Sarah Blackall of Witheridge Hill was 'burnt'. This account, in the Oxfordshire Archives, gives no indication of how the accident occurred or what age Sarah Blackall was at the time. As this Christian name occurs many times in the history of the family, it is hard to say. The Coroner at the Epiphany Session charged the usual fee of twenty shillings, plus seven and sixpence and once more this was paid by the Quarter Sessions.

Deaths in Victorian times were, in fact, so frequent that they discouraged people from forming emotional ties with their wives and children, so heart-breaking were the farewells.

******

The snow lay thick on the ground at mid-day on Monday 6th February 1843 and the sullen black skies threatened another fall before the day was out. The graveyard at the side of St Nicholas Church, Rotherfield Greys was entirely white, relieved only by the lighter covering on the heap of brown earth beside the six foot deep trench dug for the burial, immediately next to another mound.

As the funeral party came out of the church, large white flakes began again to fall stealthily, continuing their work of making all the unevennesses even, hiding every difference between the path and the graves. Most of them were no more than mounds, the older ones almost settled to ground level by now. There were remnants of wooden crosses that had been placed on some, with just a name and the dates of their brief lives carved into them. A few here and there were marked by engraved headstones but they could only be afforded by the richer families in the district.

The snow muffled almost every sound, deadening even the weeping of the women in the group. Their thin black clothes seemed to offer little protection from the cold. Gradually the family assembled around the open oblong hole, as the pall-bearers gently lowered the simple wooden coffin into the ground. The relatives and friends who stood a little further back were considerable in number, perhaps thirty of them. All had come to say 'Farewell' to Mary Blackall of Witheridge Hill who had died the week before, aged 79 years. Once everyone had sprinkled their handful of soil on top of the coffin and the Sexton had begun to replace the earth in the hole, the mourners left the scene as soon as they could respectfully do so, mindful of the hot luncheon which had been promised to them at the nearby public house, The Maltster's Arms.

This pub had been built sometime in the early 1700s, though just when no one could remember. The landlord did not know and little wonder, for he was just a tenant of Mr Brakspear's Brewery down in Henley. However, he was the epitome of a jolly landlord, with his pot-belly, beard and side-whiskers, cherry-red cheeks and broad smile.

"Why, come you in, Rector! I have built up a big fire for to warm you up. I know it is a sad day for you all," he continued, as the group slowly filed in through the door, "but she was an old lady and had enjoyed a long life!"

The Rector, the Reverend William Morgan Kinsey, BD had only recently returned from a long time spent in Portugal to take over the living of St Nicholas Church at Rotherfield Greys from the Reverend John Richards Roberts, BD. Despite his only having been in the Rectory for little under a month, he had already established a reputation among the gentry in the district. As one lady put it: "He is an Oxford divine of the old school, a ripe scholar who had travelled near and far and was learned in many tongues."

His kindness to the funeral party was typical of the man. It mattered not to him that they were poor and illiterate. He was truly compassionate and could see that, although the lady they had just buried was of a grand old age, the family would miss her especially her wisdom. However, he was fond of good conversation and realised that this was not to be found with the mourners themselves, mostly common woodsmen and their wives.

There was one exception, a man of about fifty years of age, well-dressed entirely in black, who obviously had some education and was accompanied by his wife. He wore a full-skirted, double-breasted coat, with brass buttons, trousers with a strap under the foot, black leather boots, leather gloves and a walking stick. He held his black top hat in his hand. This man appeared to have put himself in charge of the arrangements and had led the mourners to the pub. He came forward to the doorway at once.

"Good morning, Sir. I am Richard Blackhall of Stoke Row, at your service and this is my wife, Elizabeth." At this, the small lady at his side, being a rather timid creature, just murmured her greeting with the minimum of curtsy and looked to her husband to continue the conversation. She was also clad in mourning dress, wearing a bonnet lined with pleated silk, which was trimmed with black ribbons and a full-length tiered cape with braid trimming. Until she took her right hand out to shake it with the Rector, she had both hands cosily encased in a small black fur muff.

Richard Blackhall continued: "I regret we were a little late in arriving for the ceremony and were therefore not able to make ourselves known to you earlier. I am a nephew of the deceased and have tried to care for her family as best I can over the years, although my farm and my windmill up beside the Common there keep me occupied much of the time."

The Rector shook hands warmly and immediately ushered in the rest of the party, in haste to get them inside in the warm and the door closed behind him. They were a motley lot, their boots clumping loudly as they endeavoured to kick off most of the snow before entering. The men doffed their caps as they came inside and most of them mumbled thanks of a kind to the parson who had spoken so benevolently to them in the church and as they left the graveside.

Principal among them was John Blackall, a rough and ready man of about fifty years of age, although he looked a lot older. Like the other men, he was dressed in a loose, ill-fitting jacket and thick felt trousers. On his arm was a black armband. His wife, who was dressed entirely in black, made her obediences with a slight curtsy and loosened her shawl as she came into the room. "My wife, like my mother is also named Mary, sir," he said, by way of explanation. "And these are our children". One by one, they came forward and dutifully bowed their heads or dropped a small curtsy as their mother had done. John introduced them too.

"This is Samuel, our eldest. He's twenty-two and a great help to me now he's grown so big and strong. Like me, he's a woodcutter for Lord Camoys, and this is Mary, she is seventeen and named after her grandmother and her mother, of course." He looked around for his next child, who was at the back of the group. "Come along, now Jemima, don't be shy. His Reverence is a kind man and won't eat you!" Gaining confidence now, he continued: "Jemima is fifteen, sir and this is John, he's thirteen. Now here's our Shadrach, we just call him 'Shad', it's a long name for a little boy, he's only eleven. And here's Elizabeth, the baby of the family, she's nine."

"Ah, yes." Reverend William Morgan Kinsey was suddenly reminded of his scholarly days at Oxford. "He was one of the three men who would not bow down to the Golden Image that King Nebuchadnezzar had set up. They, being Jews, of course, believed only in the one God. I am sure you know the story?" He looked at the two younger children as he spoke.

"No, sir." the boy replied quietly, for his sister as well as for himself. They hung their heads, somewhat ashamed of their ignorance.

"Well, you should do. It is a wonderful tale from the Old Testament. Shadrach and his friends Mesach and Abed-nego were all in high office in Babylon, but when they wouldn't worship the idol that the King had set up, he had them cast into a fiery furnace. The wonderful thing is that they were quite unharmed! This was because they had great faith in God and prayed to Him to save them."

Looking at his father, the Rector said: "I plan to open a Sunday School to teach the young people of my parish all these marvellous stories. When I do so I know that you will send your children along."

"Yes, indeed, sir." affirmed John Blackall, dismissing his wife and children with a wave of his hand. They promptly made their obediences again and joined their relatives by the fire.

265

John turned again to the Rector and his cousin. By this time the landlord and his wife had served warmed ale to their guests, although the Rector and Richard Blackhall were both given wine in glass goblets without question.

Taking a quaff from his pewter tankard, John spoke again: "We are indeed grateful to you for your kindness to us. My mother was old and had had a good life, but we shall miss her all the same. It was something of a comfort to see her laid to rest next to my father, James Blackall. He died some thirteen years ago. It was a Sunday, 5th September 1830, as I recall. Terrible it was. He just collapsed and died suddenly. Mother was very upset."

"How old was your father when he died?" enquired the Rector.

"I think he was seventy-two, Sir. No doubt it will be in your register, should you wish to know. I have no learning and so I leave that sort of thing to my cousin, here and I am most grateful to him for all that he has done for us."

So saying, and with an inclination of the head to them both, John Blackall left the educated people to their drink and conversation.

Within a few minutes the landlord and his wife had begun serving meat and vegetables to the mourners. They sat on benches along the sides of long tables, whereas the Rector, Richard Blackhall and his wife were given a table in the corner to themselves, with fine china plates and silver knives and forks.

Here they were able to continue their conversation. William Morgan Kinsey reopened the dialogue: "It's a great age, 79. Why it's almost 80. That's quite a record for a working-class woman. To what do you think she owed her longevity?"

Richard replied quietly: "I do believe it is the way in which John and Mary cared for her, ever since her husband died. They were married for 42 years. It's a rare thing, such a long life together. Old Mary lived with them in that tiny thatched cottage down at the foot of Witheridge Hill. It's a very poor place, with just an earth floor, but they're hard-working folk."

His wife suggested tentatively: "Perhaps you would care to ride out that way in the summer, sir. It may be snowy now, but in the spring, summer and autumn it is a beautiful part of the country."

The Rector smiled. "I look forward to the warmer weather, indeed I do. This cold, snowy time does not suit me at all. I have recently

266

returned from that lovely warm country, Portugal and it was there that I learned to appreciate good wine like this. The landlord already knows of some of my likes and dislikes and I have ensured that he keeps a few bottles of this vintage for occasions such as this when I am obliged to dine here."

******

I am grateful to Mrs Juliet Noel for permission to quote from the Reade Manuscripts with regard to the John Thurlow Reade memorial.

Some of the facts about the beautiful church of St Nicholas at Rotherfield Greys were taken from the handbook on sale there.

Chapter 14. The Enumerator, the Brickmaker and the Photographer: 1851 - 1860

Early on in the reign of Queen Victoria, the government decided to start on a series of Census Returns, to be made every ten years. At first these were purely numerical but by 1841 they included the name of the parish, the name of the house (though these were rare), the full name of the head of the household, each member of his family and any visitors that were under his roof on the night preceding the Census. It also included their sex and ages and, where possible, their profession or trade or whether they were of independent means. Finally they were asked whether they were born in the same county. If they were not, no further questions as to their origin were asked.

By 1851 these enquiries had grown to include the 'condition' of the occupants of the house, i.e. whether they were married, unmarried or widowed. Also questions on their place of birth had to be answered. Later on these Census Returns were to provide family historians with much valuable information.

******

About one o'clock in the afternoon of Monday 1st April 1851, some eight years later, George Smith of Reading was delighted to find a Beer House at the foot of Witheridge Hill, just as he had been told he would. He saw the sign up on a wooden building at the side of a small thatched cottage, the roof of which at the back came down to about six feet from the ground. The cottage had two windows set each side of a wooden door in the ground floor and two windows on the upper floor. By the front of the house was a partly used small stack of hay, presumably for feeding animals in the winter.

Smith led his horse through the small wicket gate set near the end of a flint wall and tethered it to a ring at the side of the barn. In the garden, just in front of the barn was a well, with a flint wall around it. A very thin, wizened old man was drawing water up from the bottom of it, using the windlass. Turning the handle obviously seemed to be hard work for him and Smith offered to help. The man refused.

"Why no sir, thank you. She's coming up nicely now."

"How deep is this well?" Smith enquired.

"When it were sunk, about five year ago, they reckoned it to be roughly 120 feet, sir. It took about four months to dig out. Hard work it was, it's all clay and flint hereabouts, you see. You go inside, sir and I'll be in directly."

Smith entered the small barn through the door at the garden end, sat down at a table and awaited the landlord, who had said his name was John Blackall. Smith glanced around him. The long wooden room was plain, save for a couple of benches and one or two chairs. On one table was a chipped blue vase, full of spring flowers and a small collection of *fairings*, cheap ornaments often won by working class people at fairs.

Finally, puffing and panting after his exertions, the old man came in to the barn. "Bring me a flagon of your best beer, Landlord!" Smith ordered. "It's a warm day, I do declare!" Very soon he was writing laboriously with a quill pen on sheets of paper that had already been printed with lines and some words.

When he had returned with the flagon and a pewter mug, Blackall stood by, fascinated to watch Smith making entries from notes that he had already made on other scraps of paper. What interested Blackall so much was that although he wrote with a quill pen, he also stopped for a few moments from time to time and made marks on the paper scraps with another object that made a lighter mark and seemed to require no ink at all.

"If I may make so bold as to ask, sir, what is that writing tool you have there?" he asked.

"Ah, my man, this is a most useful instrument, especially for making notes in circumstances where it is not feasible to use a pen and ink. It is, in fact, a stick of graphite, encased in wood. They're called pencils and are becoming very popular in Reading now. I am an Enumerator and what I am actually doing is entering details on these sheets for the new Census Return. I will be asking you for the details about you and your family as soon as I have finished tidying up what I have found out this morning."

Blackall removed his cap and scratched his head. "I recall this was done before, sir, it would be about ten years ago now, when I was a woodcutter. I remember that the En..., whatever you said you was, came here and told my wife I had to be present in the morning to answer his questions. It was foolish for me to have to stay at home and wait until he came. I lost a half-day's wage over that. All he wanted to know was my name and age and those of my wife and children. I believe he also wanted to know what work I did and whether we were all born in Oxfordshire. She could have told him all that, she's not stupid!"

"Ah well," explained the Enumerator. "It was just something of a trial, an experiment, you see. The government wanted to see whether it would be worth the effort and the cost."

"And was it? We didn't hear no more about it."

"Yes, it was. In fact, it was very revealing. They found out how many people lived in Britain, how many of them live in the country and how many in the town and how many in each village or town. Moreover, they were able to list what their occupations were and whether they had been born in the county in which they lived."

"Why, bless my soul, sir, why on earth would they want to know all that?"

"Well, this was the first time that all the people residing in Great Britain and Ireland had been counted. It was useful to find out that there were nearly twenty-seven million, of which two million lived in London. There's probably more now and that's what we are after finding out."

John Blackall put his hand to his back and tried to straighten it. It was obvious that he was suffering some pain but he seemed hardly to notice it.

"This time it will be more detailed," continued the Enumerator, "I shall be asking more questions. I shall want to know not only your names and those of your family, your relationship to each other and whether you were all present here last Saturday 30th March. Also your ages and occupations and not only whether you were born in Oxfordshire, but exactly into which Parish you were born." With this he took another swig of beer and took up his quill again.

"Lord bless you, sir. That last bit will take a bit of thinking about. I gets a bit flummoxed about dates an' that. I'd best fetch my wife, she's better at that sort of thing than I am."

Smith returned to his work and had nearly finished listing his morning's annotations when Mary Blackall came in. She was another small character, thin and bony, her body work-worn, her greying frizzy hair tightly fixed into place with pins at the back and her blue dress much faded. The basket of laundry she carried seemed almost too heavy for her. She set it down on one of the tables.

"My 'usband says as 'ow you want me to tell you about our family, sir." she said in a tired voice.

Smith looked kindlily at the woman, who appeared to be rather afraid of him. "I am helping to complete the new Census Return, madam," he explained. "I shall need your help in setting down details of your family." At being called 'madam' she brightened a little and seem reassured.

"I'll do the best I can, sir," she responded. "What was it you wanted to know?"

"Well, let's start with the first question. Were all your family here in this house last Saturday night?"

"Yes, sir, we was all 'ere."

"Good, that makes it easier already. Now, let's start with your husband. What is his name, how old is he and what is his occupation?"

"Oh, dear, sir. One thing at a time, if you please." said the woman, who seemed to be getting agitated. "His name is John Blackall. I don't know 'ow you spells it but I once heard the Vicar say that there i'n't no 'h' in it."

Smith made notes again. "And how old is he?" he went on, patiently.

" 'e's 63, sir."

"And his occupation - what sort of work does he do?"

"Like you see, sir. 'e used to be a woodcutter, but 'is cousin set 'im up in this Beer 'ouse, so now 'e's called a Beer 'ouse Keeper."

With this statement her voice strengthened a little and there was a note of pride in it.

Smith smiled. "And you, madam, what about yourself. What is your full name?"

"I'm Mary Blackall, sir." Remembering what he asked about her husband, she went on without being bidden: "I'm 56, sir, a fair bit younger than my 'usband, but I wern't born 'ere. I were born in Bix, it's a village about three miles up the road, near Nettlebed."

"And you have children, I take it?"

"Yes, sir. They're all out at the moment, but I can tell you about 'em. They were all born 'ere in this house. There's Jemima, she's 23 and does 'ousework over at Checkendon. Then there's John," she slowed down a little to think as she continued: " 'e's 21 now and a woodcutter, like what 'is father used to be. Shadrach's two years younger than John, 'e's a woodman, too. 'e must be 19, I suppose. It's a job to keep a tag of their ages, they do all grow so fast!" She paused again for thought. "Then there's Elizabeth, our youngest, she's 17. She 'elps old Mrs Jarratt and her daughter up at the school. She's a Monitor there! [Senior pupil, given duties of keeping order]" Again, she sounded proud, if a little out of breath as she finished the list. Smith just wrote Scholar against the name of Elizabeth, because he was not sure that Monitor was a real occupation.

About an hour later, having consumed the beer, fresh home-made bread and slightly stale cheese that the woman had brought to him, Smith folded his papers into his leather satchel. He then slung it over his shoulder and went out into the spring afternoon. As soon as the woman espied him, she came over. "Be you goin' now, sir?" she enquired.

"Yes, I have more houses to visit this afternoon but I must get back to Reading before the sun goes down. I shall be back in the village tomorrow and for most of this week, so I shall probably come here again."

Thanking him for the money that he placed in her hand, Mrs Blackall smiled. Smith felt it was a rare thing for her to do. "It would be good of you, sir, to give us your custom. We don't get many strangers in these parts."

He returned her smile, unhitched his horse that he had tethered to the side of the barn, well away from the vegetable patch, at a point where it could have a good nibble of fresh green grass. He then led it through the gate again before mounting. He rode off along the bottom of the hill, beside the little stream, to where the road turned up to Highmore.

******

Stoke Row, like its neighbours, Highmore and Nettlebed, lies on the Chiltern escarpment, six miles west of Henley. It is set on a ridge, an outcrop of clays and sands of what geologists call the Reading Beds, all laid over clay with flints, interspersed with chalk, and covered with woodlands.

As we have already seen, the Beaker Folk were here for some time around 1000 BC and Roman pottery shards, dating from the third century, can still be found today in Highmore woods. Pottery making is known to have existed in Nettlebed, alongside a well-established tile and brick-making industry, from at least the later Middle Ages. For example, 35,000 tiles were supplied for the building works at Wallingford Castle in 1365. In the 15th century, Flemish brickmakers working at Crocker End, near Nettlebed, supplied '200,000 brykes to Thomas de Stonor for additions to Stonor House' and wills made in the sixteenth, seventeenth and eighteenth centuries show the continuance of kiln men, tilers, brickmakers and bricklayers all over the area.

According to the Parish Registers and the Reade manuscripts, the Swain family came to Stoke Row from Checkendon as early as 1612, probably attracted by the brick and lime kilns already in the vicinity and brickmaking may well have been continued by their descendants, as records show they were still carrying out these trades in the eighteenth century.

Another name associated with the brick and pottery industry in Stoke Row was Smith. James Smith, who died in 1791 was always known as 'Potter Smith' and was succeeded by his son, William, who died in 1834.

The Wichelows were also registered as potters and brickmakers from 1839 and George Hope, a farmer and brickmaker, who was born in Checkendon in 1817, expanded his business considerably in the mid-nineteenth century. Much of this increase in production can be traced to the removal of the tile tax in 1833 and the brick tax in 1850.

Clay pits can still be found in Nettlebed, Crocker End, Highmore, Stoke Row and Checkendon, although many of them have been filled in and even built over.

******

Martha Wichelow was a big, beefy woman, whose sharp eyes missed nothing. Her stentorian voice could be heard all over the brickyard, shouting orders that everyone could hear, despite the din that arose from the *pug mills* [horse-operated machines in which the clay was mixed with water to the correct consistency], the never-ending lines of wheeled barrows and the banging of moulds as they were broken open. The roar of the furnace in the kiln at the far end of the yard added to the incredible level of noise. Sometimes it was so great that even Martha and certainly her employees, were forced to use a sign language that they had developed over the years.

Martha's husband, William, farmer and *master brickmaker*, [one who employed others] who was born at Crowmarsh in 1793, had lived just long enough to have his name registered in the 1851 Census return. He died later that summer and his wife, who had been born in the parish of Newnham, Crowmarsh only a year later than William, realised all their money was tied up in the yard. Being a strong and able woman, she decided to continue to run the brickyard on her own. "After all," she was heard to remark soon after her husband's funeral, "I've worked here for most of my life, or at least since we came here, back in 1839. Not only that but my son, young William, is 30 now and he knows almost as much as I do about the trade!" Indeed, in 1852, when the representative from Gardiner's Directory came up to the brickyard, she was able to enter her name as 'Martha Wichelow. Manufacturer of Earthenware etc.'

In Stoke Row, the folk were breathing more easily by that September, now that the harvest was in at last. Suddenly the light seemed to be tawny, perhaps reflected from the stubble in the fields, perhaps from the dried grass on the Common and certainly from the hues of the woodlands all around, especially the beeches, the leaves of which were all shades of gold and orange. Even the bracken on the woodland floors was turning brown.

The nights began to turn colder too, as the sun set earlier and earlier and the stars could be seen in the evenings as people went down the garden to relieve themselves in their *thunderboxes* before going to bed. The first leaves began to fall, chiefly the chestnuts, which came out first in spring, followed by the beeches and then the oaks. The bushes were dotted with berries, especially blackberries. Housewives went out foraging with their children for these delicious fruits that went so well with the insect-damaged apples that had already started to fall, long before the good ones were ripe enough to pick and store.

A month later, in October 1852, in the brickyard, on the top of Stoke Row Hill, all was mud, mud and more mud. Heavy rains during the previous three weeks had produced puddles everywhere and made the ground dangerously slippery, but still the work had to go on.

William Wichelow, Jnr. and his wife, Mary, who was the same age as her husband, also lived in the village. 'Dainty Mary' as she was sometimes called behind her back, was a dressmaker and was careful not to soil her delicate hands with the clay from the works. This often led the coarser women in the village to speak ill of her, especially as they could not afford to have her make clothes for them. Her mother-in-law thought of her as a 'weakling' and often implied that in her conversation at the yard. The only person who was really kind to Mary was the wife of the Vicar, Mrs Arrowsmith, for whom the seamstress made not only clothes but also came in once a week to repair the linen.

Although St John's Church, Stoke Row had been constructed in 1846, Revd James Arrowsmith, born in Astley, Lancashire, had only taken up 'the living' in 1850. His position was known in ecclesiastical circles as a Perpetual Curate. Since that time he and his wife had been living at Scots Farm House and only just moved into the new Vicarage. This had been constructed with bricks made in the Stoke Row brickyard. Perhaps it was the fact that Mrs Arrowsmith was herself a stranger to the village that made her sympathetic to her poor dressmaker and often she listened as Mary explained, through her tears, how her husband had again bullied and beaten her the previous evening, after their five young children had gone up to bed. At Mrs Arrowsmith's request, she rolled up her sleeves to show her the bruises on her arms.

Not for nothing was he known in the yard as 'Billy the Bully', though no one ever dared to say it to his face. William Wichelow had inherited his mother's strength of arm and he used it often against his employees, and his tongue too. He would lash out at a worker for the least mistake and most of the men went in fear of him all the time.

Most of the bricks were made in the spring, autumn and winter, the summer months being set aside for field work, especially harvesting. There were twelve men working on the brickmaking while two men laboured in the kiln. Of the twelve, Thomas Clayton, who was about 50 years of age and James Beterage, who was some four years older, were both widowers and had much in common. Clayton and Beterage both lived in Stoke Row and drank together in the evenings at the Traveller's Friend (later to become the Cherry Tree), a pub in the centre of the village run by 43 year old Joel Pembroke and his much younger wife, Martha, who also ran a small grocery shop at the side of the pub.

It was one dark evening in the late autumn when the landlord noticed that Clayton and Beterage had their heads together more closely than usual. They were speaking in low tones and seemed to be hatching some kind of plot. Clayton's voice was the loudest: "I reckon Billy the Bully's gettin' worse, 'specially with this recent rain and the yard gettin' so muddy. I thought 'twas a shame to see 'im push young Willie Perrin' about this mornin', just because 'e didn't get back quick enough from runnin' up to William Thompson's man at Nettlebed. Why the lad's not much more than thirteen, I'll bet, and 'im so thin, you'd think 'e'd not be able to run a mile, let 'lone three. Not only that, but cussin' 'im too, and callin' 'im a bastard. It's not 'is fault 'e was born out o' wedlock. At least Martha's good enough to keep 'im under her roof!"

Beterage seemed to agree with him, but as Joel Pembroke leaned over, pretending to wipe a nearby table, he could only hear parts of the labourer's whispered reply: "That's as maybe, but she and 'er daughter, Emma, they treat 'im more like a slave than a servant, I say. Billy's the real rotter. One of these days 'e'll get 'is come-uppance, mark my words!"

"I'll have a word with one or two of the others, though we'd best be careful or we'll lose our jobs. I hear that even up at Nettlebed they're layin' men off, now it's winter!"

As Clayton cocked an ear in order to hear a little better, Beterage raised his voice just a trifle. "Just make sure that old 'arridan Martha Wichelow don't 'ear about our plan. God knows there's no love lost between 'er and that son of 'ers, but blood's thicker 'n water, they say!"

The landlord finished wiping the table and shrugged his shoulders, thinking to himself as he did so: "Whatever they get up to and if Billy the Bully should suffer a bit, well, serves 'im right!"

The next day was another wet one. In fact, it was even colder, due to a bitter east wind that had sprung up overnight. The noise in the brickyard started up as soon as it was daylight and by 7.30 a.m. the work of digging out the clay and feeding it into the pug mills had already started. From these small mills came ribbons of clay that were fed on to four tables on which they were cut with wires, six or eight at a time. It was from this process that these bricks became known as 'wire cuts'. By Act of Parliament in 1725 these now had to be exactly nine inches long, four and a half inches wide and two and a half inches high.

Once made, the bricks were then taken from the tables and moved by barrow to the drying stand. The wheels of these vehicles ran along a metal track, to keep them in position. However, sometimes a barrow would develop a particular idiosyncrasy and Thomas Clayton knew one in particular that had a 'wonky wheel' and had to be manipulated carefully if it was not to veer and tip the operator sideways.

Clayton and Beterage were doing this sort of work that morning, and as Clayton pushed this barrow along, he came to the point where it had to be taken over a plank that was ten inches wide and crossed one of the many large holes out of which clay had been dug back in the summer. This one was about twenty feet across and fifteen feet deep and, due to the recent rains, was half-full of water. He was part way across when he gave a loud cry: "Oh, my arm, I can't move it! Mr Wichelow, sir, I can't move my arm, it's seized up!!"

Billy the Bully came over at once, swearing vociferously: "You silly bugger, you shouldn't have started on to the plank if you knew your arm wasn't up to it!"

"It was alright when I started out, sir. If I leave it here and turn round carefully, I should be able to get back alright."

Billy darted forward at once. "We've got to keep the bricks movin'. Come you back here and let me do it. I can move a barrow faster than you any day, you bloody stupid old man. You're just a good-for-nothing these days!" With this he grabbed Clayton's arm as he extended it for help.

"Do be careful as you go, sir." Clayton warned. " 'er 'as a mind of 'er own, that one."

"Don't try to tell me my job, you bloody oaf! I've been working in this yard since I was a lad and I know more about barrows than you'll ever do!" By this time he was already on the narrow plank and had seized a hold of the barrow handles. At first, because of the heavy rainfall, he went slowly and carefully but after doing so for the length of about five feet he became irritated by the constant wet weather and the muddy, slippery surface. Then, suddenly, the barrow's wheel veered to the right and, despite trying to balance himself, Billy fell into the pit. At once he started to drown in the deep, muddy, ice-cold water.

"Hold on, sir!" Beterege shouted, as he brought up a couple of ladders and a rope which he and his mate had secreted nearby. Clayton tried to help, too, but he was supposed to have a disabled arm, so it was lucky that the commotion raised the alarm amongst the other men and soon they all came running. Very quickly they dropped the rope to the near drowning man and set the ladder against the side. The nimblest of them all, young Joseph Looker, soon scrambled down the ladder and was helping his master out of the water. Benjamin Bishop came up very soon with a large old blanket, which he fetched from Martha's house, at the edge of the yard. Although they managed not to show it, they were all pleased to have such a diversion and most of them felt that Billy the Bully had had his 'come-uppance' at last.

Wichelow was escorted back to his own house, shivering and chilled through. Fortunately, his wife, Mary, had a kettle warm on the hob and was soon able to make him a hot drink and enough water for him to wash the worst of the mud off himself. It was one of the few times that she had ever seen her husband at a disadvantage and the reversed situation made her unexpectedly sympathetic to him, for he was still basically the man she had loved and married some twelve years before. Moreover, the fact that he could still be seen to make mistakes gave the dressmaker renewed confidence in herself.

Whether it was his wife's newly-found assuredness and consequent renewed kindness, or his shame at being found at fault in front of his men, no-one knew, but for a few months at least after that Billy seemed to be less of a braggart and bully than he had been for a very long time.

******

The late 1850s was a time of great change in both Stoke Row and Highmore, largely led by the Church and the gentry.

Following the erection of St John the Evangelist in Stoke Row in 1846, a Church of England School was founded in 1853 'for the labouring, manufacturing or other poorer classes, with residence for a school master or mistress to be administered under the Ipsden Union of Schools.'

A Dame School had existed before this time on Witheridge Hill for the children of Highmore. It was conducted in a cottage next to the Rising Sun Inn, under the supervision of a Mrs Jarratt with the assistance of her daughter. Gardiner's Directory in 1852 stated: 'The school on Witheridge Hill receives a subscription from Trinity College, Oxford.' Here children received a simple education for 3d a week.

About the same time, the church of St Paul was erected in Highmore. The Post Office Directory of 1864 described it succinctly: '...it is in Early English style, and consists of a nave and a chancel. It was erected, together with the parsonage, solely at the expense of Revd Joseph Smith, BD. It was opened for Divine service in 1859. Mr Joseph Morris of Reading was the architect and Mr Robert Owthwaite, of Henley-on-Thames, the builder.'

******

In the late morning, one sunny day in May 1857, a tall elegant gentleman with dark hair and a curled moustache, dressed in country garb, alighted from his horse outside the Cherry Tree Inn at Stoke Row. He wore a hard felt brown 'bowler' hat and a lovat-green tweed jacket with patch pockets. His brown corduroy 'knickerbockers' were gathered into a band at the knee. He wore leather gaiters and short boots that were well-polished.

Martha Pembroke, who had been the beer retailer there since 1851, when Joel Pembroke had died, knew a well-to-do customer when she saw one. She promptly came out and asked whether the gentleman would like to partake of some refreshment. "Yes, my good woman," he said. "I will have a glass of your best beer, but afterwards I have a request to make of you."

The publican was a little surprised but she nodded her assent and promptly went inside. She was followed by the man, whose name was Henry Hazelwood. As he did so, he threw the rein to a young lad who was working out at the front.

Mr Hazelwood explained to the landlady his reason for coming to Stoke Row as he quickly quaffed his beer, for the day was warm and he was anxious to be getting on with his self-appointed task. She went out to the back, calling all her staff while he emerged from the front door, gave his horse a pat and motioned to the lad to help him to unpack the panniers with which the animal was well-laden. One of the objects strapped to the beast was made of light wood, consisting of a small table on three long legs. On top of this he set his camera, one that he had purchased only about two weeks beforehand. He was a professional photographer, who had his own studio in Reading, where he had been producing small *cartes de visite,* that had become so popular since royalty had started to patronise photographers. However, most of these were produced indoors, where large areas of window were a common feature, in order to provide the amount of light needed.

A number of gentleman photographers, like the artists of their time, were becoming tired of the restrictions of their studios and were anxious to experiment with taking photographs out of doors. The main difficulty, he felt, would be that of making his subject keep perfectly still for two minutes. Sitters found it difficult enough to sit motionless, moving not one muscle and blinking as little as possible, but it seemed they were quite unable to do so while maintaining a charming and natural smile and this is why early photographs made their subjects appear very formal, stiff and unsmiling.

Nevertheless, Mr Hazelwood was determined to try and take a photograph that would appear less formal. Having set up his camera that used the latest patent-free wet-collodion process, he started to arrange his subjects in suitable poses. The least important, the boots boy, the scullery maid and the gardener, he placed against the wooden picket fence that had once defined the gardens of the three cottages that had been recently converted into this public house. As Mrs Pembroke proudly explained to Mr Hazelwood: "This pub was once just a single cottage, and called 'The Traveller's Friend'. Now Brakspears have bought all three and they're planning to put on an extension next year. We shall be able to offer more bedrooms and that's why we're able to call ourselves an 'inn'."

Mr Hazelwood continued to arrange his subjects. Mary, the assistant cook, still wearing her white apron, was made to lean against a tree. Jemima, the cook, had put on a short black shawl and a black scarf over her hair. She was propped up against another and held the hand of her eight-year old daughter, Priscilla, who was a difficult child and did not wish to stand still. She was shy and would keep hanging her head, no matter how often Mr Hazelwood tried to persuade her to do otherwise.

The publican herself, a slim woman of some thirty-five years, was asked to put her hand on the white gate-post in the foreground. She also held the hand of her daughter; a plump little girl of about seven years of age, named Lily. She and Priscilla often played together.

Martha Pembroke had no time to change her clothes, nor would Mr Hazelwood have wanted her to, indeed he insisted that she even keep on the apron that she had donned earlier that day in order to protect her frock which had bands of black velvet across the front and on the sleeves.

The lad who had helped him by holding the horse was called Ned and he was set even further forward in the arrangement, being required to lean against the old white wooden gate that had long since ceased to give service. Ned was clad in ill-fitting grey flannel trousers and a navy jacket. On his head was a 'Nelson' cap and around his neck he wore a somewhat dirty cream stock, badly tied.

Finally, they were all in satisfactory positions and Mr Hazelwood thanked them for their patience before he squeezed the little rubber bulb at the side of the camera and caught the image for posterity. When he returned to Reading, he developed the picture, along with all the others he had taken that day and wrote across the bottom of it: *The Cherry Tree Inn, Stoke Row.*

* * * * * *

Many of the names in this section were taken from the 1851 Census Returns and descriptions of the brickworks came from the Memoirs of the late Josh Main.

The photograph is the oldest amongst the author's collection of over two thousand, each relating only to Stoke Row or Highmoor. This is believed to have been taken in 1857, because marks on the bricks of the extension, not visible in the picture, showed that it was built in 1858 and outdoor photographs were rarely taken before 1855. Martha Pembroke, who was the Beer Retailer at the time, may have been the woman in the centre of the picture, but the photographer and the other people in the picture, which may be seen on page 154 of Dipping into the Wells, are unknown.

The Old Place

Chapter 15. The Well Digger, the Schoolmistress and the Shooting: 1861 - 1899

Having planned and carried out many wonderful projects, especially the Great Exhibition of 1851, Prince Albert died ten years later, plunging not only Queen Victoria but also the rest of the country into deep mourning. Within a year, however, the country, if not the queen, came back to the reality of life without this great motivator.

Times were certainly changing in Stoke Row and Highmore. Today we have come to accept change, even to expect it, but before the mid-19th century any form of alteration to the *status quo* was regarded with suspicion.

In 1862, a National School was erected on Witheridge Hill. Sadly, unlike Stoke Row School, few details of life here prior to 1901 have come down to us.

On the other hand, the *School Log Books* for Stoke Row are now in the Oxfordshire Archives and date back to 1865. They make fascinating reading.

However, it was the sinking of the wells in both Stoke Row and Highmore, in 1864 and 1865 respectively, following a severe drought in 1864 that brought the greatest benefit to the villages. It was a curious fact that, although Britain was at the head of a great Empire 'on which the sun never set' and she was constructing railways, bridges and buildings all over the world, people in remote rural districts like the Chiltern Hills were still desperately short of water.

If they did not have wells or *cisterns* [large underground brick storage tanks], they collected very unhealthy water from old clay pits.

******

The children making their way through the village to the new school at Stoke Row on Tuesday 10th March 1863 were mystified as to what was happening on the common land almost opposite their destination. An old cart, somewhat the worse for wear and drawn by a sturdy cob, was parked there. The horse seemed grateful for a chance to feed on the new green grass. It was a fine, spring day and the birds were singing in the few stunted trees that grew on the common, most of them still too slender to have been cut for firewood during the previous winter.

They gave a shout of greeting to two of the men, who they recognised at once. 'Grandpa' Grace and a younger man, Jimmy Wells each had picks and spades and seemed to be about to start some form of work. They were dressed in their usual knee-length coarse linen smocks and large straw hats, with red kerchiefs tied round their necks, but they were obviously being supervised by a man dressed more smartly and who they had never seen before. They stared at him as they slowly made their way into the schoolyard. "He's not from the village, he's from Henley or Wallingford," stated Robin Goodenough with the air of one who knows everything.

"What's it say on the cart, then? " asked his youngest sister, Jessie. "You can read, go on, tell us then!"

"It says," pronounced Robin slowly, " John Wile-der, then... I don't know the next word, but the last one's Wallingford. I know that one, even though it is long. I've seen it often when me an' Dad goes down there."

Finally, at the school gate, they stopped completely to stare at the Wallingford man, for a stranger was rarely seen in those parts. For one thing he was dressed differently from their fathers and uncles who, for the most part, wore simple clothes. One or perhaps two garments were all they owned.

This man also seemed to be taller and straighter. Another fact was that, unlike the men they all saw every day who wore beards and side whiskers, this man was clean-shaven, except for a small curled moustache. He sported a hard, brown felt bowler hat and a double-breasted waistcoat under his tweed jacket with patch pockets. His knickerbockers were gathered into a band at the knee and his long socks were tucked neatly into a pair of short brown leather boots.

It was the trousers which particularly fascinated the boys in the group of about a dozen children who by now had gathered to watch the men who seemed to be staking out a patch of land some distance from the road. "I've never seen trousers like those!" commented one lad, who was used to seeing his father in thick, coarse grey felt ones with a band tied beneath the knee to stop rats from running up his legs when they were working in the fields.

The school bell rang a second time and the irate schoolmistress shouted to them to "Hurry up, you children. You should have been in here ages since!" The group turned away reluctantly and made their way into the school building.

As they began to dig, the men could hear through a slightly opened window the drone of children reciting their tables: "Twice times one is two, twice times two is four, twice times three is six . . ." and so on, until the sound of men's hammers knocking in the stakes drowned out all other noise. Meantime, the stranger, Mr Wilder's foreman, Jeb Parsons, was measuring and making notes with a stub of a pencil in a small book.

Older folk passing by knew what was happening, even if the children didn't. Rumours had been going around the village for some time that Squire Reade's son, had arranged for a well to be dug. "They say his son, you know, the one what's been out in India, he's gettin' it all done," Jimmy Wells' 27 year old wife, Sarah, confided to her neighbour, Emma Messenger. "At least, it's givin' my Jimmy a job."

"He's got the right name for it, all right! Wells, that's a good one for a man what's digging one." laughed Emma.

"Yes, the Vicar said his people probably used to look after wells years ago. He's being helped by Grandpa Grace, though I dare say it'll be Jimmy that goes down the hole. I'm scared! I hope he doesn't have an accident. It don't sound very safe to me!" Sarah confessed.

"Oh, don't you worry." Emma consoled her friend. "He'll be alright!" Fortunately he was, although the work was arduous and dangerous. Men were often killed in the process, usually as a result of the sides caving in.

Every night, Jimmy Wells came home and told his new young wife about the work. "Don't you worry, love!" he said cheerily, when he returned from a day's digging. He was just thirty years of age, strong and confident. He and Sarah had only been married a little over a year and both of them were hoping for a child. "One of these days, our children will be glad of this well, when we've finished it. They won't have to drink dirty water no more!"

"How long's it goin' to take?" asked Sarah.

"I dunno, about a year, Wilder's man says. Seems that's what it usually takes. This one will be hard though, 'cos there's so many flints in the ground!"

"What's to stop the earth coming down in on you, then?" his wife continued to worry.

"Ah, well, we gets over that by puttin' specially curved bricks all around the sides of the hole and then we puts stakes   under them to stop them droppin' down further. When they're dry we'll pull the stakes out, dig further down and then put more bricks on top, so they all slip down, section by section. That way we'll have a long brick wall all the way down the hole. It won't be hard, you'll see!" With that he tucked into his supper, having worked up a voracious appetite from the day's work.

After the first day's work he came home quite excited and told Sarah: "When I was diggin' today, I found a little tiny silver coin. Squire Reade was there and he took it at once; he said it looks Roman. He says he'll take it up to Oxford to find out more about it. Roman, eh? Grandpa Grace and I wonder how it got there. Mr Reade says it may have belonged to a Roman soldier. I never knew there was any up here."

In fact, Jimmy Wells had to lay bricks to a depth of thirty feet, each time filling buckets with gravel and subsoil and sending them up to Grandpa Grace. After each period of digging he had to adjust the ladder, taking the greatest care because the hole in which he was working was only about four feet in diameter.

Several weeks later, he came home to Sarah looking very tired and somewhat frustrated. "Jeb Parsons reckons we've dug about fifty feet now but already the water's seeping in. We had to stop late this afternoon. It's all chalk now and some of it's very wet."

Nevertheless, the work had to go on. Fortunately, summer was coming and Jimmy hoped for better light down his dark hole.

"It's a good job he don't mind working in tight spaces." Sarah confided to Emma one day. "He says he's used to it, but I keep worrying about what'll happen if they strike sand. Jimmy says it'll be alright and that he'll be able to shore up the walls, but I do fret so, especially now they're getting so deep."

In fact Jimmy did encounter sand, at about 130 feet deep and again about another ten feet deeper down. These bands of gravely material had to be shored up with planks. It was a blessing that Jimmy Wells did not seem to suffer from claustrophobia. The bravery of the men who did this very difficult job cannot be under-estimated. It was very much a question of teamwork, Jimmy relying wholly on the trustworthy Grandpa Grace who, high above his head, never failed him.

"The air down there's dreadful." Jimmy told Sarah one Saturday evening. I'm glad tomorrow's Sunday so I can get my chest filled with clean air for a while." But he still had to start again on the Monday.

The two men, under the supervision of Jeb Parsons, with occasional visits from Mr Reade and Mr R J Wilder, continued with the work through the summer and into the autumn. However, for a few months in the hard part of the winter, by which time Jimmy had reached a depth of nearly 250 feet, they were allowed to stop. The hands and feet of both the men were badly chapped by the awful damp and cold conditions under which they had to work.

In the spring of 1864, the work was taken up again. Edward Anderdon Reade rode over one day in April to meet Mr R J Wilder on site and to explain to him his idea to open the well on 24th May 1864, the birthday of Queen Victoria. Mr Wilder, in his turn, urged Jeb Parsons and the Stoke Row men to work harder. This was increasingly difficult because the well was by now so deep, nearly 360 feet, but still the water level had not been reached.

Nevertheless, a few days later, the great cry went up as Jimmy Wells signalled that he had reached the water table. To prove this he filled a small bottle that he sent up in the bucket of chalk and shells, proving to Edward Anderdon Reade that Stoke Row, like the Chiltern Hills and indeed, all of Britain, had once been under the sea.

Jeb Parsons rode down to Wallingford at once to summon Mr Wilder who then showed him the latest stage of the work on the beautiful Indian superstructure that Mr Reade had designed, based on a cupola which he had remembered existed in the Maharajah's palace. "Tell Mr Reade it's almost ready to take up to Stoke Row," he instructed. "Tell him I'll ride up directly, as soon as I've finished in the foundry."

All this time, few people outside of the Reade family and Wilder's yard knew of Edward Anderdon Reade's plan to erect a dome over the hole which had been dug for the well, nor of the beneficence of an Indian *Maharajah* [Great Ruler]. In fact the story did not come out fully until several years later.

Edward Anderson Reade, fifth son of the Squire of Ipsden, spent almost 35 years with the East India Company and worked closely with the Maharajah of Benares on various projects and the solving of many problems. As far back as 1850, prior to the Indian Mutiny of 1857, the two men were discussing the sinking of wells in Benares. This arose from Mr Reade's wise and kind act in purchasing a piece of disputed land from two brothers and on it sinking a well for the use of travellers in that arid countryside.

Mr Reade explained it all in the Oxford Times in 1872, when a delightful picture of the Well was drawn to accompany the article. He wrote: 'The scenery (in that part of Benares) is not unlike that of the Chiltern Hills; the inconveniences, owing to deficiency of water supply were the same. The measures the Maharajah was adopting for the relief of his people were the subject of much of our conversation, in the course of which it would seem I must have mentioned the results of boyish knowledge in the upland of my own district, such as the people being dependent for water retained in dirty ponds and deserted clay-pits. In dry seasons the water used in cooking in one cottage was passed on to do like office in others, urchins being cruelly thumped for furtive quenchings of thirst and washing days being indefinitely postponed.'

The Well was indeed, formally opened on the birthday of Queen Victoria, Monday, 24th May 1864. It had cost £353. 13s 7d. The price of the machinery for lifting the water and the gold elephant, which was added later, amounted to £39. 10s 0d. A small octagonal cottage was also erected for the Well Warden to live in and cost £74.14s 6d.

A tiny remuneration was assured this guardian by the provision of a cherry orchard, some four acres in extent. Cherries grown here through the following years were picked and sold to the Reading markets.

The village celebrated the reaching of the water table and the erection of the cupola over the Well in grand style. Sports were arranged and a grand feast prepared, money having been provided for the purpose by the munificence of the Maharajah. In the evening fireworks were let off in the adjoining pleasure ground, much to the surprise and joy of everyone, especially the children.

The first Warden, a Mrs Whittick, had to admit people by unlocking the gate, watch over their bringing up the water and to 'guard against mischief and abuse'. It was also her task to ensure the machinery was maintained in good order and to report any malfunction. The water was raised in one of two nine-gallon, counter-balancing metal containers with narrow tops, to minimise spillage. From there it was ladled out into small wooden buckets with metal bands and carried home on wooden yokes across the shoulders. When in use the depth of the water was generally 15 to 25 ft and a regular daily yield of 600 to 700 gallons of water was recorded.

Sarah Wells was one of the first to benefit from the new water supply and was extremely proud of her husband's achievement in digging down so deep. "To tell the truth," she confessed to her friend Emma, "I'm so glad that it's all over at last. I really was worried that Jimmy would get trapped down there and that the earth would all collapse in on top of him. Still, now he's safe, I'll admit that the Well is a wonderful thing and the water is so pure and good to drink."

Not everyone agreed with her, though. It took some time for the local rustics to accustom themselves to the 'new water from far underground'. Most of all, it was the sight of the brightly painted cupola, which stood some twenty-three feet high and dominated the skyline of the village, which was the hardest to get used to. There were few trees in the vicinity and the sight of something so foreign and painted in such bright colours, dark red, blue and gold, standing up on the horizon was almost too much for the older folk.

"It don't seem natural." said some, but others realised the expensive machinery needed a roof to protect it and recalled Mr Reade's words about sending a picture to the Maharajah, taken with the newfangled device called a camera, because he couldn't just send a drawing of a hole in the ground to show the Indian ruler how his money had been spent!

Gradually the villagers got used to the sight of the strange edifice and came to realise the benefits of drinking pure water. Moreover, as time went by, more and more visitors made their way from Reading to see this wonderful device and to taste the beautiful clear liquid.

Soon other benefactors followed suit, as an excerpt from the Reading Mercury in October 1864 goes to show. [Curiously enough, the writer of the following newspaper articles made a mistake at the time in his spelling of the name of the village. He obviously did not realise that the way in which he spelled it was not the one used locally at that time].

The Sinking of the Highmoor Well

An unusually interesting ceremony took place at Highmoor, on Monday last. The great drought of last summer having forcibly shown what an inestimable boon a constant supply of water would be to the inhabitants of that high range of country; the Rev Horace Munro, the Incumbent of the parish, generously determined to sink a well at his own expense, and present it for the use of his people for ever.

This good work was begun on Monday. There was a short and appropriate service in the Church at 11 o'clock, after which the congregation, headed by the village choir, walked in procession to the site chosen for the well. There the Old Hundredth Psalm was joyously and heartily sung by the assembled parishioners. Their pastor then begged God's blessing on the undertaking, praying that the well might soon afford a bountiful supply of water for them, their children and their cattle, and that they might all have grace to see the same with thanksgiving for the glory of God's name, through Jesus Christ our Lord.

The day was lovely and the whole scene most interesting. The association of a religious service with the act of well

290

digging appears to be of very ancient origin. The 'Song of the Well' recorded in *Numbers XXI*, is a case in point, and a remnant of the custom is still retained in some of our English villages, for instance at Tissington in Derbyshire, where there is an unusual ceremony called the 'Well Dressing'. It was by a fitting arrangement therefore that on this occasion, prayer should be solemnly offered up to Almighty God, the Giver of all good gifts.

At the conclusion of the ceremony, it was announced that Miss Elwes, of Highmoor Hall, had kindly made a handsome donation, for the purpose of providing a suitable covering for the well.

Less written material has survived about the well at Highmore, but the Reading Mercury again sent a reporter to record the opening ceremony. It was, by this account, a very grand affair:

The Opening of the Highmoor Well

About four months ago we recorded the commencement of a good work of Highmoor, the sinking of a parish well under the auspices and at the expense of the Incumbent, the Revd H Munro. On Thursday last, the work having been brought to a successful conclusion, the well was formally opened with one of the most joyous meetings remembered in this part of the country.

At half-past six in the evening, there was a special service in the Church, when suitable psalms and hymns were loudly sung by the village choir, assisted by the neighbouring choir from Kidmore End, the whole body of the singing being led by the choirmaster, Mr W H Strickland.

A most moving and telling sermon was preached by the Bishop Coadjuter of Edinburgh, on the many 'well lessons' to be found throughout the Bible, and especially on the 'well blessing' of our blessed Lord himself.

At the conclusion of this address, the whole of the congregation, together with the choir, the clergy and the Bishop, walked in procession accompanied by a hundred torch-bearers, to the well-house. The scene of this event was picturesque in the extreme. The Bishop stood on the well-house steps, overhead was the elegant roof and in front was a dense crowd of parishioners, with uncovered heads, lifting up their thankful voices with one accord in the well-known strain of the 100th Psalm. One or two short collects followed, and the whole concluded with the Apostolic blessing.

Three hearty cheers were then given by the people for their Pastor and benefactor, and, after a brilliant display of rockets, accompanied by a large party, adjourned to the Schoolroom, where a most bountiful repast was provided, and a most happy evening spent. Among those who partook of Mr and Mrs Munro's hospitality on the occasion were the Bishop Coadjutor of Edinburgh, Charles Lane, Esq., and party, the Rev North Plader, the Rev J W and Mrs Cobb, the Rev and Mrs Arrowsmith (of Stoke-row), &c.

The well-house is a very handsome hexagonal building. The works have been executed by Messrs Godwin of Stoke-row, and Messrs Wilder of Wallingford; the stained-glass window being by Messrs Powell, and the brasswork by Messrs Hart. Such a day was never known at Highmoor, and as long as the water springs up from the 'great depths' of that parish well, so long will the remembrance of this happy dedication feast be kept in remembrance.

Although the Highmore well was not quite so deep, its pretty little octagonal well-house, with its tiled roof, could be said to be more in keeping with its surroundings. This time it was not the generosity of a foreign potentate which supplied the good pure water and a pretty little well-house to protect the person drawing it, but that of a wealthy clergyman and a lady of the manor.

The well beside the church at Highmore was not as deep as the one at Stoke Row, just 284 feet, but that, too, was a remarkable feat of engineering. In fact, it was said at the time that if a piece of string the same length as the depth of the well were attached to the well machinery and extended along the church wall, it would reach to the middle of the Village Green. It continued unfailingly to supply clear pure water to the villagers of Highmore, including the hamlets of Witheridge Hill and Satwell, for a further three-quarters of a century.

******

In the early nineteenth century there were two small daily schools held in the parish of Ipsden, which included Stoke Row. One was commenced in 1831 for thirty-three females and was supported by Mr John Reade, Squire of Ipsden while the other for eleven males was financed by private contributions.

However, it was not until the church of St John the Evangelist was built in Stoke Row in 1846 that a Church of England School was founded close by, seven years later, 'for the labouring, manufacturing or poorer classes in Stoke Row, with residence for school master or mistress.'

In the mid-nineteenth century, children were only taught Reading, Writing [taking down dictation], Arithmetic [chiefly multiplication tables, learned by rote] and Needlework. A great deal of time was devoted to Religious subjects, such as Scripture, Hymns, Prayers and Catechism [learning set answers to questions on the Bible].

In the beginning, very little attention was paid to attendance figures, only as and when they were particularly low or high. The reason for them was then given, sometimes sickness or holidays, but usually the prevailing weather conditions, which were extreme at times. School continued up to Christmas Eve and the holiday was generally just one week but summer holidays were often long. Despite the *Agricultural Children Act* of 1873, one frequently reads in the School Log Book that 'the length of the Harvest holidays depends greatly on the weather.'

In the school's Log Book of 1865, the dimensions of the single School Room were given as being: 'Length 28ft 6 inches. Breadth: 16ft 3 inches. Height: 14 feet.' By 1867 there was 'an average attendance of 31 and an annual grant was made in the sum of £14.5s.8d.' Separate *offices* [toilets] were provided in 1870, but the Inspector noted in 1878 that they were 'roofless' and 'should at once be put into a thorough state of repair.'

When the school began, a resident master, Mr William Crews, assisted by his wife, Mary, were appointed. A year later a Miss Sarah Needle was installed to teach about thirty children. She stayed for nine years. Thereafter came a series of short-lived appointments, often supported by an Ambulatory Master. Miss Kate Stannard stayed for some five years, followed by Mrs Kate Francis who lasted for a record eleven years. There was an attendance of fifty-two by this time, which she appears to have managed alone. It is hardly surprising that the most frequent entry in the Log Book were the words 'Ordinary progress'. It makes the reader think how dull it must have been, especially for the pupils.

On 2 December, 1878, a Miss E S Carter, Certificated Mistress, began her work. Her entries occupy 63 pages of the Log Book and almost every one is covered with complaints about the children.

* * * * * *

The winter of 1879 was a particularly hard one. It began on 2nd December 1878, the day Miss Elizabeth Sarah Carter started her work as Mistress of Stoke Row School.

She had arrived the previous Saturday, 30th November. Because of the icy conditions, the carter's horse had had difficulty in getting up the hill from Henley, where she had arrived in the late afternoon on a train run by the Great Western Railway. The Henley branch line had opened in 1857 and brought many benefits to the town. The Vicar, Revd John F Mackarkness, had left a note on the door, suggesting that she call at the Vicarage early the next morning, but apart from this, there was no one there to receive her as it began to get dark.

"Will you be all right, Miss?" enquired the kindly carrier, patting his skeletal horse. "I think it's cold enough to be havin' snow soon. I'd best be gettin' back to Henley before old George here finds it too slippery to get down the hill."

Elizabeth Carter nodded but she was not pleased by the sight that greeted her as she entered the School House that was to be her future home. Removing her black silk-lined bonnet and cape, she looked around her. The furniture was plain, just a table, two wooden chairs and a small cupboard. She lit a small candle. A small, rather antiquated upholstered chair reposed in one corner of the room. "That's obviously seen better days!" she noted to herself, but it sufficed for her to sit on and remove her black high-buttoned boots. These she replaced with a pair of old felt slippers taken from the capacious carpet bag which she had insisted on carrying personally throughout the long journey.

Miss Carter was a small, slim, woman, with thin, wispy hair, combed back into a bun at the back of her head, a fashion started by Queen Victoria when she was young. Her face was that of a frustrated spinster, one who had rarely known love, brought up as she had been in the workhouse for most of her life. Her expression, in repose, was hard-lipped and grim and she wore a permanent scowl. She was obviously not one to tolerate fools gladly. However, she had always had ambition and the chief of her aims was to get out of the clutches of the Windsor Poor Law administrators and make a new life for herself. "Not only shall I do that," she promised herself, "but when I am settled, I shall bring Mother up to stay with me."

Mrs Margaret Carter had been widowed with several small children when they were very young. Because she had tuberculosis, she found herself quite destitute, unable to continue her profession, that of schoolteacher. The only thing she could do was to fall upon the mercies of the Poor Law Guardians and enter the dreaded Workhouse. Somehow, probably because of the children, she managed to survive her terrible illness, but was still too weak to return to her profession.

Fortunately for her, life in these institutions had improved somewhat in recent years and certainly since earlier in the century when Charles Dickens had brought their appalling conditions to the attention of the 'great and the good.' The replacement of the Poor Law Board by the Local Government Board in 1871, when the health and sanitation of these institutions had come to the fore, was the cause of much improvement.

Young Elizabeth worked hard in the grim little workhouse school-room where the pauper children were taught only to read and write and to do simple sums. They also learned their basic mathematical tables by rote and some of them could give answers learned by heart to questions on the Bible put to them by the Chaplain. 'Lizzie', as she was known to her family, studied harder than the others, poring over her few school books by a guttering candle in the evenings. During those hours in the day that she was allowed to see her mother, the frail woman encouraged her daughter to 'read as much as you can', but she was often teased by the other children. Nevertheless, Lizzie was determined to better herself to a point where no one would ever know the background that she came from.

When she was older she helped in the Workhouse School as a Monitor and was finally found a place as Assistant Teacher in the local National School. Later she was properly trained and finally passed her Teacher's Certificate examination. At times throughout her training she had met a pleasant young man or two, but she was not interested in being courted. "I am going to get myself a life of my own, with a home of my own." she was once heard to remark with startling firmness.

"And here I am, at last!" she announced to the rather mangy ginger cat which was already well settled in the School House. "Well, I hope you're a good mouser." she continued. "This place looks none too clean and I'll warrant there are a few mice about, this being a country district." Immediately she set about cleaning the room, even before she went upstairs, so that she could put out some of her few belongings.

Finally, when she had set out her things to her satisfaction, she climbed the narrow, steep stairs, holding her carpet bag in one hand and the candlestick in the other. The bedroom was as plain as the downstairs room and offered only a single iron bedstead, with a pillow, two sheets and a couple of grey blankets. Under the window was a washstand, with a bowl and a jug. "At least it's filled with water," she thought to herself. She had been told that there was a large brick-lined cistern in the garden. This pleased her, since she was not willing to take a post that did not offer a house with its own cistern.

Against the far wall was a large wooden wardrobe. The varnish was scuffed and one of the handles was missing. Elizabeth began to make a mental list of items that would have to be replaced or repaired. "I hope the Vicar will avail me of his garden boy in the morning to help get my box up here," she thought as she returned downstairs to try and light a fire in the tiny hearth.

In the minute kitchen she prepared a meal for herself from the few items that had obviously been left there for the purpose. Elizabeth started to feel slightly lonely and even sorry for herself, but she soon shook off her depression as the fire began to blaze and the cat fell asleep, purring on the small homemade rag rug in front of it. "At last, I have what I have always wanted," she comforted herself as she settled down to sleep later that evening. "Now I have a home and a school of my own and one day, as soon as Tom and John leave the workhouse, I'll bring Mother up here to live with me."

Before eight o'clock the next morning Revd John Mackarkness, who was still having breakfast with his wife, it being Sunday, was surprised to be told by the maid: "Miss Carter to see you, sir."

"Thank you, Mrs Wixen," the Vicar said. "Come in, Miss Carter, do. This is my wife, Anne." He was a bony man, tall, grey-haired and somewhat stooping. "I hope you were able to settle yourself in comfortably last evening." he said in a strong Scottish accent.

His wife smiled wanly. Her voice also bore traces of her Scottish background and was obviously a woman of few words. "Mrs Wixen said the carrier managed to get you up here just before dark. I trust you found all you needed."

"Yes, sir. Thank you ma'am. I have all I require at present, but I would be grateful for some assistance if you have a boy who could help me to get my box upstairs?"

"Of course." assented the Vicar, pulling the sash beside the fireplace. As soon as the elderly maid appeared he charged her with finding the garden boy for that purpose.

"Matins will be at ten o'clock. We shall, no doubt, see you there." were the parting words of Revd Mackarkness, as he saw her to the front door. Elizabeth nodded her dutiful assent.

After Moses Johnson had helped Elizabeth Carter up the stairs with her box, she locked the door of the House and went into the schoolroom. Again, the expression on her face was disdainful as soon as she looked around. There seemed to be no chairs for the infants and she realised they probably squatted on the floor. The older children appeared to sit on various types of chairs alongside oblong wooden tables on which lay the children's slates and chalks. The teacher's desk at the end of the room, by the tortoise stove was itself just a table, but it did hold two small drawers. On top of the table was a bamboo cane of the standard type. Miss Carter picked it up and flexed it before she put out her few books and looked around for more. In a small cupboard she found a pile of worn red-covered *Readers* and very little else.

By now the Churchwarden had begun to ring the bell for Morning Service. Elizabeth quickly left the schoolroom and returned to the School House. There she ascended the staircase, and took from her box her one and only 'Sunday best' dress, made of black bombazine. This garment, which she herself had sewn, was of a twilled material, worsted with cotton, severely cut and very plain. She made a quick toilet, put on her cape and bonnet and walked hastily along to the church.

Everyone in the village was anxious to see what the new schoolmistress was like. "She looks like she won't stand no nonsense!" was the universal opinion. After the service, Revd Mackarkness and his wife invited Elizabeth to take tea with them in the afternoon.

The weather was getting even colder by the time she rang the bell at the Vicarage door, sharp at four o'clock. The elderly maid opened the door. "Good afternoon, Miss Carter. I'm Mrs Wixen. I'm a widow and the Cook General here. If I can be of help to you in any way, since you're here on your own, I shall be pleased to do so." she offered, as she took Miss Carter's cape and bonnet.

"Thank you, Mrs Wixen." Elizabeth replied, a little surprised at her unexpected kindness. "I'll bear that in mind."

Tea at the Vicarage was a somewhat gloomy affair. Rev Mackarkness was a dour Scot and his wife only a little warmer in spirit. However, they were able to explain to the new Schoolmistress something of the village, its people and its past, especially the story of the sinking of the Maharajah's Well, which the teacher had seen from the upstairs window of her house. She decided to go and look at it as soon as she could. By the time she left the Vicarage, though, it was too dark. As she entered the dimness of the house she mused on how pleased she was to see the cat, to which she had given the unromantic and hardly imaginative name of 'Ginny', rather than 'Ginger', as it appeared to be a female.

The next morning she was up early and immediately after her bowl of porridge went into the schoolroom to light the stove as snow had fallen overnight and it was continuing to do so. By a quarter to nine she had everything in order to her satisfaction and the first children started to arrive, keen to see what the new teacher was like. They were disappointed at the words with which she greeted them: "I am Miss Carter, your new teacher, and I wish you to know that I do not stand silliness from anyone!"

Gradually more children arrived, most of them having trudged through the snow for some time. As soon as her pocket watch read nine o'clock she rose from her chair and closed the door firmly.

"Some of them might be late, Miss." said one little girl, nervously. "Especially the Higgses; they have a long way to walk from Scotts Farm and the snow's quite deep now."

"Then they'll have to turn around and go back home." Miss Carter enunciated loudly and clearly, determined that this statement should impress the children. "This school begins at nine o'clock and not a minute later!"

Sure enough, several minutes later, when ten-year old William Higgs and his younger sisters, Mary and Susan, having been playing snowballs along their two-mile walk, arrived at the school door, they found it shut. Miss Carter opened it a few inches and said sharply: "You are seven minutes late. You will now go back home and tell your mother to get you up earlier and make sure you are here in good time!" So saying, she banged the door shut again.

Having started as she meant to go on, Miss Carter marked the register and so began her new life as a teacher at Stoke Row School. Like most schools of the period, it reeked of damp coal struggling to get ignited, wet boots, blue ink and white chalk, together with the odour of the children themselves, especially when they had just entered the room fresh from their long walks to the school or great activity in the playground. At the end of each week after the children had gone home, Miss Carter sat in the cold schoolroom and wrote her entries faithfully in the School Log Book in a clear copperplate hand, before the ink could freeze in the inkwell.

By the March of 1879, the weather had eased somewhat and the children had learned not to displease Miss Carter in any way, if they could possibly avoid it. This was not always easy, because her ideas of the standards of work required were very high. Moreover, with only one older girl, not really senior enough to become a Monitor, to help her manage the Infants, Miss Carter was finding it hard to keep order at the far end of the room.

The Infants sat in a ring around the girl and while she was reading a story they were fairly attentive, but her reading was painfully slow and lacked expression, so it was hardly surprising that the three and four year olds would start to wander, some tried to come up nearer to the front to see their older brothers or sisters. Miss Carter was then quick with the cane, giving a twitch to any child that made so bold.

Despite her every endeavour, though, three boys in particular made life very difficult for her. Many a Friday evening after school she wrote their names clearly in the Log Book and noted that they 'incited the others'. She gradually seems to have found this book a sort of confidential diary for her own feelings about these 'unruly, dirty children', who she came to think of as being 'quite impossible!'

In late April 1879, a Mr James Clinch came to the school door as soon as the children had left. He had with him a pretty little girl of about five. He was a well-built man, stocky and quite well dressed. However he had what seemed to Miss Carter to be a strange type of accent. His 'burr' was a good deal broader than the Oxfordshire one to which she was now becoming accustomed.

"Good afternoon, Ma'am," he said, doffing his cap as a mark of respect for the teacher about whom he had heard a considerable amount since he and his wife arrived in the village some days beforehand. "My name is Clinch and this is my daughter, Clarinda. I am recently come from Tewkesbury in Gloucestershire and I am a cabinet-maker. We are now living at The Oak at the top of the Henley road. I am also the publican of that establishment."

Miss Carter was not impressed. "A foreigner and a publican to boot!" she thought to herself disparagingly, but said aloud: "And you want me to take your daughter into my school, is that it?"

"Yes, Ma'am. Her name is Clarinda."

Again Miss Carter pursed her lips, thinking it was far too fancy a name for a child. "Very well, come in then." She said as she reluctantly led the way to her desk and took out the register. "When was she born?" she asked.

"On 25th April 1874." he stated clearly. "She is just five and this is her School Book. Her name, Clarinda W R Clinch, is at the top."

"Thank you, I can see that for myself." was Miss Carter's acid response. Eyeing the child up and down, she continued: "She can start tomorrow."

In May 1879 she had trouble with one boy in particular and wrote in her careful hand: 'I had occasion to chastise this boy for which he was very violent and passionate." [sic]

The Inspector came on 8 July, 1879 and afterwards wrote laboriously in his Report Book:

Many children at this school have made fair progress in Reading and the 1st class have been taught Dictation well, but there is a wonderful lack of method and school-keeping power, which doubtless has been the main cause of the poor arithmetic and of unsatisfactory work done by the Infant classes. It seems now the time to provide more suitable sitting accommodation for the Infants. Great improvement will be expected next year, especially in Arithmetic...

Some of the deficiencies are likewise due to absenteeism... Many have been scarce three months out of the past six months, on account of the long and exceptionally hard winter from December to March being almost continuous snowy weather. Even now we have cold winds and unfailing rain and very few fine days. There were 55 children present yesterday but only 47 today.

Clearly Miss Carter was not succeeding as much as she had hoped, but fortunately the governors were tolerant and trusted she would do better in future. Life became a little easier for her in the summer months, as the numbers of pupils dropped dramatically. During August she found herself writing remarks in the Log Book like: 'Numbers still decreasing, several being detained from school to be employed on the Harvest.' and in September: 'Fine weather this week, but the children still have further fallen off in their attendance due to Harvest work.'

The school closed for several weeks as a consequence, but even when she reopened it on 6th October 1879, she made her entry in a tone of annoyance: 'Recommenced school work after the Harvest holidays. Very few children came today.'

Still, she continued to teach those who did come but the ways of country children seemed to cause her displeasure. On 31st October 1879 she wrote: 'Eating beech nuts has transpired very much in school this week. Two boys have persisted in doing so after repeated reproofs and corrections.'

Another month went by and the autumn was well advanced in the village. As a part of her entry for 5th November she stated: "Half holiday for there [sic] bonfire." Not only was it surprising that a schoolteacher could not use the correct spelling of a common word, but the tone of the whole entry gives the impression that she did not approve of the celebration of the traditional Guy Fawkes' Day.

December of that year started as cold as the year before and snow fell before Christmas. One Tuesday a small boy came to the door of the schoolroom. Alice Messenger, the Monitor, seated at the back with the Infants, heard his knocking and went to the door. "Come in quick," she said sharply. "Why it's young Johnny Blackall, isn't it. What 're you doing up 'ere?" The boy was shabbily dressed and his snow-covered boots were very worn. In his hand he held a small piece of folded paper, sealed with a dab of red wax.

"Please, miss, I've got a note for Miss Carter." he explained.

Alice took him up to Miss Carter, who had been walking up and down the rows of tables, with her cane held in her hand at the ready.

"Well, boy. Who are you and where do you come from?" Miss Carter demanded, as she took the note from him.

"Please, Miss Carter, Miss," he said, touching his cap before he remembered to take it off. Miss Carter instantly frowned at the snow that dropped on to the floor. "My name's John Blackall and I live in the cottage at the bottom of Witheridge Hill. I go to Highmore School up on the hill and Miss Muskett sent me with this note. She says I'm to wait for a reply, Miss." Having delivered his pre-prepared speech, he fell silent.

Miss Carter returned to her desk, read the missive and wrote a few words at the bottom of the sheet. "Take this back at once." she ordered. "And don't mess about on the way!" The boy took the note and gladly left the room as quickly as he could. There

302

was something daunting about the teacher that he had not encountered in the happier atmosphere of the school up on Witheridge Hill.

Arrears in payment of their nine pence a week 'school money' was one of the many problems that Miss Carter had to endure at Stoke Row School. In January 1880, she confided in her Log Book: 'School very small today, only 30. The weather has been very foggy and bitterly cold. I have sent several children home for coming after nine o'clock and several have also been returned for the arrears in their school money.'

School Visitors, who were sometimes local gentlewomen, also proved a great inconvenience to the Mistress. After school one Friday in February she dipped her pen into the ink bottle and entered the complaint: 'The elder children have derived a notion from the Visitor (which accords with their own convenience) that they are not necessitated to attend more than two days a week. Several of them told me so and acted in accordance.'

As she wrote, she remarked to the ginger cat, lying lazily by the fire: "It really is too bad. The older ones are getting very uppity these days!"

The following winter was disastrous. On 21 January 1881, her hands stiff from the cold, she wrote: 'All Wednesday there was a heavy fall of snow, with driving wind which blocked up the roads so that no children could come. By Thursday noon footpaths had been cut through the snow that, up to Uxmoor was five feet deep and three feet up the school door. Friday was so bitterly cold that only three children came and even they could scarcely gain any heat all day, though they were seated close around the stove.'

In March, shortly before Easter, it was Shrove Tuesday that caused Miss Carter to speak to the Vicar about the absence of some of her pupils when he called in later that afternoon, having left his Alexander dog-cart outside. "Two of the boys were absent today, Vicar!" she complained. "The other children tell me that they went 'shroving'. It seems to be a deplorable custom in these parts. Do you know of it?"

"Yes, Miss Carter." the Vicar replied, in his strong Scottish accent. "Sadly, I do. They go around the big houses begging for eggs, milk and flour with which their mothers may make pancakes. I agree they should not be away from school, but it is a great temptation for them, since many of the families have insufficient food."

However, on a cheerier note, later that month the children were allowed to leave school at three o'clock the next day 'on account of a lecture on Figi [sic] being given for our entertainment in the evening by Capt Meade, R.N.'

In April, the School Visitor came to see Miss Carter and explained that, as she wrote in the Log Book, 'he now had powers to enforce the regular attendance of the children and could exert them. Yet others have stayed away, regardless of his warnings.'

Over the brief Easter holiday, Elizabeth Carter returned to Datchet to fetch her mother to Stoke Row. "I have been told the clear cold air up on the Chiltern Hills will benefit your lungs, Mother." she reassured the ailing woman, who arrived just in time to be entered into the 1881 Census Return that June. Whether it was the presence of her mother, who was able to help a little at times, or the stiffer legislation now in place, can only be imagined, but by the end of the year Miss Carter had begun to confide a little more optimistically in her School Log Book.

On 4th November she wrote: 'The children are getting on capitally with their work, unpunctuality is a rarity, the lessons are more thoughroughly [sic] and energetically pursued.' Her spelling was still rather weak for an educated woman. In December, more cheerfully still, she entered the intriguing phrase: 'Most of the boys can now knit.'

She even gave a little money to a group of her children who came around to the School House singing carols that Christmas. It is true that their version of *God Rest Ye Merry Gentlemen* and *The Holly and the Ivy* were not as tuneful as they might have been, but her mother was cheered by the singing and this moved Miss Carter a little, especially since the boys and girls who traipsed around the village that snowy evening were not the ones who usually caused her annoyance.

The winter of 1882 was not as bad as previous years and in May of that year a great event occurred in the village. Monday 15th May was celebrated by the school as a Fete Day. Gifts of a delicious tea and other items were given to the poor in the village and the children were presented with toys and sweetmeats. This event was financed by the Maharajah of Benares in thanksgiving for Queen Victoria being saved from assassination. A photographer came to the school and took a photograph of the children, mostly sitting or kneeling on the ground, wearing an assortment of hats, whilst their mothers stood behind them. Miss Carter and Mr Henry Morris, Headmaster of the Dogmore Academy, a nearby private boarding school, were standing in the doorway.

The Diocesan Inspector, Revd Constantine G Wodehouse of Mungewell Church, examined the children in their Scripture that June and 'commended the children on their behaviour, intelligence and their industrial [sic] work, viz: sewing, knitting and crochet.' He gave First Prize to Charles Busby and commended Sophia Clargo, Edward Hillier and Robert Absalom.' All the children cheered the winners. It seemed as if, at last, Stoke Row School was becoming a happier place.

On 26th July Miss Carter announced to the assembled children: "You may all have a whole day's holiday tomorrow, so you may go to the Flower Show in the village. This afternoon we shall all go out and pick wild flowers. Then we shall come back and make nosegays for you to enter into the competition."

Absenteeism continued through the Harvest period, of course. Many of the older children helped with the gathering in of the corn, whilst those not yet strong enough to do so had to stay at home and look after the young ones whilst their mothers worked in the fields.

Before she closed the School for the week's Christmas holiday, Miss Carter was able to write in the Log Book: 'the boys and girls, big and little, produced much finished work in needlework, herring-boning, [a type of stitching] crochet, knitting and netting work. Fred Busby and Frank Hillier finished excellently the printing of a book.'

In 1883 the winter was very wet and Miss Carter found that 'as a consequence of the continuous wet weather this winter, colds, coughs and diarrhea [sic] have been prevalent among the children attending school.'

Early in June the Visitor called in. She remarked sharply to Miss Carter: "This room smells dreadful to me. You have no ventilation and since the children are so dirty, the smell in here is appalling!"

"I will open the window at once and ensure that the room is thoroughly washed and cleansed tomorrow, Madam" Miss Carter replied, dutifully, although she herself had not noticed the odour, as she was so accustomed to it.

Again that summer there was considerable absence, due mainly to cherry picking at which most of the children, especially the boys, were very nimble and adept.

On 17th September Miss Carter confided in her Log Book: 'One child lost her father before the holiday and is again sent to school by the Relieving Officer, who had paid for her schooling. The four children are all absent, playing about in the road. They all owe for more than a year's irregular schooling. Sixty-seven on the books.' She made no mention of any assistance. The teaching of all these children at once must have been very trying for her.

Guy Fawkes Day still seemed to be a problem for her. On 9th November 1883, she wrote: 'About half the children took a bonfire half-holiday without leave and with rude self will, meaning to secure another the next day which was not given...' and a week later: 'The three children have again returned to the school, with the promise of paying weekly fees of 9d to clear up their long arrears. One boy is not particular as to the truth.' Miss Carter underlined the latter statement so as to give it the emphasis she felt the fact deserved.

Still, every day was a struggle for her to keep order, especially with regard to punctuality.

On 30th November, her hands cold from the damp foggy day that it had been, she inscribed: 'Three children came at 9.1/4. I told them they were better away, so they went away.'

At the end of that term, Miss Elizabeth Sarah Carter left Stoke Row School. Before she did so, she made one final entry in her School Log Book, in which she had confided all her hopes and fears throughout the previous five years. This entry, in her clear copper-plate hand, was a good deal more optimistic and kindly than almost any of the others had been:

'The children have been very well behaved this quarter, which has enabled me to get them forward better. They have made great and continuous efforts to suppress their restlessness all through and the elders have often been great helpers, getting through their own and the little ones' work. If they could be kept at interesting employ-ment with due relaxation they would be excellent. All have a tendency to untruth, but some are quite reliable. I think they are generally well-informed, intelligent, polite and willing. This is the opinion of

E S Carter.'

Shortly after this period, the Education Department made great strides in improving the buildings, the books and the general interest level of the schools under their jurisdiction.

******

At a time when it was the custom for the Assize Judges to travel between Oxford and Henley, they usually took short cuts through narrow back lanes, so as to avoid the towns and villages where they might encounter trouble from those who had come up in court before them in the past, or even their relatives. They often rode up from Wallingford via hamlets like Ipsden, Hailey and Well Place, and by-passing Stoke Row by means of a bridleway that ran in front of The Black Horse public house, where they sometimes stayed overnight. From there it was but a short canter through a path that became known as 'Judges Ride', down to 'Splashall Bottom' to Neal's Farm and thence to Rotherfield Peppard and Henley.

A little way along that path, about half a mile east from The Black Horse, was a small cottage that had originally been an ale-house, known as The Jockey. Why it was called this, no one could remember, but it may have originated in the former occupation of the previous landlord. After he left the house it went through a series of owners. By 1868 it belonged to Mr Edward Reade of Ipsden, who sold it to a Major General Waddington, no doubt with other property. Finally, the General sold it to Revd Henry Gibbons of Wallingford who leased it to a baker from North Oxfordshire in 1881.

******

Joseph Lawrence, a short, rather fat man, with a balding pate, had been born in Bishopstone, Wiltshire and had met his wife, Mary Ann, when they were both in service in Barton, North Oxfordshire, where she was born. She was assistant cook in a large manor house and he was a coachman. However, Joseph had always aspired to having a little business of his own and so, urged on by Mary Ann, he left the services of his employer and became an assistant to Frederick Holloway, the Barton baker.

It is true that the hours were hard. He had to be up at four o'clock in the morning to rekindle the ovens and continued until twelve noon, with just a brief respite for a bit of breakfast. The bakery was a busy one and supplied not only the village of Barton, but also others in the vicinity. As soon as the bread was ready it was taken out for delivery by Amos Clutterbuck with the pony and trap that bore the baker's name. By the time he returned, Frederick and Joseph had finished most of the baking and it was Joseph's turn to take the remainder out around the area.

The young man proved to be a good baker and a polite delivery-man that often earned him good tips, especially from the big houses at Christmas.

Eventually, he had saved up enough to ask Mary Ann to marry him. "I've got enough now for us to start up on our own," he promised her, "and you could help me by selling groceries. You'd be good at that!"

And so it was. The couple were married and, through the Vicar who performed the ceremony, heard of another clergyman who had a house to let in the south-east of Oxfordshire. "It's not all that far from Wallingford, a country market town," the Vicar assured the couple. "And Revd Henry Gibbons says in his letter that there is no baker in that part of the uplands. You should do well!"

In due course, the Lawrences moved down to Dogmore End, [which had once been the home of the pottery-making Beaker folk], between the villages of Checkendon and Stoke Row.

They moved in over Easter, 1881, and in June of that year, 40 year old Joseph was proudly able to tell the Census Enumerator that he was a 'Baker and Grocer' as well as being Head of the Household. He had to confess that he and his wife, Mary Ann, had had no children, but he declared that he had a young visitor staying there, 22 year old grocer whose name was James King. "He's my nephew," Joseph explained. "He's here with us for a while to show my wife how to start a small shop here. At the moment I'm too busy, having to set up these ovens and doing the baking here on my own."

Certainly their neighbours in the hamlet of Dogmore End were glad of the opportunity of buying their groceries from Mary Ann, because the other nearby shops were on the far side of Checkendon, in Stoke Row or on Witheridge Hill, all a tidy walk away. People nearby included not only the landlady of The Black Horse, who provided a meal occasionally to travellers who passed through, but also their neighbours who occupied the four houses either side of 'Berncote', as Joseph and Mary Ann had just renamed their cottage, with the consent of their landlord.

More importantly, a stone's throw away was the Dogmore Academy, in Basset Manor, that had been set up by a Mr Henry Morris and his wife, Rosetta, in January 1867. Mr Morris took the whole morning to list for the Enumerator not only his wife, Rosetta, their own five children, his Cook and General Servant, but also to give him details of their twenty-nine boarders, most of whose parents were out in government service in the colonies. Mrs Fanny Smith, the cook, usually purchased her ingredients and other household items on her weekly shopping expedition to Wallingford, but she was often grateful to be able to send Emma Wells over to Mrs Lawrence at the Berncote Grocery Stores to buy a few odds and ends when she ran out of them.

However, they did not find her an easy woman to deal with. Several miscarriages had caused her much back pain and as she often grumbled: "Carrying all these boxes and panniers about don't help matters, neither."

Later that year James went home and the couple advertised in the Oxford Times for a youth to help them in the bakery and the grocery store. Finally a young man of sixteen answered their advertisement. His letter of application was written with great care and in it he explained that he was Stephen Buckner, son of a shoemaker at Aston in north Oxfordshire. He came the weekend following Joseph Lawrence's letter accepting his services and as Mary Ann said to her husband as they got ready for bed that evening, "He seems a nice enough boy."

Nevertheless, as the years went by, she began to find him lazy and even suspected him of being dishonest, though she couldn't quite prove it. Gradually, his manner began to turn surly and one day in September 1884, when she found him sitting outside in the autumn sunshine instead of doing the work she had set him to do, she became really angry and hit him several times around the shoulders with the broom she had in her hand. "I don't pay you and give you board and lodging so as you can sit around out here!" she shouted at him as she did so.

"I'm fed up with you, you old hag!" Buckner shouted back, as he ran away down the garden. Later on he returned, red in the face and announced to the baker and his wife: "I've had enough of this place and of you two! I'm going up to pack my bag and I ain't never coming back!" He then rushed up to his room and came down later, his small carpet bag in his hand.

The Lawrences let him go, since he was becoming so disagreeable, and decided to advertise for another assistant. "I'm sorry now that I hit the boy." Mary Ann confessed to her husband that evening. "But my back plays me up so that when I saw him sitting about, it just got my goat!"

"Never mind, my love. We'll find another, I'm sure." comforted her husband. "I'll put an advertisement in the *Oxford Times* next week."

It was quiet in the shop the following Wednesday morning, about half-past eleven, when Mary Ann was sitting in her kitchen, peeling potatoes for their dinner. Her husband had gone down to the flour-mill at Mapledurham for more supplies. It was a long journey but the old windmill on Stoke Row hill had been out of use since the 1840s and was, in fact, beginning to decay. It was a dull day and Mary Ann was quite alone. Suddenly, she thought she glimpsed a figure advancing towards her from the back door but thought to herself instantly: "I'm seeing things, it's this fog, plays tricks with your head, it does." In the same second she noticed that the man was wearing a black mask over his face.

She started to laugh because she remembered that it was 5th November, Guy Fawkes Day, and thought someone was about to play a joke on her. "Perhaps one of the boys from the Academy?" was the idea that came into her mind, until she saw the man raise a pistol.

Before she could speak, he fired a shot at her that entered her right side. She was so astonished that all she could find to say as she fell sideways to the floor was the obvious statement: "You've shot me!"

"Yes, you bugger!" the young man replied. "And I'll shoot you again!" but instead of doing so, or making any further attempt, he ran out of the house as fast as he could. Mary Ann gradually raised herself from the ground, staggered to the front door and fell again. There she slipped into a state of unconsciousness.

It was a full half an hour after this that a groom in the service of Mr Morris at the Dogmore Academy, close by, came in for some tobacco. Finding no one in the shop and no reply to his calling out, he looked around and observed Mrs Lawrence lying on the floor. Blood was oozing from her dress and he could not be sure whether she was still alive. However, his knowledge of horses stood him in good stead. He put his fingers on her pulse and noticed that her breathing was shallow but steady. He promptly left her lying there and returned at once to alert his master.

Mr Morris lost no time in giving instructions to his groom that he was to "ride hard for Doctor Horne at Wallingford, and bring him back with all speed. If necessary, he can ride Trojan and you can walk back." As he said all this, Mr Morris himself mounted Cleo, his wife's horse and rode as fast as he could to the police at Wallingford, though the smaller horse could not for long keep up with Trojan, which was a thoroughbred.

Finally, Dr Horne arrived at Dogmore End and found the patient being cared for by Mrs Rosetta Morris and her cook, Fanny Smith. On examining the poor woman he found a problem. He explained to the ladies: "The bullet has traversed her ribs from the right side round by the blade bone, but I am unable to find it. I must send to Reading Hospital for an experienced surgeon. It is a great pity that her husband seems to have gone on an errand."

In the meantime, Mr Morris, together with Mr George Hope, a local farmer and owner of the brickyard at Stoke Row, had waited for the police and their dogs. As soon as they arrived, they got on the scent of a man on the highway at Woodcote. They followed on the same track and down at Moulsford, by the river, they came upon a young man sitting inside the Beetle and Wedge Inn, eating some food.

As a reporter from the Oxford Chronicle concluded in his long article a couple of days later, under the headline:

". . . Mr Hope went in and sat down by him, noticing that he kept his hand in his right hand pocket. As soon as the man saw the opportunity, he bolted but was captured by the police-man outside. In his right pocket was found a small pistol, loaded, and he also had five cartridges. He offered a desper-ate resistance, but was eventually captured.

. . . the unfortunate fellow, who is charged with having com-mitted the strange act, appears to be the son of Mr Buckner, a shoemaker of Aston, a most respectable man.

He is barely nineteen years of age, and what his motives were are not clear. It is said on one hand that he worked for Mr Lawrence and was badly treated. On the other hand it is stated that a cash-box was taken, containing over three pounds and that the money was found upon him."

It was many months before the local gossip about Mrs Lawrence died down, but it is believed that she did recover from her wounds eventually. However, the Lawrences probably moved away after the tragedy, because by the 1891 Census, another occupant was listed at Berncote Cottage.

******

Much of the first part of this chapter comes from the Reade Manuscripts. *I am most grateful to Mrs Juliet Noel [nee Reade] for loan of these documents.*

The Log Books of Stoke Row School *are to be found in the Oxfordshire Archives, along with Clarinda Clinch's Schoolbook.*

The attempted murder at Dogmore End was reported in the Oxfordshire Chronicle *in November 1884. The old house was demol-ished a few years ago and rebuilt.*

Chapter 16. The Widow, the Murderer and the Great War: 1900 - 1920

When Queen Victoria died in 1901, it brought to an end a reign of 'sixty glorious years'. Actually it was sixty-three years. In that time she demonstrated by example the place that the Crown could occupy in British political life and as a link between the peoples of the vast British Empire.

Despite the immense wealth of the nation though, poverty at home was still rife. Matters improved a little with the advent of the Old Age Pension in 1908, but that was only for persons over seventy years of age and was 'means-tested'. Apart from this, there was virtually no social security except for the little that was administered under the Parish Relief system. Vicissitudes in the life of the labouring poor in those times often meant considerable hardship and sometimes complete penury.

* * * * * *

In 1906, Ellen Franklin found herself widowed when her husband, a hay-tier and thatcher, was killed in an accidental fall from a roof. Their two sons, Charles, fifteen, and George, fourteen, accompanied their father's body home. The sight of his mutilated corpse shocked her deeply when it was brought back to their cottage in Judges Lane, Checkendon on a cart. Her elder daughter, Daisy, who was ten years old at the time, said later: "she never really recovered from the blow."

However, Ellen was a strong-minded woman and decided after a few days that she would have to move. "I can't stay 'ere," she

313

explained. "Not with all the memories this 'ouse 'olds for me." This decision was confirmed following a visit from the Vicar of Checkendon when he suggested to her that the three youngest of her children, Dorothy, aged seven, Ann, three and John, just a few months old, should be put into the Wallingford Orphanage. "They 'int goin' to take my children away from me!" she vowed the next day to her neighbour, Jane Warner of Scots Common.

"But how'll you manage all of them?" asked Jane. "I suppose the boys bring in a bit, now they're bigger, but the others, how'll you be able to feed them all?"

"I'll manage some'ow!" Ellen vowed. "I do washin' now up at Checkendon Court, I'll just 'ave to do more. Daisy and Dolly'll 'ave to look after the younger ones. Another few years and Daisy'll be able to go into service - that'll 'elp a bit. And the Vicar says 'e'll try to get me Out Relief from the Parish. I just in't goin' to let my kids go to no orphanage and that's flat!"

Several weeks later Ellen heard that Mr George Page of Highmore had a cottage to let at the foot of Witheridge Hill. As she and the five children crowded around the fire that evening she explained her intentions to them, breast-feeding the baby as she did so. "Now, it's a terrible thing what's 'appened to us, but we've got to make the best of it we can. The new cott's a bit smaller 'n this and the rent is 6d a week cheaper. Lady Rothbart at Checkendon Court's talked to some of 'er friends and they reckon as 'ow I could get enough work doin' washin' at one and six a day and earn nine shillin' a week. What with that and what Charlie and Georgie brings in, I reckon as 'ow we could manage."

The children wondered about their new home and asked their mother a lot of questions. Daisy was the most inquisitive. "What's it like, this cottage, then?"

"Well, I walked over yesterday when you was at school and looked at it with Mr Page. It's only about a mile away or p'r'aps a bit more, down at the bottom of the 'ill and ... "

"Is there a well?" interrupted Charlie, always the practical one. "We don't want to 'ave to go up the 'ill to 'ighmore well to get water, that's a long way."

"Yes," replied his mother. "Luckily there is a well there, not a big one, but it'd be enough for us. It was dug there when the place was a beer-'ouse, Mr Page said. There's the remains of an old wall at the side of the garden and a big old shed, too but it's not much good now. It lets in the rain I think. It's a bit broken down, but it might be useful for keepin' the animals in."

"Can we go on keeping Lucy?" piped up Dolly, in her high-pitched voice.

"Of course, we can keep Lucy, what'd we do without a pig?" was her mother's reply. "In fact, Witheridge Hill's commons land, so we can keep any animal we wants and of course, there's lots of firewood 'andy. We'd still be able to keep the chickens in the garden, there's quite a big garden, bigger 'n this and you boys can grow us our own vegetables, like what you do now, only more of 'em. We shall need more as you all grows bigger and 'ungrier!"

They moved the following Saturday afternoon with the assistance of Bert Wheeler, Jim West's man at Stoke Row Farm. "We in the farming community have to help each other. I admire your mother, keeping your family together as she is trying to do," Mr West declared kindly when Charlie went and asked him for the loan of one of his carts and a horse to pull it.

Luckily the spring day, though cold, was a sunny one and Ellie kept the children happy by singing songs to them and encouraging them to join in as the cart came up the rise to Uxmoor and turned the corner to go through Stoke Row and down the hill to Witheridge Hill bottom, Although she had little time to go to church, she usually sang hymns for they were the only songs she heard. Her favourite hymn was *The Church's One Foundation*, but she couldn't always recall all the words, so when she came to the end of what she remembered, she went on to another:

When I look up to yonder sky
So bright, so fresh, so very high,
I think of One I cannot see
Who thinks of and cares for me.

He does my daily food provide
And all I could want beside
And when I close my sleepy eyes
I rest in peace, for he is nigh.

315

As they bumped along, she cuddled the youngest close to her and thought sadly of the two that she had lost in childbirth in the early days of her married life. "Good thing, really, I 'in't got them to feed as well, though!" she realised, practical woman that she was.

Finally they came to Witheridge Hill. The younger child had never seen it and Daisy had only been there occasionally, on an errand from Checkendon School to Highmore School, on top of the hill. Along the bottom was a broadsward of bright green grass. Here and there animals were nibbling the new spring growth, a donkey, two pigs, two goats and three old cows, their udders almost dragging on the ground. Lucy, their pig, tied into the back of the cart, raised her nose in the air and seemed to like the idea of having new grazing ground. Well-worn paths criss-crossed the common land where the gorse flowers were now bright yellow. "That's a lovely sight!" said Ellie, brightly, pleased to be leaving the past behind her.

As soon as they reached the cottage, Ellen told Charlie to get a fire going in the hearth. "There's no range, then!" he said, sounding disappointed. "That means we'll 'ave to 'ave boiled food all the time, no roasts any more!"

"That's right," agreed his mother. "That's why it's 6d a week cheaper. We'll 'ave to keep a wood fire going all the time if we wants 'ot water, even for a cuppa tea. Anyway, we couldn't afford coal for a range now," she sighed. "Still, at least we're all together!"

As soon as they arrived at the gate, Charlie commanded: "You young 'uns 'ad better go out to pick up some firewood, quick, while Bert, Georgie, Mum and me gets this stuff off the cart! This bit o' kindlin' we brought with us i'n't goin' to last long!" Happy to be free to go roaming, Daisy led Dolly and Annie out into the copse at the side of the house and soon they were gathering firewood and bringing back bundles of it.

The fireplace was large and simple, with a door to a small bread oven on the right hand side. At the base were four bricks with a couple of iron bars across them on which to stand an iron pot and their big black kettle. On the outside of the cottage was a brick-built, tile-roofed wash-house, the chimney of which led into the main one.

Later that afternoon, Daisy was dispatched to find her way down to Sonning Common, some three miles down the road from Highmore where, her mother told her, she would find a butcher.

"e's Mr Brind. Mr Page said 'e'll let you 'ave a scrag o' mutton for 8d. Now 'ere's the money. Tie it in your hankie and put it in your pinny pocket, so you don't loose it! As soon as you gets back, I'll start a stew." Ellie promised.

They all worked for several hours while the baby slept blissfully in an old drawer near the fire. Charlie put up an iron bar across the top of the hearth, so his mother could hang a pot over the blaze and cook them a pudding, made with some flour and suet and a few currants. The bar would also hold more water in a tin drum that had a handle. He knew this would burn thin after a while but hoped they would by then be able to buy another one down in the general store in Sonning Common. This village was thriving now and more houses were being built there every year as it was not too far from Reading.

Ellen put her flat irons in the hearth, at the ready. Then she laid down a colourful rag rug in front of it over the brick floor. She felt it cheered the room a little. Putting her hand on the beam over the fireplace, she leaned over and poked the fire until it flamed up again. She had made the rug a couple of years previously, she recalled, sitting by the fire with her husband in their home at Checkendon. "Now stop that, my girl!" she said to herself, sharply. "It don't do to mope. Remember, Grandma used to say 'Laugh and the world laughs with you, cry and you cry alone!'"

That evening they all had some of the stew and pudding. Ellen gave the meat to the boys while the younger children had the gravy and vegetables. Finally she was able to sit down in the one uphol-stered chair she owned. "Your Dad bought this at a sale, many years ago." she told the children. " 'e paid 18 shillin' for it. I said at the time that it was a terrible waste of money but I'm glad I've got it now. It's good to ease myself into at the end of the day, especially a day like this one!" She glanced around her.

At the far side was a wattle and daub wall with a plain wooden door. They dubbed this room 'The Back House' and had put in it the wheelbarrow, the buckets and digging tools, along with their boots and the vegetables they'd brought from their previous home. "They'll keep dry in there. At least this 'ouse has a brick floor and not an earth one like some of 'em in Checkendon." Ellen had said to herself, thankfully, that afternoon as she had placed a small old table in there, with a bowl of water, a piece of soap and a towel for them to wash their hands. One of her mottoes was: "A wash is as good as an hour's rest." Beside the table she placed the old tin bath in which all of the family would have at least one hot wash a week.

In the middle of their part of the room was a somewhat rickety table at which they had just eaten, now with a candle in a pottery candlestick on it and around it six chairs of various designs. Also on it was a chipped jug containing bluebells that the little girls had picked. "Go and get some, not too many and don't pull 'em up!" she had bade them. "If the white part comes out they'll never grow from that bulb again." she explained. "Just pick enough to fill this jug. This is our new 'ome now and we must make the best we can out of it."

After about an hour, she bundled the three girls up the steep stair-case that rose through a hole in the corner of the room. On top they found a similar divide to the one downstairs. Each room had a window and Ellie opened one of the casements. "We must 'ave fresh air. The nights are not so cold now and this 'ouse needs airing!" she remarked as the girls looked a little dismayed. They took off their outer garments and snuggled into the double bed in the manner to which they were accustomed, the two older girls in the top part and young Annie across the bottom. Daisy had brought up the drawer into which Ellen carefully placed the baby who, as he began to grow older, they were now calling 'Jack'. "The boys'll be asleep in the big bed next door, so don't you make a noise in the night if you use the *guzunder* [chamber pot, ie 'goes under' the bed] and wake 'em up." she warned. "You can hear the owls in the wood here already, like you 'eard the cuckoo this afternoon, it's much the same as 'ome." their mother reassured them.

The next day being Sunday, they were all at home and Ellie's first job was to inspect the brick-lined pool at the back of the house. Having satisfied herself that it was water-tight, she drew water up from the well and filled the pool which had long since dried out. It was here that she would keep the butter and cheese and the milk from the goat that she was expecting to be brought any minute. The previous afternoon, Granny Slade, a near neighbour, had promised to lend her a 'nanny goat' for a few days until she could find one for herself.

The children spent most of their time exploring the surrounds of the house, gathering firewood and kindling, while Ellie and the boys started to tidy up the garden and to patch up the old shed. "Did you say Mr Page told you it used to be a barn, part of an ale-house?" George enquired. "Looks a bit duff to me. I'll bet there's rats in there. Can't have been much of a pub."

"No, I don't think it was," replied his mother. "But that was a long time ago. It used to be run by a family called Blackall, Mr Page said. It was called the Yew Tree. P'r'aps that's why there's those two yews out the back. 'e also said the last of the Blackalls, I think 'e said his name was Shadrach, used to be publican up at the Rising Sun, on top of the 'ill here, about fifteen years ago, but 'e died soon after 'e got there. Seems 'e and 'is wife, Fanny 'ad twins, a boy called Frederick and a daughter called Mary but they were grown up by then and went off somewhere. Frederick was a gamekeeper so 'e might've gone anywhere. Certainly they're not 'ere any more to tell us what it used to be like when it was a beer 'ouse. Pity, really, it might 'ave been interesting."

"Well, I'm not interested in 'ow it used to be, I'm more keen on seeing 'ow it's goin' to be in the future," said Charlie, ever practical. "Now, where shall we be puttin' this vegetable patch?"

Their mother took a spade and started to pull out some of the weeds. " 'ere, though there's a lot of ground elder. It's so 'ard to get rid of. Charlie, you'd best be looking at the Guzzle Hole. I'll wager it's not been cleaned out in years. I looked at it earlier, it'll need a new plank over it."

"Oh, I'll just throw some dead leaves over it. Maybe that way we can use the stuff in the bottom for manure next year." suggested George.

Later that afternoon, Revd Francis Russell Harnett, M A, who had been the Vicar of Highmore since 1899, called to see the newly-arrived family. His unannounced visit startled the Franklins who were busy in the garden when the cleric, his white 'dog collar' standing out sharply against his black formal clothes, stopped at the gate in his trap which was pulled by a light fawn pony. "Good afternoon, Mrs Franklin." he bade her, somewhat stiffly. "Welcome to Highmore. I trust you are settling in well?" He decided not to leave his trap, since the garden looked rather muddy.

"Yes, thank you, sir." Ellen Franklin replied, wiping her dirty hands on her apron and brushing back her thin, greying hair.

319

"Is that your son up there?" he enquired. She nodded. "What is he doing, pray?"

"He's tippin' piles of leaves on the guzzle 'ole, sir. It 'a'n't been cleaned out in a long time."

"You mean this is where your chamber pots are emptied?!" asked the astonished Vicar.

"Yes, sir. It seems so. We 'ad a brick privvy where we was before but there i'n't one here."

"Then I must have a word with George Page. Fancy him letting this cottage to you with all your young children and having no enclosed latrine. I am appalled!"

"Thank you, sir." Ellie half-smiled, gratefully.

"I shall hope to see you all in church on Sunday!" he charged her. "You may come up and see me at the Vicarage if you have any need." he concluded as he touched the pony with the whip.

In fact, as it transpired, Ellen did have need of his help some months later when Revd Harnett received a letter from the Henley Union [formerly the Henley Workhouse] to say that they disputed the assumption that it would be their duty to pay Parish Relief to the widow. "They say here that because you actually live at Witheridge Hill, which is, in fact, in the parish of Mongewell and not in the parish of Highmore at all, you should continue to be paid by Wallingford, just as you did during the period after your husband died when you still lived at Checkendon. I shall write to them again and see if we can obtain more clarification of the situation, but it may be necessary for you to go up to Oxford to establish your claim to benefit."

This controversy went on for several months and eventually Ellen did have to go up to the court at Oxford to fight for her right to Parish Relief. "You're never going to walk all the way to Oxford and back, Mum, are you?" asked Daisy that morning, before they all went up to school. "It's an awful long way. Our teacher says its more than twenty miles to Oxford."

"Yes, my duck, I shall walk there and I shall be able to rest when I get to the court. There's sure to be somewhere to sit down a while," her mother said, trying not to show her fears. "I 'a'n't got money for the carter to go all the way there and back, it'd be an awful lot. What's got to be done has to be done!" she finished, going out of the door resolutely.

That evening though it was a very worn and tired woman who returned to the little cottage. Her face looked drawn and pale as the children gathered around to hear the news. "Wallingford's got to pay," she stated as she tried to pull her muddy boots off her swollen feet. "Get me a bowl o' hot water, Daisy, there's a good girl. My feet are killin' me!" As she gradually revived she told them about her day. "They were kind enough, but I felt some'ow bad about it, 'aving to beg for money like that." she explained. "And I 'ad to 'ave my photograph taken. They said it was for their records. The man was very nice, but there was a big flash when 'e took it and I couldn't look up. I was quite scared, really, I've never 'ad my photograph taken afore."

Despite the Parish Relief and all her 'scrimping', Ellen did fall behind with the weekly rent of two shillings and nine pence after a while and when the landlord, George Page, came to collect the money one week, he pointed out to her that she was thirty shillings in arrears. Ellen had never been able to fully understand figures and so she took his word for it and agreed to pay another three pence a week until the debt was paid off. Even then he did not put the rent back to its original rate.

That autumn, Dolly came home from school with a letter in her hand. In the evening, Ellie read it carefully. "It says you should 'ave glasses, love. They say your sight's bad and that's why you're behind the others with your school work, but glasses will cost five shillings!"

Dolly looked mystified. "Ha'n't you got the money, then, Mum?" She asked.

"No I a'n't, duck. You see, it's like this. I gets one shilling and six pence for every day's work. I works six days a week and that's nine bob [shillings]. Out o' that I got to pay three bob rent and even though the boys brings home some, we all got to eat and you kids 'ave got to 'ave new boots this winter, them others is wore'd out. No, I'm sorry my duck, you'll have to manage to see your books as best as you can."

So Dolly continued to fall behind with her schoolwork. Eventually it was decided that she was only fit for housework or gardening.

******

The first entry in the Highmore School Log Book for November,

1907 was made on Monday 18th, when the new Headmaster wrote: 'I, John Harold Baker, took charge of this school, with my wife, Beatrice Annie Baker as Infants' Mistress.'

John Baker had been an Assistant Headmaster and his wife a certificated teacher. The young engaged couple had been to view the school the previous summer, when on a warm, sunny morning in late July, they cycled out from Oxford in the direction of the hills of South Oxfordshire, a journey of some twenty miles. They eventually reached the village of Highmore and upon enquiring found the School perched on the picturesque Witheridge Hill. Around it were a few cottages and a small public house called the Rising Sun.

The School, built of brick and flint, was of modest dimensions, consisting of a main room and a small room for Infants, with entrance porch that faced Common land. This greensward provided an attractive place for the children to play. The School House was joined on to the school and boasted a scullery, living room and pleasant parlour also overlooking the Common. Two bedrooms upstairs completed the accommodation. With its red tiled roofs, flint walls and diamond-paned windows, the school and the house made a pleasing picture, in character with its rural surroundings.

The young teachers were favourably impressed with what they had seen and sent in their application immediately. Having been interviewed several weeks later by the School Managers, amongst whom were the Vicar and the Squire, they were accepted and their appointments confirmed by letter.

They then had but a couple of months to arrange their wedding and to select a few items of furniture for their new home. Following their marriage, they enjoyed a week's holiday and were fortunate with the weather for their brief respite. The genial autumn of that year continued into early November, so that the seaside amenities were still enjoyable without the crush of the holiday crowds of summertime.

The brief interval of leisure was soon ended and the weekend found the couple on their journey to their new home. With the help of Mr Baker's sister, the School House was arranged into a comfortable home. It was compact and convenient for the early days of the twentieth century. They were days of oil lamps and hip baths, but no piped water.

The important thing for this young couple was that it was their first home of their own, where they had freedom to plan their lives, a welcome change from the restrictions and limited privacy of their previous lodgings. The rent of the School House was about £12 a year, inclusive of Council rates.

Exchanging an assistantship with a rural headship was not a financial advantage for the salary was twenty pounds less than his previous pay of ninety pounds a year. His wife's salary was fifty pounds instead of her former seventy pounds. Even so, they felt themselves to be passing rich on a total of only one hundred and twenty pounds per annum. Their income was supplemented with the fifteen pounds that John was paid for playing the organ in the church of St Paul at Highmore. They learned to live comfortably but simply.

After his experiences as a single class teacher, Mr Baker found himself faced with an entirely new situation as head of a village school. The pupils numbered about sixty boys and girls from five to fourteen years. Of these about twenty were infants and seven-year olds. They were put into three groups and taught by Mrs Baker in the Infants' classroom.

In the main schoolroom the forty or so pupils were arranged according to the old-time plan of standards and ages and again taught in three groups. In this work Mr Baker had the help of a Monitoress, a bright senior pupil or sometimes a student teacher, which was a great help with the younger children in the main school-room. By this time denominational schools were beginning to benefit from the new Education Act when all publicly maintained schools came under the direction of the County Education Authorities.

For Mr and Mrs Baker it was a very agreeable change from their struggles with large classes in town schools. They found the attitude of the country children to be in great contrast to that of their former pupils. The village children seemed to be more stolid and less precocious. Some appeared to be rather dull and retarded but their responses were natural and agreeable. The children evidently liked coming to school and the fact of having new teachers aroused their natural curiosity and interest.

The situation of the School was exhilarating in itself, with the Common forming a natural playground for the children. The furze and bracken-clad hillside behind the building, with its view of the valley and the wooded hills beyond, stretching up to Stoke Row was very attractive. A road ran round and across the hill, making it an island site. In spring the woods presented a scene of magical greenery and in autumn it was a pageant of varied tints of brown and gold. Immediately to the rear of the School House was a large and obviously very old oak tree. "It is my guess that it is well over five hundred years old." John said to his wife one summer Saturday when they were seated in the garden. "I'm sure it could tell you many a tale, were it able to speak!"

The Bakers gradually found themselves drawn into village life at Highmore. On Sundays there were the church services when John played the organ and in the summer he played cricket, while his wife helped with the teas as was customary. He also became a member of the Parish Council, along with the Lord of the Manor and the Vicar and both husband and wife enjoyed the annual Flower Shows held in the district. Like many other social events these brought together people of all types and ages in the locality and soon the couple knew many people and were themselves acknowledged cheerily wherever they went.

Town shopping presented one of the few difficulties owing to an inadequate means of transport. Bicycles were excellent for getting about the village and to others nearby but to go to Henley or Wallingford meant they had to hire the Grocer's pony and trap or travel by the carrier's horse-drawn van that started out from Nettlebed. This meant a morning's journey and a need for a lunch out. Often one had a long wait in the late afternoon while the carrier executed various commissions for his village clients before the slow evening ride home, made even more tedious by the various stops and business calls along the way. It was particularly onerous in winter when, except for mothers with babies and the elderly, the passengers were requested to alight and walk up the hill, which they invariably did cheerfully, so as to lighten the load for the horse.

John H Baker really loved music and greatly enjoyed the convivial Thursday evenings in the church when choir practice took place. After the strain of teaching young children all day, he particularly looked forward to walking from his home up to St Paul's. It was one such evening in the summer of 1910 when he observed a stranger on the path, coming down from Highmore towards Witheridge Hill. As soon as he could, he returned to the School House and recounted his experiences to his wife.

"I was on my way to choir practice when I saw a dapper figure approaching from the upper part of the village. He was dressed as though he was on a walking tour. He carried a walking stick and from a strap over his shoulder was suspended a small leather pouch for holding binoculars. I instantly recognised the small, neatly dressed man as resembling the portrait I had seen that morning in the Telegraph of Dr Hawley Harvey Crippen. He's wanted by the police for the murder of his wife. Do you recall, I showed the picture to you?"

"Yes, dear, I do. He looked very smart, but rather mean, I thought." replied Beatrice.

"Well, I was due at the church for choir practice, so I only had time to take a good look at him before I continued on my way. I knew you were over with old Mrs Styleacre and just hoped he would not call at the house, because I remembered that Annie was there on her own with the baby."

"Yes," said his wife. "When I came back Annie told me about the visitor. She said she had answered a knock on the front door with young Noel in her arms. It seems the stranger asked if he could see the Schoolmaster as he wished to request a night's lodging. Annie told him that she expected the master to return from church any minute, though she knew it would be over an hour before either you or I would return. She hoped it would deter him and it did. As you know, Annie is always suspicious of anyone she has not seen before. She's so nervous, that girl!"

Mr Baker immediately rang the bell for the maid. "Tell me what happened this evening," he asked her, gently. "What did he say to you when you told him I was out?"

"I told him sir, that anyway, there was no room in the house for a visitor, as there are only two bedrooms and they're occupied by the family. When I told him that he just said 'Good evening' and went away."

Mr Baker dismissed the maid with assurances that she had done the right thing in the circumstances and immediately opened his oak bureau and prepared to write a couple of notes. His wife promptly suggested she should go out on the Common and find some boys who would be able to run fast to the Police Constables at both Nettlebed and Stoke Row. "I know the Franklin girls are out there, but they're a bit young. With any luck the Eggleton boys will be there too, they're fast runners." With that she looked out of the window and said, as he was writing furiously, "Yes, there they are, I'll call them at once."

Later that week, the Bakers heard that Ethel le Neve, Crippen's companion, dressed as a youth, had been seen walking on Nettlebed Common. It was thought that he and she had been to the home of her parents at Maidenhead, prior to their coming out in the country beyond Henley to escape detection.

It also transpired that although he was not able to find accommodation in a private house, Crippen was able to stay at the Dog and Duck Inn at Highmore. The landlady, Mrs Page, told her story to the Vicar and Mr Baker when they requested her to do so. "Good thing I didn't know he was a murderer. I don't get time to read newspapers. My hubby would have done, God rest his soul, but now I'm here on my own, I don't. Anyway, I offered him a late tea. We serve Beech's jams here, you know." The Vicar nodded and she continued: "When he agreed, he asked me for a type with no pips in it. He said they're an annoyance to him as he has artificial teeth. After the tea he noticed my late hubby's violin on top of the piano and asked if he might play it. There was no one else in the bar, so I agreed. He played quite well really."

The Crippen affair caused some sensation at the time. He was an American and a dentist practising in London. He and his wife, a former variety actress, had led a 'cat and dog' life for some years in their flat over his dental practice. He got so fed up with his wife's behaviour that he began to take an interest in his lady assistant, Ethel le Neve and eventually fell in love with her. However, instead of adopting the simple expediency of disappearing with his chosen companion, he committed what was called by the press 'a cold and heartless murder by administering poison in his wife's morning cup of coffee.' It seems he followed this up by burying her body in a hole dug under the cellar floor.

As Mr Baker recounted later in a letter to a friend in Australia:

'Crippen's subsequent trial made a great sensation. Some

sympathy was aroused for the misguided criminal, as he stood a lonely, diminutive figure in the dock, making a recital of the purgatory of his ill-assorted marriage, but the inevitable verdict condemned him to expiate his crime upon the scaffold.'

What actually made the Crippen affair so memorable was that he was the first person to be arrested on board ship as it docked in New York, following a shore-to-ship radio message, one of the first to be sent.

******

Like so many villages in England, both Stoke Row and Highmore suffered a great deal in the First World War, chiefly in the loss of so many of their men. Not only were nineteen men from Stoke Row and fifteen men from Highmore killed, many came home wounded both physically and mentally. Throughout the War the women at home were kept in a state of constant anxiety, every day fearing the sight of the village Postmaster or his assistant coming to the door with a yellow envelope that would hold a telegram bearing bad news.

******

Edward Evans and his wife, Alice, were at the Village Fete in Stoke Row on Bank Holiday Monday in August 1914. It was a warm, sunny day and with them was their five-year old son, also named Edward, though he was always known as 'Ted'. This young lad was extremely keen to have a go on the Swing Boats that were brought to the Recreation Field by the owners of the local fair which not only came to the village every June, but also brought small items of equipment to local fetes throughout the summer. Ted kept pestering his mother, who was more anxious to buy food items, such as cakes and jams that had won prizes for their producers in the Flower Show the previous month. "Please, Mum, can we have a go on the swing boats?" pleaded Ted.

"That's the umpteenth time you've asked me!" his mother shouted, over the noise of the little silver band that was playing in the middle of the field. "Go and find your Dad, perhaps he will. He's got

327

more time than I have," she said, picking up another jar of raspberry jam to compare it with the one she already had in her hand.

So the little boy ran off. He knew where his father would be and, sure enough, he found him there, in the Beer Tent, chatting to his friends. "Please, Dad, can we have a go on the swing boats?" he pleaded. "I think Mum doesn't like them and she won't take me."

"Oh, all right then, you little pest!" Edward replied with a smile, swinging the boy up on to his shoulders. "Just one go mind, I haven't too much cash to spend on those things!"

With that he bade his pals "Cheerio for a while!" and winking at them as he did so, he took the boy by the hand and began to cross the field. Suddenly, he saw, coming through the gate at the entrance to the field, Mr W J Taylor, the postmaster, who was making his way over from the Post Office. This was in the nearby London House, where a board over the door announced that he was a 'Baker, Grocer and Draper'.

"Sorry about this, Mr Evans," the Postmaster said, with a look of apprehension on his face. "But I thought that, it being a telegram, I ought to bring it over to you at once. I knew as it was the Fete day you'd be over here. Luckily I was in the house when the telephone rang, because, as you know, the shop itself is shut on Bank Holidays."

Edward took the envelope from Mr Taylor's hand and opened it with a grim expression on his face, for he felt he knew what command the contents would hold. Leading Stoker Edward Evans had already served in the Royal Navy for twelve years, but had left when his term was up, returning to marry Alice Green on 4 August 1908. After this they came to live in The Terrace in Stoke Row and Edward found work as a forester on the nearby Nettlebed Estate. War had already been declared on Germany some three weeks earlier and Edward knew that it would not be long before he would be told to return for duty again.

"Sorry, lad. There'll be no swings today. Where's Mum?" Edward scanned the crowds of people, women in large decorated hats, pushing *bassinets* [hooded perambulators], men carrying glasses of beer and children everywhere. Finally, he spotted Alice, still talking to the lady behind the Preserves stall. "Alice, Alice!" he called and eventually she heard him above the merry-making and, seeing the purposeful look on his face, put down the jam jar. With a farewell nod to the saleswoman she came towards her husband.

"As she neared him, she saw the yellow envelope sticking out of his clenched hand. "Is it, is it...?" she asked, falteringly, for she too, had been dreading this telegram for weeks now.

"Yes, it is. It says I have to report back to the Royal Fleet Reserve in Portsmouth for training." Edward read the scrap of paper out loud to her.

"We'll come with you, love." his wife comforted. "I'll bring young Ted with me and we can stay in lodgings until you sail."

"Well, alright. Just for a while then, until there's a ship for me."

Gradually other men in the area received similar cables, if they had been on the reserve lists of any of the armed forces. At the same time they knew in their hearts that life in the villages would never be the same again.

Up in the School on Witheridge Hill, the Headmaster, Mr John H Baker, wrote in the Log Book on 18 September 1914: 'In view of the great crisis in our country's history, viz: the war between Germany and Austria and the Allies, Belgium, France, Britain and Russia, the following features have been introduced into the school work:

Drawing: Flags of the Allied Countries.
Singing: The National Anthem, the Marseillaise and other patriotic songs being learned.
Recitation: Poems of patriotism and valour will be taught.
General Information: Important dispatches and war news are read each day during Reading or Composition lessons.
Geography: Sketch maps from the newspapers will be cut out and studied with the atlas and the position of the chief towns in the war will be noted. The positions of the great armies will be followed.

Young men were being called up fast throughout the land and in October 1914, Mr Baker wrote: 'Owing to the War... the Education Committee feels there will be insufficient youths to form an Evening Class... and will make no grant.'

The Franklin boys, Charlie and George, living down in the little cottage at the bottom of Witheridge Hill, were also called up for duty in the Army. They served throughout the War but rarely wrote more than the occasional postcard home. Their mother worried constantly about them. Every night she knelt by her bed, listening to the breathing of the three younger children and prayed for the safety of her sons.

One slightly brighter aspect of their being away from home was that Daisy, now eighteen and Dolly, now fifteen, were able to sleep in the boys' big bed in the adjacent room. "It don't half seem big, there's so much room!" Daisy laughed. "I only wish it weren't because Charlie and Georgie was in the Army." She was fortunate in being able to find work as a maid at Highmore Hall and was able to come home each night, providing she was up at the Hall again by six o'clock in the morning to lay the fires and lay the table for breakfast, among her other duties.

The timetable up at Highmore School was revised in January 1915, in accordance with suggestions made by Mr C B Hunt, His Majesty's Inspector of Schools. Mr Baker's entry for that week included an explanation of the changes that were to take place: 'Physical exercises will consist of twenty minutes lessons per week. Additional lessons in Recitation, Oral and Written Compositions, substitutes for English grammar lesson for the Lower Group. Drawing lessons once a week for the boys and girls...' The regimented curriculum of Reading, Writing and Arithmetic only was beginning to change.

The Great War, as it was beginning to be known, was already affecting the village, like all those in England. On 18 June, 1915, Mr Baker made the entry: 'Two boys, H Earle and F Randall, granted permission to be absent...for agricultural labour, owing to the scarcity of labour, due to the War.'

In the November of that year, Mr Baker wrote: 'Mr Hunt, HMI, has taken a commission in His Majesty's Army and will be replaced by Mr H J Dean. The Committee has decided to give certificates in lieu of books for Attendance and Good Conduct.' Economies, both financial and practical were becoming necessary.

Boys were especially needed to work on the land as so many of their male relatives were being killed or wounded. When they were old enough, a 'Labour Certificate' was given to children, usually boys, and this allowed them to finish school as 'half-timers' and go out and earn a little money. This was of some help too, to their mothers living on the very small allowance paid to the armed forces. On 31 March 1916, Mr Baker wrote: 'Jack Randall was successful at the recent Labour Examination and so will be eligible to leave the school.'

From time to time, both the Franklin boys had spells of leave and were able to come home from the trenches in France. They were always transported from Southampton or Portsmouth to Reading by train but were expected to walk the nine miles home.

Dolly herself, from the age of fourteen had been working in the mornings up at the Stoke Row Vicarage, scrubbing floors and cleaning saucepans with sand. The work was very hard and rough on the hands of a young girl and she often had chilblains. The Vicar's wife, Mrs Hutchinson, was very critical and finally, Ellie decided it was enough for Dolly to care for the children and the house. "We'll manage." she assured her daughter.

"Mum, you're wonderful!" said Dolly tearfully when her mother made the decision.

"Oh, I'm no 'ero!" exclaimed the woman, regardless of all that she had been through in the past ten years.

So, Dolly stayed at home and cooked and cleaned for the whole family. Unfortunately, neither of her brothers was at home when, one hot summer's day in 1916, the wall of the old well in the garden of the cottage caved in. Daisy had gone into a better paid job as a resident maid over in Buckinghamshire by then, so the management of the house and her two younger siblings was left entirely to Dolly while her mother was at work doing laundry in the local 'big houses' all day every day except Sunday.

However, the seventeen year old was appalled when she heard the flint stones plopping down into the water, for she knew it would mean a lot of fetching and carrying of water in buckets on yokes on her shoulders until it could be repaired. The nearest public well was the one up at Highmore Cross, by the church. Since it had been sunk in 1865, the grateful villagers had used it constantly, but most of them lived up nearby and on the same level.

Luckily, the Vicar of Highmore was at home when she called at the back door and told her story to the maid. Revd John Hughes came out to see the girl and assured her that he would 'engage the services of a well digger as soon as it could be arranged.'

Dolly soon found the climb up the hill with a yoke across her shoulders and two buckets clanking at her sides to be very hard, even though the containers were empty. Every day, when they were full, she was thankful to be able to walk downwards to the bottom, on the surfaced road known as the 'Hard Hill' on the north side. "I never realised how valuable our well was until I had to go up to the Highmore well every day," she told her thirteen year-old sister, Annie and ten year old brother, Jack. "I think you two will have to do a bit more now to help. There's so much for me to do now the boys are in France." Eventually the well was repaired and never was a girl more grateful than Dolly when the well digger pronounced it 'all safe and sound now!'

In February of 1917, up at the school on top of the hill above the cottage, Mr John H Baker was writing yet again in the School Log Book: 'Special lessons have been taken this week on the National Food Supplies and the Great War Loan.' and four months later: 'Special lessons were given on Birds, Insects and Crops and others on Food Economy.' Food production was becoming a major national issue. Later that month, the Headmaster wrote again: An extra ten *poles* [pole = 5.1/2 yards] of ground is being cultivated by the Gardening Class, owing to the urgency of food production. A return of the particulars of the above has been made to the authorities. Potatoes have been planted in eighteen of the thirty poles of ground cultivated.'

At the end of that month, 'Lieutenant Eric Blore, RFC, kindly gave the children an account of his work at the Front in an 'Observation Balloon', which he illustrated with sketches made on the blackboard.' [This gentleman was a Highmore resident.]

In the September of that year, when school started again after the summer holidays, Mr Baker received 'papers from the Education Secretary with Government proposals for collection of:

(a) Horse chestnuts. [These were used for the manufacture of a type of gunpowder]

(b) Blackberries for the Government jam factories to supply the Forces. It is proposed that the authorities grant the schools about two half-day holidays per week until the middle of October, so that children may gather the above under the supervision of their teachers.'

On 12th October he was able to report 'During the past four

weeks the total quantity of blackberries picked by the children and teachers amounted to four hundredweights.'

But still the War went on. Every few months a soldier would be reported as having been killed or a wounded man was sent home. Belts in the villages had to be tightened even further as food shortages began to tell. Several local women also joined the QARANC [Queen Alexander's Royal Army Nursing Corps] and reported dreadful stories about life in the trenches and in the hospitals at the front when they returned home on leave.

On Wednesday, 30th April, 1918 the school was closed: '...owing to the Children's Concert for the benefit of St Dunstan's Hostel for Blind Soldiers' and this was brought home to people when a photograph was published in a magazine showing a line of blind soldiers, each with his hand on the shoulder of the man in front, being led by a sighted man.

About the same time, Mrs Alice Evans received a telegram to say that her husband, Leading Stoker Edward Percy Evans was seriously ill with double pneumonia in the Royal Navy's Haslar Hospital, Portsmouth, having been torpedoed on HMS *Terrible*. She immediately took young Ted with her again, as she had done several times throughout the War when he had written to say that his ship would be in port for a few days. In a small and rather dingy boarding house they had all known a few hours of happiness together before it was time for his ship to sail.

This time, when she stood by his bed, Alice realised her husband was not going to live, so she went out into the corridor and told Ted to 'go to the cinema with young Bert for a while.' Later that afternoon, the usherette came down the aisle to the two boys and whispered to the older one: "Your mother's sent word, you've got to go home at once."

When he arrived back at the lodging house, his tearful mother told Ted what he had dreaded hearing. His father had died and would not be coming home again. Leading Stoker Evans' coffin, draped with a Union Jack, was later carried through the village of Stoke Row, followed by a long line of mourners. His seaman's cap was placed on top of it and was buried with him.

That autumn, blackberries were gathered again but 'these were sold to the Red Cross Hospital at Henley, being refused at the Railway

Station, owing to the Railway Strike.'

Eventually, on 11th November 1918, an Armistice was signed between the Allies and Germany. Those who had survived this terrible War rejoiced as best they could. A few went to London to celebrate but those in the villages organised joyful events to mark the closing of one of the worst periods in the nation's history.

Charles and George Franklin came home one Sunday in December 1918. They had been fortunate enough to meet up on the ship that happened to bring them both back. They walked up from Reading to Highmore but it was George who ran down the hill to the cottage. His young brother, Jack, was the first to see him coming down the lane.

Dolly was to tell their neighbours later how he had "hollered out to Jack: 'Tell Mum I won't come in yet. Tell her to put a bowl of water out by the gate. It may be cold but I'd rather wash out here, I'm alive with lice!' Both my brothers did the same, took all their clothes off and put the fresh ones on that Mum had put out with the bowl of water before they would even come into the house. I swear they still stank when they did come indoors, though. Later that evening they burnt all their old clothes on a bonfire at the top of the garden!"

A week or so later, George divulged what he had brought back in his kitbag, a small brass shell. "It's empty, so it's alright." he claimed, but Ellie made him bury it deep in the ground at the bottom of the garden.

Several months later, George's *gratuity* [government grant to soldiers] arrived. "Mr Page says he's selling this cottage and the garden, Mum and I've decided to buy it. He wants just a hundred pounds for it and I could do that out of my gratuity money."

"Don't be silly, boy!" his mother counselled. "It'd be a millstone round your neck. Even though Mr Page's recently put this tiled roof on instead of the old thatch, you'd never be able to pay the rates!"

George was disappointed but felt his mother was probably right. "After all," he thought. "I've yet to get a job." A terrible winter followed and the undernourished population fell easily victim to an epidemic of influenza that was to kill a large number of the people. This and grave unemployment, made life almost as hard as it had been during the four long years of the Great War.

******

The story of the Franklins comes from the Memoirs of Miss Dolly

Franklin, *published in the* Stoke Row News *in 1980.*

The Highmore School Log Books *are in the Oxfordshire County Archives. Mr John H Baker's book* A School on the Ground Floor *also provided much of the information in this part of the chapter, especially the story of Dr Crippen. Mr Baker also wrote several other books about this area, including* The Ipsden Country *and* The Land of the Gap.

The reminiscences of Mr Ted Evans were published in his Memoirs *in the* Stoke Row News *in the 1980s.*

The Old Place

Chapter 17. The Sawyer, the Actress and the Farmer's Wife: 1921 - 1938

The years following the First World War were full of difficulties for the nation. The epidemic of influenza had killed hundreds of thousands and left many very weak. This, together with rife unemployment and the consequent poverty meant very hard times for most people. Even so, the people of Henley and Wallingford managed to collect money to build War Memorial Hospitals and Memorial Crosses were erected in every village. In Stoke Row and Highmore, where times were especially hard, brass plaques were placed on the walls of the Churches and the Chapel.

A beautifully illuminated scroll, listing the almost one hundred Stoke Row men who had served in the War, together with the names of their regiments and whether they had been wounded or killed, was framed and placed on a wall in the 'Iron Room' as it was known, a building constructed of corrugated iron sheets at Stoke Row. This had been erected in 1909 at the expense of the Vicar, Revd Hubert Harben Appleford, on Glebe land which lay between the Vicarage and the Church. For many years it served as a Reading Room for the local men. Later the Scroll was moved to the newly-built Village Hall.

******

Edward John ('Ted') Evans, whose father had died in Haslar Hospital in May 1914 as a result of being torpedoed when he was aboard HMS *Terrible*, was twelve years old by 1921 and was desperately trying to help support his mother, Alice, and his ten-year old sister, Kathleen.

Although they were still at school, he and his best friend, Harry Webb, cut wood for Mr Arthur Chapman in the late afternoons as soon as their lessons had finished and in the summer evenings as well. Mr Chapman felled the trees and cut them into six-foot lengths. It was then up to the boys to saw them into six inch lengths and split them into sections, so they could be sold as firewood. On Saturdays and in the holidays they helped Mr Chapman on his rounds. They reckoned to be able to cut five hundred logs a week and thus earned themselves six pence a week each. An extra bonus was that Mr Chapman allowed them to take home any wood that would not split and all the chippings that burnt well on their kitchen ranges.

One sunny, warm day in the 'long, hot dry summer' of 1921, Mr William Lester, the carter, asked the lads to take his sow up to Highmore Farm. "She's to go to the boar," he explained to them. "I'll give you a penny each if you manage to get her there and bring her back safely." As soon as they nodded their glad assent at such a seemingly easy job, Mr Lester warned them "She has a mind of her own, does Peggy. You take care as how you goes with her!"

So off the boys went, leading the pig by the rope and, just as they had imagined, it was easy. "Easy peasy, easy as pie" Ted laughed.

"Easy money, too!" rejoined his pal and they and the pig trotted down Stoke Row Hill and past the little cottage at the foot of Witheridge Hill.

"That's where the Franklins live, isn't it? Lucky the Franklin boys got through the War. Not like my poor Dad." said Ted, wiping away a tear on the cuff of his shirt as he recalled how his father had swung him up on top of his shoulders on that fateful day in 1914.

It was harder work walking up the hill by which time they had to pull the pig by the rope in order to get her up to the top. By the time they reached Highmore Cross the lads were hot and thirsty. Suddenly the pig sat down. Despite all their efforts she would not budge an inch. "There's still a way to go to Highmore Farm!" said Harry, getting alarmed in case they should not be able to fulfil their task and earn their penny.

"Let's just sit down and rest a while here on the Green." Ted suggested. Anyway it's so hot! Perhaps Peggy could do with a rest, too. My goodness, I'm thirsty!"

Luckily for the boys, the Postmistress, Mrs Baldwin, came out of the Post Office and saw them there. "Why don't you boys go to the well, over there, by the church and take yourselves a drink They say this is the longest drought on record, we've had no rain since February, you know, but the well water is clean and pure and you can get a drink from the cup on the chain in the little recess at the side." Gratefully, the boys took it in turns to go over to the well and drank their fill.

By the time they had finished, the pig got up slowly and seemed to know that it was time to go. "I hope Mr Page let's us see what happens when she gets to the boar!" said Harry.

"Don't s'ppose he will - you know what an old misery he is." Ted replied.

True enough, Mr Tom Page took the sow from them and told them to go to the farmhouse kitchen door. "The cook'll give you a drink and something to eat. I'll send David Jenkins round with her as soon as she's ready." he said.

The plump, round-faced cook, Mrs Megan Jenkins, was much more cheery. "Come you in, my lovelies." she cooed in her soft voice, which brought with it the sound of Welsh valleys, far away. "You must be thirsty, even if, as you say, you stopped off at the Highmore well on the way. Here we are, have some of my home-made lemonade. You'll be here a while yet."

In fact, they were there for several hours and were able to partake of a nourishing lunch, one of the best meals they'd enjoyed in a long time. Finally, David Jenkins came to the kitchen door and gave the rope into the hands of Harry Webb.

Going back to Stoke Row was quite a different matter to coming up to Highmore. "Peggy seems to be almost skipping along!" Ted noted to his friend. "Shame old Tom Page wouldn't let us see what happened in the pig sty. I know what the boar does to the sow, but I'd like to see it for myself, wouldn't you?" His pal nodded his agreement.

In the autumn of that year he and Harry also went out picking up acorns from the woodland floor and sold them to Mr Lester who sold them on in the Reading markets as pig food.

On Boxing Day, 1921, Mrs Chapman sent her seven-year old son round to the Evans' house. "Mum says can Ted come and see Dad? He's very bad with his chest and she's hoping he'll be able to take the logs down to Reading!"

"Of course he'll come." Mrs Evans reassured the boy. "Run home and tell your Mum he'll be there in a few minutes. He's just having his breakfast and, in any case, he'll have to go round to Harry's house and get him, too."

The two twelve year old boys were partly overjoyed at the idea of being able to take the horse and cart themselves to Reading and yet somewhat apprehensive lest they should not be able to manage the horse in the busy streets of the town. "Luckily Billy's a calm old boy and he's used to the traffic anyway." Harry said to Ted as they hurried over to Mr Chapman's yard.

"Yes, that's true. I reckon he knows his way round the houses and shops in Reading just as good as we do. You notice how he stops at each one and seems ready to go on to the next as soon as we come out." Ted agreed.

Again, the boys showed how well they could do when the need arose, delivering logs to Reading and collecting the money from the buyers as well, for two whole weeks. Even when it snowed, old Billy seemed to be able to keep his footing and they had no accidents, although Alice Evans, Jane Webb and especially the Chapmans were very glad to see them return safely each time. Fortunately Arthur Chapman was well enough to take the work over again by the time the new term started at Stoke Row School.

Thanks to increased legislation in connection with education, the situation in Stoke Row and Highmore schools, along with others in rural counties like Oxfordshire, had improved greatly. In 1916, the club-footed, harsh Headmaster, Mr Frederick Dakin, decided to move on after only two years,. He was replaced by a much fairer, kinder man, Mr George Wilson, along with his stout but pretty wife. The local women noticed immediately her beautiful skin and naturally curly hair.

Miss Cecily Turner, who had come to live with her aunt and uncle, Mr and Mrs Hewitt, on the death of her parents when she was only seven, was now in charge of the Infants. She had gained her Teacher's Certificate and continued living with her widowed aunt in the tiny octagonal Well Cottage, where Mrs Hewitt herself was now

Keeper of the Maharajah's Well.

George Wilson was known as a fair-minded man, but was not one to 'spare the rod and spoil the child.' He carried his cane wherever he went and did not take misdemeanours lightly. One day, after he had been in charge of the school for about a year, Mr Wilson found some rude words written in a book and determined at once to find out who it was.

Ted went home and told his mother what had happened: "He went through all our handwritings and ruled out all the kids until he got to mine and Jake Smith's. It weren't me, Mum, honest!"

Alice Evans believed her son. She realised that he got up to larks sometimes, but because she had always insisted on no one in the house doing so, she knew that he would not use bad language verbally and certainly not write it.

All the boys then had to go before the Governors of the school. One by one all the boys were interviewed and finally the offender confessed. Because he owned up and apologised sincerely, Mr Wilson forgave him publicly and, perhaps to compensate the rest of the children for this great upset, he and his wife gave a party for the whole class.

Life was not all book-work and learning, even at school. All the children played games at break times, mid-morning, after lunch and on the way home. Among these was the 'flicking' of cigarette cards, usually provided in packets of 'Woodbines'. These cheap cigarettes came in packets of five for tuppence [two pence] or ten for four pence. Ted explained the game to his young sister, Kathleen. "The idea is to flick the card the furthest. The winner collects the whole lot that's on the ground, then!" The cards were about three inches long and one and a quarter inches wide and came in an assortment of themes, such as Film Stars, Flags, Footballers, Regiments, Trains, Royalty, etc. Collecting sets by 'swopping' was a favourite pastime.

Another way in which Ted entertained his friends was by playing his mouth-organ for he was quite musical. Other boys had to make do with whistles from tree boughs. One of them demonstrated to Ted how he made his: "Young ash is the best wood. You cut it down with a sharp knife, put it into your mouth like this, to wet it, and then you twists it and the bark comes off, like this, see! Now then, you makes a V shape in the top with the knife and, Bob's yer uncle! You just blow through the top and push the bark up and down to vary the notes. It's easy peasy!"

Girls like Ted's sister, Kathleen, preferred to play with their rag dolls and to make straw rattles with a pebble inside, for new babies in the village. They rolled hoops made by the local blacksmith and even played marbles when the game 'came into season', usually around Easter time, as soon as the roads became drier and provided a better surface. Those children who could afford them had marbles with stripes in varied colours, whilst the poorer ones had to do with glass stoppers from ginger beer bottles. They loved skipping and Hop Scotch, too, chalked on the school playground.

In the winter they had to do with verbal games, often puzzles like 'As I was going to St Ives I met a man with seven wives'. Woe betide the poor child who did not know the rhyme and tried to calculate four times seven! A less kind trick was often sprung on a new child by the school bully:

> *Adam and Eve and Pinch-me-tight went down to the river*
> *to bathe*
> *Adam and Eve were drowned, who do you think was saved?*

Kathleen was just in time to save little Mary Maundle from a nasty pinch on the arm when she caught Ned Callow playing this trick on her. "Don't you dare!" she cried as she pushed him away. The other girls soon crowded round and prevented the bully from hurting either of them.

'Tipcat' was another favourite pastime. This time it was Ted who showed one of the younger boys how to play this game. "You get a bit of stick, like this, cut it to about four and a half inches long and whittle it down with the knife until its about three quarters of an inch thick, like this. Now you shave off both ends to a point. Now," he said, laying the stick flat on the ground in the middle of the road, "You hit it with a bigger stick like this one!" As he did so, the pointed stick spun up into the air and within a split-second of its having done so, Ted hit it again with the stick. "Now let's see how far it'll go!" The stick flew ahead quite a long way. Ted could see that the younger boy was impressed. "The winner is the one whose stick flies the furthest," he concluded. "Come on, we'll be late for school, mucking about like

341

this!"

Despite being a disciplinarian, Mr Wilson was an excellent and knowledgeable teacher and taught his pupils a great deal. Two of his favourite subjects were physics and chemistry. To make his lessons more interesting he made a 'volcano' from ground pumice and sand. Then he made the whole thing explode with home-made gunpowder mixed from salt-petre, charcoal and sulphur. He was not to know that some of the boys, including Ted and Harry, made their own pyrotechnics this way, even putting some of the gunpowder into a bottle! As Ted was heard to say many years later over a beer in the Cherry Tree: "It's amazing no-one was hurt by those home made fireworks!"

About this time, the Vicar of Highmore, Revd John ('Bravvy') Hughes, gave a series of lantern slide shows on weekday evenings in Highmore Church. The programme started with a few hymns and the slide show then followed. The pictures were often of the Holy Lands. There was no charge for entry but a collection was made as the villagers left the church.

Like other boys of his age, Ted Evans left school in July 1923, when he was fourteen. He and Harry Webb continued to work together for Mr Chapman and by this time they were bigger and stronger and their employer started them on 'chucking'. This work consisted of finding a tree stump that was on the point of rotting. "Mr Chapman calls it a 'druxy'," Ted explained to his mother and sister after his first day at this work. "Then we use a *beetle* [a wooden mallet] and a wedge to split the stumps up, so they can be burned on an open fire. Mr Chapman showed us how to cover them up when we were finished, so they can dry throughout the summer."

"What do you cover them with?" asked Alice, curious as to what her son's work involved.

"Old tarpaulins, corrugated iron, anything to keep most of the rain off." Ted replied. "Mr Chapman says they burn jolly well in the winter. I expect he'll give us the smaller bits that he can't sell in Reading market."

That winter, when it became too cold to work outside, Ted applied for a job in the newly built sawmill at the far west side of Stoke Row. This was considered at the time to be the finest one built in England, as its revolutionary design provided for all the *banding* [the belts which drove the machines] to be carried down from the pulleys and shafting overhead and thus increase safety at work. The logs came in and had to be sawn up, usually using a band saw. Ted was started on this work with an older man and he soon learned how to control these powerful machines. He soon earned himself the nickname 'Ted the Sawyer'.

His mother was delighted to find her son now had more money to give to her each week and also to buy new clothes for himself on his Saturday afternoon bus rides to Reading. "He's become a real natty dresser!" Alice boasted to a neighbour proudly one Sunday afternoon as she watched him go down the street with one of the local girls. "He bought that new suit in Burtons, you know, the shop that's got the motto: 'We are the Fifty Shilling Tailors!'"

Ted was not only smartly dressed when he was not at work, but he also had an eye for the girls and many of them were delighted when, on a Saturday, he took them up to the Working Men's Club at Nettlebed. Here, watching silent films, they enjoyed the humorous antics of Charlie Chaplin, Harold Lloyd and Tom Mix. Sometimes there were exciting serials like *The Phantom Foe*. These 'pictures' always ended with a 'cliff-hanger' which encouraged the young people to walk the three miles up to the Club the following Saturday, to see how their hero and heroine were faring. Now that Ted and his friends were working they were expected to pay six pence, whereas while they were at school the entry price had only been three pence.

The fact that it was dark did not bother them, for the boys had carbide lamps and knew the roads well. They loved to look up at the bright stars on a winter's night and Ted prided himself on being able to point out to his girl-friends the Milky Way and even a few of the major constellations, like Orion and the Big Bear and showed them how to find the North Star. It was so quiet that all they heard was the hoot of the owls as they walked down Stoke Row Hill, through the woods, past the little cottage at the bottom of Witheridge Hill and on up through Highmore to Nettlebed on the 'New Road' created in 1926. Motorcars were few in those days and people rarely drove out at night.

In 1928, when he was just nineteen, Ted met a pretty girl called Beattie Rogers who lived at Kingwood Common, two miles from Stoke Row on the Reading road. For this dashing young man it proved to be 'love at first sight.' He went home and told Alice and

Kathleen that he intended to marry Beattie. "You've only just met her!" protested his mother. "How do you know you will be happy with her?"

"I just know, I knew it as soon as I met her. I said to myself at once: 'That's it, she's the one!'"

Three years later, on the first day of October 1928, they were married and had a large family of seven children, four girls and three boys. They lived most of their married lives in Stoke Row where Ted continued to work at the Star Brush Sawmill.

******

Just prior to the Great War, parts of the Highmore Hall Estate were put up for sale and this included a small, old thatched cottage on top of Witheridge Hill, next to the school. Mr John H Baker, the Headmaster, had just come into a small inheritance that enabled him to gain possession of it. The property was a very attractive one, consisting of a small orchard at the side of the cottage and a long stretch of garden on the other. Like the school, it stood on the brow of the hill adjoining many acres of common land, sloping down to the valley below. Beyond this was the magnificent view over the beech woods, rising to the village of Stoke Row on the opposite side of the valley. However, the house was in a poor condition and the garden overgrown.

John Baker paid one hundred and fifty pounds for the property and immediately set about restoring it as best he could in his spare time. It had been a tenanted home for a farm worker for generations and had suffered badly from neglect. Fortunately the summer holidays were about to begin, so John and Beatrice made up their minds firstly to clean out the cottage and then to repaint it. John was good at woodwork, having come from a family of builders, and soon he was putting in cupboards and shelves. Between them they soon had the cottage in 'apple pie order'.

That September the couple put the word around the village that the cottage was to let for four shillings a week. As the standard rent for these properties was only three shillings or less, it is not surprising that they had no takers. "I think we should try and rent it to someone in London," advised Beatrice. "We could advertise it in my magazine, *The Lady*. There's sure to be someone up in the city who would like a country cottage like this to come down to at the weekends. So many people have motor-cars now."

John agreed this to be a good idea and not long after they had done so, one fine Sunday afternoon, a taxi drove up to the Schoolhouse and a lady and gentleman alighted. The visitors turned out to be well-known theatrical people. Miss Hilda Trevelyan had been playing the part of Wendy in J M Barrie's *Peter Pan* for several years already and was also renowned for her role in *What Every Woman Knows*. Her husband, Sydney Blow, was an impresario and the two of them were seeking a cottage in the country.

Hilda was entranced with the little thatched cottage, especially the view from the windows and its secluded position. True it had no bathroom and only primitive sanitation, but the couple agreed to pay ten shillings a week. Both the Blows and the Bakers were delighted at the arrangement.

The curious fact was that Sydney Blow and his wife had been to this spot before. Several years later he explained to John and Beatrice Baker, as he showed them a picture postcard, exactly what had happened some years earlier. "The other day, I was turning out some old photographs and postcards and came across this one of Witheridge Hill, with our little thatched cottage on it. You can see here, the back of the card I had written in my own hand: '24th June 1908. A delightful place, where we should like to live one day.'

It came about in this way," he continued. "After the second year of Peter Pan, Hilda said she felt she wanted to have a holiday in some quiet country spot, but where should we go? She suggested all sorts of places, but I urged her to make no plans and just leave the holiday to Fate. 'There is nothing like an unplanned holiday, not knowing where you are going to.' I said."

He lit a cigarette and went on: "Hilda did not agree; she is a deal more cautious than I am, but eventually she gave in and I introduced her, not without many misgivings on her part, to the scheme which starts with your selecting some London terminus at random.

You then arrive at that terminus with luggage to last you a week. You next choose any letter of the alphabet and then find out from the platform indicator which is the next train out. You note the name of the last station on that route which begins with the letter you decided upon, and buy your tickets.

"What!" exclaimed Beatrice Baker, "Not knowing anything about the place you are going to!" She seemed astonished at the idea.

"That's right." Sydney Blow continued. "You take the train, you arrive at your random destination, you hire a conveyance and direct the driver to take you to the most charming inn in the most lovely surroundings in the neighbourhood. And you have a week's delight of unplanned happiness – that is, if you are the right couple to play the game.

In the case of Hilda and myself, we chose Paddington and 'H' was to be the letter. The first train happened to be a Henley train. At Henley my instructions to the driver of the conveyance led us to arriving at the Maltster's Arms at Rotherfield Greys, you probably know the one I mean. We spent a lovely week there and during our walks there we came up here. It was then we came across this cottage, although it did not look like this then. In fact, as you know, it was rather shabby but I could see that it would be much improved with a lick of paint."

"What an extraordinary co-incidence!" remarked John Baker. "Of course, it was let to one of the local woodsmen then."

"Yes, so we did not go inside, but I went over to the little shop and bought this postcard as I didn't have my camera with me. As you can see, I have kept it for many years and had quite forgotten about it."

"Life is full of strange happenings like that!" commented Beatrice. "And you are happy here now?"

"Oh yes!" Sydney replied. "I often tell my London friends that there is nothing like a country cottage to blow the theatre cobwebs away from one. There is always a new joy and a new thrill each day in the garden you 'do' yourself. Of course the love of the garden must be yours, otherwise you will never make a success of it or enjoy it. A garden can get a big hold on one, as you well know!"

Mr John H Baker and his wife left Highmore School in 1924 for Goring Heath School where he took up the Headmastership and his wife again became a teacher. In their fourteen years on Witheridge Hill they had seen many changes at the school, especially since the end of the Great War. Among these were the provision of motor transport, milk during the morning break and catering for school meals at lunch-time. The long walks in all weathers and slices of bread and dripping with just cold, and often icy water, to wash it down at lunch-time were a thing of the past. In consequence the children very soon became visibly fitter, brighter and easier to teach.

After the Great War, the Blows came down regularly to Witheridge Hill at every opportunity. When they were not there, their housekeeper, Jane, cared for the cottage and Jim Green kept the garden in immaculate condition.

Philip ('Pa') Braham, a musical director and composer of *Limehouse Blues* and other well-known songs, with his wife, Faith, also bought a property nearby, which they named 'Fipps Cottage'. Several of their show business friends also bought dwellings around Witheridge Hill. One of them was the famous dancer and singer, Jack Buchanan, [often spoken of as being 'England's answer to Fred Astaire'], who was a frequent visitor at 'Fipps', and was a very generous and kind man.

A little later, Jack purchased an old cottage next door to 'Fipps Cottage' and developed it into a beautiful house that he named 'Bucks Barn' and used as a 'weekend retreat'.

Several years later, one weekend when the Blows were having a restful time, Sydney once again met John Baker outside the school gate. "I hear that Philip Braham's wife has opened a restaurant in Reading. That should give her an interest as well as an income now that she is a widow." John remarked.

"Yes," Sydney agreed. "Jack Buchanan has been helping her with it. He has a heart of gold and will do anyone a good turn if he can. Last weekend Jack promptly rallied round and served behind the snack bar on the opening night. You may have seen the picture and the report in the *Reading Chronicle*. There was a long queue waiting outside 'Sallie's' that evening and it had to be controlled by the police. They were all marshalled in good order and patiently waited their turn to be served by Jack Buchanan - it's not every day you get served by a famous star of stage and screen!"

"No, indeed." John agreed. "She is very blessed, having a friend like that. Like the old saying: 'A friend in need is a friend indeed'."

In the meantime, Hilda Trevelyan was continuing to play Wendy in *Peter Pan* which was becoming ever more popular as the years went by.

Hilda's career started in *Little Mary* and it was at a performance of this play that the Scottish playwright, J M Barrie first saw the girl that he turned into the immortal Wendy, said to have been Barrie's favourite in the part. In his biography, *A Ghost Walks on Fridays,* her husband recounted his memories of how it all began:

'When the rehearsal of *Peter Pan* started, you can well imagine the astonishment in the minds of the company. Was there ever such a household as that of the Darling family? No play so far had had a big dog for a children's nurse. No fairy so far had come flying through a casement window into a night nursery. Not on the stage, anyway. Fairies strode majestically on and were very often five foot ten inches high, with tiny wings and shimmering with diamonds and bejewelled wands. The first *Peter Pan* company was staggered when they learned that Peter, just an ordinary boy, made his first entrance flying with no wings, right through the window and landed on the nursery floor.

Hilda used to meet me in the breaks of rehearsal and tell me scraps of the many odd things that happened on the Duke of York's stage. She was quite at a loss to know what the play was about. During a lunch together she announced that she was going to learn to fly. "What!" I said, "Are you a fairy, too?"

I don't know yet; we haven't got that far. It's all very strange and puzzling.' And yet, as we know, she did 'fly' and the whole thing was a wonder at the time, so long before 'special effects' gave us the terrifying thrills we see in modern entertainments.

Miss Trevelyan, as she became respectfully known in Highmore, was often to be seen working with her husband in the garden of their country home, which they called Garden Cottage. Usually in the summer she wore a 'milkmaid's cap', which came down to the shoulders at the back and shaded the wearer from the sun. Later she took to very large-brimmed headgear, which became known by the cinema-going public as 'picture hats'. Sometimes photographers from picture magazines or newspapers managed to track her down and occasionally were privileged to take portraits of her in her lovely home.

She often popped up to the village shop, run appropriately enough by a Mr Sweet, on the 'New Road' that had recently been created down the south side of the hill and was wide enough to take buses. Here she posted letters and caught up on the local gossip, for as she explained to Mrs Sweet: "We have come to look upon Highmore as our second home."

"And we always think of you as 'Wendy', Ma'am," Mrs Sweet replied. "Even though we've never seen the play ourselves."

It was not only for her role in *Peter Pan* that Hilda Trevelyan became famous. A well-known critic of the time, J T Grein, wrote:

"She is the most modest of artists. She is rarely lured into an interview and then scarcely speaks of herself. She expresses no opinions in – mainly futile – symposia when actors and actresses are supposed to have the last word in wisdom and omniscience. We don't know what she wears, or where she walks, dines or maybe dances. Yet we all know and love her, this unobtrusive little 'country mouse', who has more heart and intelligence than a random dozen actresses. When she does not act, and wisely she selects only parts into which she can throw herself, she retires and is not heard of.

Yet she dwells in memory, a clear-cut cameo to be treasured and cherished. From the day that she leapt into fame in Frederick Fenn and Richard Pryce's *Op o' my Thumb* – a slip of a girl, so tiny that she was nothing to look at – but she looked at you with those big eyes of hers and made you laugh and cry at will – her portrayals stand out when so many others are forgotten. And when we talk of Barrie, our most poetic playwright, up looms the name of Hilda Trevelyan, with visions of *Peter Pan, A Kiss for Cinderella, What Every Woman Knows* and *The Twelve Pound Look*."

The Blows often said they owed their 'wonderful country life' to John H Baker, the headmaster of the School on Witheridge Hill, who had bought and restored their cottage many years before the Great

War.

Not only did the Blows purchase Garden Cottage but, as the years went by, they bought and restored several other properties on Witheridge Hill, including the one which had been the Dame School. The Blows rebuilt this residence, called it Witheridge Hill Cottage and in the garden erected a little thatched 'summer house', which Hilda called her 'Wendy House'.

In the early 1930s, they bought the small cottage with two yew trees outside it on the road that ran along the bottom and which had once been a beer house. It had no formal name, so they decided to call it Old Place, that being the translation from the Saxon [Han Lley] of near-by Henley. Sydney Blow's brother, Julius Blow, was an architect, well enough known to have had articles about his work published in *Country Life* and the journal of the Royal Institute of British Architects. He had a remarkable flair for restoring vernacular buildings that previously had only earth floors and outside sanitation.

As the Blows restored each of five cottages, they sold their current home and moved into the next, creating lovely country homes for London people. Very soon the whole ambience on Witheridge Hill had changed from rural hovels to comfortable second homes for the 'well-to-do' burgeoning middle-class.

In consequence, the local woodmen and their families were soon forced to move. The Franklins were one such, but were found homes in the new Council houses that were erected in 1928 at Highmore Cross. They were well built, had long gardens and an open outlook on to farmland beyond. For all these villagers they were a considerable improvement on their previous abodes.

******

By 1938, Henley, Wallingford and Watlington had each developed into pleasant market towns, notwithstanding the severe unemployment that blighted the 1930s. Henley was the most prosperous. Its railway and nearness to London brought a surge of house building in the area, as the town was ideal for the more prosperous daily commuter to the metropolis.

Wallingford had seen a new hospital built on the Reading Road and the old one converted into a police station. The old Corn

Exchange, built in 1856, was used in the 1920s and '30s as a cinema until the purpose-built Regal Cinema opened its doors in 1934. This was enjoyed by many people, some of whom had come recently to live on the new council estates. Walter Wilder's foundry, which had made the canopy and machinery for the Maharajah's Well at Stoke Row in 1864, was one of the few light industrial companies in the town.

Watlington continued to lead its usual quiet life. A charming little town at the foot of the Chiltern Hills, from the Saxon *cilt* [chalk] it was much-loved, both by its residents and by the few London people who owned country homes in the area.

Reading, however, had burgeoned into a very large town. Not only did it have a station on the GWR [Great Western Railway, affectionately known as 'God's Wonderful Railway'] line from the West Country to Paddington, but a considerable number of industries had also grown up in and around the town.

Probably the most important of these was Huntley and Palmer's biscuit factory. This had started in 1822 as a modest biscuit bakery and confectioner's shop run by Joseph Huntley, opposite the Crown Inn, where several times a day coaches stopped to change horses. In order to stretch their legs, passengers often strolled across to the shop. In the early years all biscuits were sold loose and had to be eaten fairly quickly, but after a while Joseph Huntley had the idea that if they were packed into tin boxes they would keep fresh for far longer.

In this way another company was founded, that of Huntley, Boorne and Stevens, whose decorative tins were eventually to carry Huntley and Palmer's biscuits all over the world. Joseph Huntley also delivered them to villages throughout southern and central England by means of the well-organised canal system, part of which also flowed through Reading.

However it was in 1841, that this company really grew, when Joseph Huntley went into partnership with George Palmer, whose energy, initiative and interest in mechanisation were to transform this thriving family concern into the biggest biscuit enterprise in the world. By the end of the nineteenth century, Huntley and Palmers employed over 5000 people and the tin box factory also expanded, making not only biscuit tins but many other kinds as well. By the twentieth century their tins were mass-produced in many original and unusual shapes. The invention of offset litho printing in colour on curved surfaces added to the many varieties. Their novelty Christmas boxes were especially attractive and much sought-after.

The tile and brick works at Tilehurst, the Reading Iron Works which made agricultural machinery on the banks of the River Kennet, and Suttons Seeds, which went back even further than Huntley and Palmer to when John Sutton had started to sell seeds in 1807, all became major industries, helped greatly by the presence of both the canal and the railway.

In fact, the railway, being a busy junction, provided even more employment for this prosperous town. Many other smaller firms thrived in the shadows of them all. Not the least of these were the large stores and smaller shops in the centre of the town. Heelas Department Store, which had begun in 1854 as a small drapery in Minster Street, had grown into a large and well-conducted emporium, but it faced competition from other clothing stores such as Bulls and McIlroys as well as Jackson's, which occupied a valuable site on the corner of King Street. Individual shops selling a whole range of goods also lined the roads all around the town centre. A few, like the Home and Colonial Stores and The New International Stores were part of large chains, but the majority were run by their owners and provided the town and outlying villages with practically everything imaginable.

Notwithstanding all this wealth in the nearby towns, life in the countryside in the 1930s had changed little since the nineteenth century. With few exceptions, the owners of the same seven farms in Stoke Row and two in Highmore were still struggling to make a comfortable living.

******

Church Farm, in Cox's Lane, Stoke Row had been so named because it was once owned by the Church of England. Before the advent of St John the Evangelist in 1848, services were held there about once a month, thereby saving the local people from having to go all the way to Ipsden.

By 1935, however, it had come into the hands of the Wells family, one of several of the same name in the village. As far as they knew, they were not related. George Wells was the current owner, following the death of his father, early in 1937. George was a big man with a countryman's gait and large hands that had grown horny with much rough work. He had married Eileen Mason in the June of that year and sometimes smiled to himself as he thought back to how it all began.

Eileen was the younger daughter of Alfred and Ethel Mason of Caversham. They had another daughter, Joyce, who was two years older and still lived at home with her parents. Alfred was 47 years old, an engineer in the employ of Huntley and Palmers, the biscuit manufacturers, and cycled each day into their factory in Reading.

His wife, and was somewhat younger, worked as an assistant behind the counter at the Home and Colonial Stores, while Joyce did similar work at the New International Stores. Having both women in the grocery trade ensured that they were well provided for with food at very cheap rates, especially as they were allowed to buy unsold perishable produce at the end of the day at very low cost. Their younger daughter, Eileen worked as a clerk at the Reading Iron Works, where she had none of these benefits, but seemed happy enough.

Because they all worked, the Masons were able to afford a mortgage on a comfortable semi-detached house in Caversham, just above the town, on the north side, on the Emmer Green road.

They seemed to be a very contented family, but when early in 1938, Eileen started to court a young farmer the Masons became slightly concerned. They had met when he came down to the Iron Works for some new farm implements, Her parents had both always lived in the town or its suburbs and had no desire to see their daughter move out into a country district. "Never mind, Mother," Alfred comforted his wife. "Perhaps nothing will come of it."

However, as the months went by and the young couple seemed to be increasingly devoted to one another, their fears grew. Finally, one Sunday morning, when she had been out to the cinema with George the previous evening, Eileen asked her parents if she could invite him to tea the following Saturday afternoon.

"Well, of course, dear," her mother agreed, trying to hide her concern. "You know your friends, and Joyce's friends as well of course, are always welcome here."

The following Saturday eventually came and Ethel prepared a delicious tea. The girls both made scones and cakes, so there was plenty to eat. It was fortunate for Ethel and her husband were both amazed at the quantity of food the young farmer ate. "It comes of working outside, I suppose." said Alfred quietly to his wife as he helped her in the kitchen to make more tea.

When the meal was finished a very nervous George sat on the edge of his seat and, with Eileen beside him on the settee, facing his hosts and their elder daughter, he began to say that he and Eileen would like to get married, but he was not quite able to get the words out in a proper order. Alfred smiled understandingly. "Of course we're happy to give you both our blessing. Goodness knows, it's rare these days that a young man comes and asks the father of his intended if they may get married."

"Ah well, sir," George replied. "Me and my family, we're the old-fashioned sort. We believe in doin' things properly."

"And you say that you will be able to live in the farmhouse. Will your mother continue to live with you, then?" enquired Alfred.

"No, sir. She and my grandmother have been allocated one of the new Council houses in School Lane. They were only built about ten years ago but there's one vacant now, so the Council are goin' to let them rent it." George stated with some relief.

"How old is the farmhouse?" asked Ethel.

"Oh, it's quite old, ma'am. I think it dates back to the late seventeenth century, but we've always tried to keep it in good order. We've got a big underground cistern full of water from the gutters, so we've hardly ever run out of water and even if we did, the Maharajah's Well is only just up the road. Eileen wouldn't have to carry the buckets, I'd do it myself, with a yoke." he hastened to add.

Luckily, George did not notice the slight intake of breath on Ethel's part as she thought of the tap water that they had always had in their kitchen.

"And we've got electricity in Stoke Row now, we've had it for four years. It's made a lot of difference to life in the house and in the cowshed." George continued. "We've even got a telephone, too. Our number is Checkendon 23. I see you have a telephone here, too, so Eileen can always speak to you. Stoke Row may seem like a long way, but it's only six miles, really." This long speech seemed to have calmed George's nerves somewhat and the normally taciturn man began to smile again.

"Well, as you probably know, Eileen's twenty-one now. We gave a lovely birthday party for her and her school chums last February - pity you missed that!" Alfred laughed and went on to enquire: "When do you plan to marry?"

"We hope to make it next June, sir. I am very fond of Eileen and the quicker we can get married, the happier I shall be." George answered.

"In that case, you'd better start calling us Mum and Dad, then. You can't keep addressing us as sir and madam, can you now?" laughed Alfred.

"Oh, thank you, Dad!" exclaimed Eileen as she rushed over and kissed her father and mother. "We plan to go and buy a ring next Saturday." She also embraced her sister, but noticed as she did so that the older, rather plainer girl looked far from happy.

"I shall miss you so much, we've always been such good pals." Joyce said, with a slight glint of tears in her eyes.

"Oh, that's alright. Like George said, we've both got the telephone now. And you'll be able to come and stay at weekends. You can come up on the bus."

Joyce looked startled at the suggestion. "What, me. Go out and stay in the countryside?"

"Yes, of course, you'll love it. It's beautiful!" Eileen assured her sister, although Joyce looked doubtful.

The couple were duly married in Caversham Church on Saturday 25th June 1938. It was not a big affair, just their close relatives, but George Wells, his mother and certainly his grandmother, all looked decidedly uncomfortable in their 'Sunday best', having travelled with George to the church all the way from Stoke Row in a black Ford car, hired from Mr Briggs, who drove them there. It was rare enough for them to travel in such a vehicle and the confined space made old Mrs Wells feel quite sick, but fortunately she managed to conquer her fears before the journey was over.

In the church they sat with several other relatives on the 'groom's side' and glanced nervously over to the smarter folk, of whom there were quite a few more, on the 'bride's side'. Thankfully, the Vicar was

355

cheerful and did his best to make everyone feel at ease.

Alfred and Ethel Mason held the reception in their Caversham home. Again there was a good spread and once they had enjoyed a couple of glasses of wine, everyone began to loosen up.

Nevertheless, the country folk felt somewhat out of place in the suburban house and they were thankful to return to their village, once the young couple had been taken by Mr Briggs to Reading railway station, where they took the train for a week's honeymoon at Torquay.

George had to admit that he had never been away on a holiday before and almost all the time he was worried about the animals he had left behind in the care of a neighbouring farmer, who he telephoned every day from a call box in the resort. Despite enjoying the sea air and the love of his new wife, he did not really relax until they had returned to the Stoke Row farmhouse and settled back into the way of life that he had always known.

Eileen found the transition from town life to country life made big demands on her. "I love you dearly, George." she whispered one evening, "but it's so quiet here. It makes me feel nervous."

"You'll get used to it, love." he reassured her. "I tell you what, we'll go into Readin' next Saturday and buy a *wireless* [radio]. You'll like that. It'll keep us in touch with the outside world!"

"Yes, that's a good idea," returned Eileen "and we can pop in and have tea with Mum and Dad and Joyce. I'll 'phone them now and see if it's alright. Maybe Joyce could come up and stay soon. After all, we've been home a month now."

The radio certainly made a big difference to life in the farmhouse. Eileen had it on when she was doing the housework, the cooking or the ironing and loved to hum the tunes played by the dance bands in the evenings.

Joyce had agreed to come up the following weekend on the bus that ran from Reading to Woodcote, via Stoke Row. Eileen met her at the bus stop and carried her case for her. "I've brought my Wellington boots like you said." Joyce confirmed. "I do hope it's not too muddy, though."

"You have to get used to mud when you live in the country, especially after a thunderstorm like we had the day before yesterday." Eileen informed her sister. "I hope you've brought your slippers, too. We always change as we come indoors. I even try to wipe the paws of the dogs, too, if I can catch them!" she laughed.

"You said on the phone about the dogs. I hope they don't bite."

"No, of course not. Well, not when they're with us they don't. They're sheep dogs really, collies. There's Gem, she's the mother and Jack; he's the worker now. He's very good with the sheep."

"How many sheep do you have?" asked Joyce, avoiding a puddle in the road as they neared the farm.

"About forty, I think." Eileen stated. "George sees to the farm mostly. I mainly look after the geese, the chickens and the pigs."

"Pigs! You've got pigs??" Joyce sounded disgusted at the thought.

"Well, of course. Just two. They eat the scraps and next year the sow'll have piglets. I'm quite looking forward to that. Actually, I'm getting quite fond of the animals."

Gradually they came to the corner of Cox's Lane with the main road and as they turned, Eileen pointed out the ivy-clad Georgian brick and flint farmhouse ahead of them. "We're nearly there now," she said happily. "You'll love it here, really you will."

Joyce looked nervously at the dogs that had come out barking to greet them. "They'll be fine, as you're with me and once they get used to you they won't bark any more, I promise. And the geese will stop making that racket too, as soon as we go indoors," comforted her sister who was already beginning to sniff the air.

"Coo, what a pong!" she announced. "How can you live with this smell?"

"You get used to it," replied Eileen, taking off her boots and putting on her slippers. As soon as they reached the kitchen, she put the kettle on.

"I see you have to pump the water up before it comes out of the tap," her sister observed.

"Yes, but it's got a lovely taste to it. It seems better to me than what we get out of the tap at home." and then quickly she added "But don't tell Mum and Dad I said that."

It took Joyce some time to find her way around the big old rambling farmhouse but she gradually remembered the layout, thankful that George and Eileen had had a toilet put in the house, even if it was downstairs. The idea of still using a chamber pot in the bedroom was an anathema to the suburban girl.

After they had enjoyed a hearty supper, George and Eileen settled down comfortably to listen to the radio. Joyce was impressed by this addition to their life and was glad to find that they were not so much out of touch with the outside world as she had feared. In fact George, who read the Daily Mail every day, seemed to be quite conversant with the international situation and spoke several times of the threat posed by the Germans across the Channel.

Nevertheless, most of his conversation was concerned with the farm and the animals. "I hope Mary, our cow-girl, will be able to get better at using the new milkin' machines soon," he said. I find it quite easy, but she's used to the old way."

"What do you mean, the old way?" asked his new sister-in-law.

"Ha, ha!" laughed George. "I suppose you're like most town folk. You probably think we still employ pretty mob-capped milkmaids who sit on three-legged stools in the open air. You can't imagine the filth that we worked in when Dad was alive. We used to get up at 5.30 in the mornin' and milk the cows in that shed over there." He motioned to the building on the other side of the yard. "We worked just by a flickerin' oil lamp and the roof was always in danger of collapsin'. When I got old enough, I patched it up and now I hope to be able to get a new roof on it."

He lit a cigarette. "Cows are about the most filthy animals you can imagine. Within minutes of workin' with 'em you too, are mucky. When they come in from the fields they are covered in mud. You have to try and get it off 'em, especially off their udders to try and keep the milk reasonably clean. Sometimes you gets kicked by 'em, too and then you really are in the mire!" He noticed his sister-in-law shudder at the idea, but he continued, nonetheless.

"Mind you, things is better now than when Dad was younger. He told me once about a man who used to work for his father. His name was Bert Green. He was very fond of a drink and one mornin', when it was obvious that he had had a bit of a session the night before, he was sitting under one of the cows, nursing his hangover, when she flicked her tail and knocked his pipe out of his mouth." George flicked his ash into the ashtray as he said this, as if in memory of the tale.

"Dad always used to laugh when he told this story. It seems Bert always had a ferret in his pocket and a whippet at his heels. He was as mucky as you could get, out in all weathers with almost no protection, save for an old sack over his head, but even so, he leaned over, put his hand into the bucket of milk and pulled out his pipe. He then knocked it out, dried it, filled it up, lit it again and continued milkin' as though nothing had happened!"

"Why! That's dreadful!" shuddered Joyce. "When did it happen?"

"Oh, quite a time ago, maybe fifty years. It's gettin' much better today. The government are beginnin' to introduce new measures to help us improve the health of our cows and the conditions under which we keep 'em and milk 'em. That's how I've been able to buy these milkin' machines, now we've got electricity. One day I plan to install a proper milkin' parlour." he concluded.

"How many cows have you got?" she asked, trying to show an interest while at the same time wondering how clean the milk was that they had recently had in their tea.

"We've got twenty-six dairy cows at the moment and thirty-one beef cattle. That's enough for the moment as we only have ninety-seven acres all told, includin' about forty-three acres of arable, that's corn and root crops to you. We can't grow much corn here because of the hilly nature of the land and the flint stones in the soil do terrible damage to any machinery, especially the ploughs. I plan to buy a tractor before long. I'm afraid ploughing with horses is finished. We've got four, but they're going to have to go, much as I love 'em."

Eileen took up the explanation of their ambitions. "We've been reading about the machinery they have in America, not only tractors, but combine harvesters as well now. It'd make all the difference if we could afford even a Fordson, that's a tractor. Still, we're saving up for one. We don't want to borrow the money, the future doesn't look at all certain, with all this talk of another war."

Joyce and her younger sister had always been protected from the fears of another war by their parents. "I went all through the Great War." their father had said a year or so before and added with finality: "And I don't ever want to talk about it!"

"I'm sure the politicians will be able to arrange a peaceable end to all this talk of another war. Like so many other people of our age, your Dad and I remember too much about the Great War to ever think of another one. All that suffering, it would be unthinkable." their mother had explained at the time.

When they were washing up the breakfast things next morning, Eileen asked Joyce if she had slept well. "No, I'm afraid I didn't go to sleep for ages. The dark and the silence here is spooky, really. I did hear the hooting of the owls as I eventually dozed off and then it seemed no time before I heard the cockerel out in the yard. Still, somehow I am getting used to it."

Eileen smiled. Joyce continued by confiding in her sister: "I realise now how lucky you are, being married and with a home of your own. I'm twenty-eight now and sure to become an old maid, 'left on the shelf' as they say."

"Oh, no. Don't say that." replied Eileen. "You're young yet." At the same time she knew in her heart that her older sister was not only less attractive than she was, but also she had very little ambition and made no effort to make something of herself. "You should try and have your hair done, wear some make-up and buy a few new print dresses for yourself. We'll have a look in Heelas next time I'm down in Reading." she promised. "I must come down soon. I need to get some 'Wintergreen' in Boots the Chemist. I have to rub it in to George's back when he pulls a muscle. It sometimes happens when he's handling one of the animals. It smells awful, but it does work!"

The following Saturday, Eileen took the bus down to Reading and called in for her sister. As they walked through the suburban streets they met a Wall's Ice Cream man, pedalling his tricycle. "Ah, there's the Wall's 'Stop Me and Buy One' man - I fancy a choc ice, would you like one?" Joyce offered.

The September day was already proving to be a warm and sunny one so Eileen accepted with pleasure. "This is one thing we don't have in Stoke Row," she had to admit.

They did buy a couple of pretty floral print dresses for Joyce in Heelas and when they were in Woolworth's store, Eileen decided to buy some china. "I want to buy some more to match the set of six that Auntie Kath gave us for our wedding. The china in the farmhouse is all old, chipped and crazed, in fact, there's not much glaze left on any of them. I like this design with hollyhocks and lupins on them. I think I'll go mad and buy another four cups, saucers and plates because we plan to invite Mum and Dad up to tea. We'll get George's Mum and his Grandma to come over, too. They weren't at their best at the wedding. They don't like towns."

When they got back to Caversham again, Eileen made all the arrangements. "You can come up on the number seven Thames

360

Valley bus. It leaves at three o'clock from outside the Library," she explained. "It only takes about an hour - you'll be in Stoke Row by four o'clock and then you can come home in the evening, before it gets dark.

Alfred and Ethel, accompanied by Joyce, came up to their youngest daughter's new home on Saturday 24th September 1938. They were not to know until they read the Sunday papers the next day that, as they were doing so, the Prime Minister, Mr Neville Chamberlain, was returning to England from Germany, clutching a piece of paper and announcing to the world that there would be: "...peace in our time."

The bus up to Stoke Row was a number 7, a single-decker, painted red with a cream band and cream roof. Alfred liked buses and was pleased to note that it was a 29-seater Leyland 'Lion'. The journey seemed to take ages, although it had its benefits. "Actually you can see much more from a bus than from a car, even a single-decker like this," he pointed out to his wife.

Joyce, who had made the journey several times by now, told them the names of each of the villages as they passed through them. "This is Emmer Green. Well, you know that anyway, you've walked up here on a Sunday afternoon, haven't you?" and then, a little later: "This is Sonning Common and in a minute we'll be going up the hill to Peppard. It's not far from there to Highmore and then we turn left down to Witheridge Hill and go on up to Stoke Row."

It all looked fairly normal until they reached Witheridge Hill and the woods at the bottom. "It's so dark in these woods!" exclaimed Ethel. "I shouldn't like to live in that little cottage there, even though it is pretty." As the bus climbed the tree-lined hill, she continued to feel nervous until it came out into the sunlight again at the top.

At last the bus reached their stop, outside the London House Stores and they all alighted, glad to see Eileen there to meet them. "It's lovely to see you here!" she exclaimed. "I'm so glad it's a fine, sunny day. Did you notice the beauty of the trees as you came up through the woods?"

"Well, they were a lovely colour but I did feel nervous as we came along. I found myself hoping the bus wouldn't break down and we'd have to walk." her mother replied.

Joyce noticed that Eileen and George had gone to some trouble to tidy up around the outside of the farmhouse and was pleased to find that George's mother and grandmother were already ensconced in the sitting-room.

Once formalities had been exchanged, the two girls went into the kitchen to prepare the tea. "You have made it all look so much smarter since I was here last." commented Joyce. "What with that and the new china, I'm sure it'll all go well. I've brought up some scones and a cake, like I said I would."

"Thanks a lot, dear. I wonder though how much they'll notice what they're eating. George's Grandma is already telling them her memories of life on her father's farm up the road when she was a girl. I love to hear these tales, let's hurry up, I don't want you to miss any of it."

Grandma Wells was already in full swing by the time they wheeled the trolley in. She was a tiny, wizened woman, dressed entirely in black, who had obviously been a powerful character in her younger days. Her voice was high-pitched, but still strong and clear. "This is about the dairy. I think it's about 1920." Eileen whispered in Joyce's ear.

"It was fascinating to watch the milk being put into the cooler," the old lady recalled. "It went round and round all the glass pipes, finishing up in the churns ready for selling. The transport people picked up the churns and delivered them to the station and cheese factories. A certain amount of milk had the cream taken off; this was made into butter and curds and whey. We had lots of skimmed milk for making lovely rice puddings and porridge and there was always plenty to drink. We also had cocoa every night before we went to sleep."

Helping herself to a ham sandwich, she scarcely paused for a munch before she started again: "We had our own threshing machine. It went from one farm to another. With a father and two sons having three farms between them, they would help each other at all times, which is the best thing to do.

When it was thrashing time we used to find some lovely large swedes and potatoes and put them in the furnace of the thrasher and bake them all hot to eat. They made a lovely supper with pepper and salt and bread and butter. Nothing could be nicer and very filling. The other people working with us loved them too and Dad would pop some into the furnace later in the afternoon to take home for our tea.

In the oven at home there was a nice large pie dish of rice pudding, with butter and grated nutmeg all over the top. It did not just smell beautiful, it tasted good, too!" With that she decided to have some more to eat and left the chatting to the others.

Once she had had her fill of all the sandwiches, scones and cakes she could eat, the old lady started up again on her memories. In fact, Alfred, Ethel and Joyce found it all quite absorbing, hearing about a way of life that they scarcely knew anything about.

"When we had a long hot, dry summer, like 1921, we had to suffer for it because there was no water in the cistern, so we had to fetch water from Stoke Row Well with yokes on our shoulders and two large buckets. Dad had to go with a large horse-drawn water cart, carrying 50 gallons of water to put in the cattle troughs for the horses, cows and pigs, large and small. Of course the hens, ducks, swans, turkeys also had to have water." She took another sip of the freshly made tea as if to assuage her thirst at the memory of those dry days.

"It was a very bad time for washing clothes, and impossible to rinse them thoroughly. We had prayers in the Schools, Churches and Chapels, all to no avail. The corn was all stunted. The growth was very short and resulted in a quarter of the quantity of grain, making it very hard for the farmers and people alike. There was very little bread about and you couldn't make bread without flour and you couldn't buy any, whatsoever. We used to have a lot of potato scones every day to keep us all going. Lots of cattle died from thirst besides the insects and fowls of the air. It was not an easy time anywhere, you even saw frogs and tadpoles lying about, all dried up."

"Tell Mr and Mrs Mason about the cows, Grandma." George urged her. "I was tellin' Joyce something about the old ways when she came last time."

"Well, we always went to bed early, for my Dad had to be up at five o'clock again next morning. At that time of the day he had to fetch all the cows and put them in their stalls ready for washing down and get the milking gear ready. In the winter he had to give the horses their hay and fill their nosebags with chaff, oats, barley and corn and then get them ready for their work in the fields.

Sometimes my brother would go with Dad and help to wash the

cows' udders with a cloth and hot water before the hand milking started at six o'clock by the light of hanging lanterns. They cast eerie shadows as they walked backwards and forwards past our bedroom window. It took an hour and a half to milk the cows and put the milk into the coolers. Then the cows had to be turned straight out from the milking sheds into the grass fields." She took another gulp of tea, anxious to continue before anyone else should speak.

Her audience allowed her to do so and so she continued: "Then the sheds had to be washed down with hose pipes and Jeyes fluid, all the utensils and churns had to be taken to the Buttery to be thoroughly cleaned, rinsed and dried and everything put away until 4.00 pm. Every cow was milked twice daily and everything had to be cleaned twice daily too. You see, farming is a ritual that must be properly carried out. It makes a lot of difference to the milk yield if the milking is early or late. Cows can be very stubborn, especially if a different pair of hands milks them, sometimes they hold back and refuse to yield – they have their likes and dislikes, the same as we do."

"I love to hear 'Grandma' talk about the old days." George's mother remarked to the others. "It does make me appreciate how lucky we are to have electricity and buses today."

"Ah well!" the old lady took up the thread again: "In the early 1900s, the wages of Oxfordshire agricultural labourers were some of the lowest in the country. I always remember my grandfather saying: 'I started work at the age of nine as 'horse boy' at Uxmoor Farm. My wages were 3/- a week and I had to start at five o'clock and work on Sundays, too. Many a morning I've pulled a turnip for my breakfast. Cruel times they was!' so you see, even our forefathers fared worse than we did!"

The whole visit was a revelation to the 'townies' as they were unkindly called in the village. In fact, it was many years before the oldest folk would even accept Eileen as one of themselves. Nevertheless, the farmer's new wife gradually did become assimilated into the life of Stoke Row, while at the same time keeping her connections with the town where she had grown up. As she explained to her parents when she went down for the day: "It's quite a different life up there. I know everyone in the village and they know me. Because of the farming, we also know people in the other villages, like Highmore and Checkendon and they know us. Down here we don't know anyone, do we?"

"Oh, that's not true, dear." her mother replied reproving her gently. "We know Mr and Mrs Bell next door this side and the Smiths the other. And then we get to know the customers in the shops, Joyce and I do, and Dad knows the men at the factory."

"But it's not the same as village life, somehow." continued her daughter. "Up there we have so much going on which we do together. We all know each other and we help each other. It's something to do with being away from the town. I find it hard to explain, really. I wouldn't be able to settle down in the town again with all these bright lights at night. In fact, I don't know how I survived the noise here for so many years."

"Well, the main thing is that we can still visit each other and keep in touch by 'phone." her mother said comfortingly. "I suppose we're a bit like the story of the Town Mouse and the Country Mouse, aren't we?" she pointed out with a smile.

* * * * * *

Much of the first part of this chapter has been taken from the Memoirs of Mr Ted Evans, *published in the* Stoke Row News *in February 1995, with kind permission of his widow, Mrs Beattie Evans.*

For the second section the author drew from Mr John H Baker's book, A School on the Ground Floor, *Sydney Blow's autobiography*, The Ghost Walks on Fridays, *and her researches for her own book* Dipping into the Wells *which contains many photographs of Hilda Trevelyan.*

Some facts in the last part of this chapter have been taken from The Story of Reading *by kind permission of Daphne Phillips. Stoke Row Farm did exist as such, but the characters are purely fictional. However, many of the reminiscences have come from the* Memoirs *of various villagers recorded by the author and published in the* Stoke Row News *during the 1980s.*

Chapter 18. The New War and the Evacuees: 1939 - 1943

Many men, in the towns of Henley, Reading, Wallingford and Watlington, as well as in villages like Stoke Row and Highmore, seeing the possibility of another war looming ahead of them, volunteered for the Territorial Army as early as 1938.

Thousands more were 'called up' as soon as war was declared on 3rd September 1939. Most of those who lived in Stoke Row and Highmore were lucky enough to survive the Second World War, which, in the beginning, many people called 'this new war'.

Fewer were killed or injured than in what was still then known as the Great War, but the names of those who did give their lives are recorded on brass plates in the chapel and church at Stoke Row:

To the memory of those who gave their lives: 1939-1945

J H Bird, L/Cpl.Royal Marines. Killed 6th June 1944, aged 19.
P L Clayton, Pilot Officer, R A F. Killed 6th June 1942, aged 20.
G L F Hopkinson, Flying Officer, RAF VR.
Killed July 8th, 1943, aged 21.
B Lambourne, Stoker, R. N. H M S *Gloucester*.
Killed May 22, 1941, aged 24.

Little is known about the first three, but we do know that the last of these to die was twenty-three year old Stoker First Class Basil Lambourne, whose family were the Stoke Row bakers. During the Battle for Crete, he was aboard HMS *Gloucester* when it went down leaving only eighty-four survivors. A telegram brought the news that he was posted as 'Missing', but his death was not confirmed until after the war. His parents, George and Annie Lambourne, always hoped and prayed that their youngest son would return safely after all, as had his four brothers, but it was not to be.

John Meheux, whose family also lived in Stoke Row, was killed in England whilst training despatch riders. Usually there was a column of fifteen trainee riders, with an instructor at the back and another at the front. On this particular day the front instructor was not at work, so John came from the rear to the front, but was killed on a bend by an approaching lorry.

Seven Highmore men died on active service. A brass plate in the church of St Paul records no more than their names and regiments:

William Archer	Royal Air Force Volunteer Reserve
John Denham	Pioneer Corps
Paul Enfield	Oxon & Bucks Light Infantry
Alfred Evans	HMS Dunedin
John Hanutt	Royal Air Force Volunteer Reserve
Geoff Nares	Royal Lancers
Cyril Symonds	Royal Air Force

William Archer was in the RAF and was killed over Arnhem, Holland - his grave is there still. He spent much of his youth at 'The Barn' Lower Highmore and in Satwell Close, Satwell, Highmore.

John Denham was the eldest son of Mr Arthur Denham of the Little Manor House, Witheridge Hill. John was the son of Mr Denham's first marriage, and when he grew up he went into accountancy and law. He volunteered during the early part of the Second World War and went into the Pioneer Corps as an accountant. Then he got a commission and went through the invasion of France in 1944. However, it was while he was in a car being driven by a Frenchman that he was killed when the car hit an allied tank. He was a very charming and able young man and many people loved him.

Paul Enfield was firstly reported missing and then presumed dead. He and his wife, Rose, lived in the cottage that was down a path opposite the Dog and Duck, recessed from the road. It was then known as Green Man Cottage.

Alfred Evans: Known to his friends as 'Niley' Evans, he was in the

Royal Naval Reserve, was 'called up' at the beginning of WW2 and was killed when the minesweeper *Dunedin*, on which he was serving, was sunk.

John Hanutt: Sadly, nothing whatever is known about this man.

Geoff Nares was the son of Owen Nares, famous actor and 'matinee idol'. Mr and Mrs Nares lived at Lower Highmore, in a little cottage in the beechwoods.

Sgt Cyril Symonds, Gunner, RAF. No. 2235152. Killed 18.12.1944. 'He gave his life for his country'. (War Graves Commission headstone in Highmore Churchyard Extension). Cyril Symonds was in the RAF. He lived in one of the Henley Trust cottages, next to the Church at Rotherfield Greys.

John Jackson Hamilton, BA, AMICE. Killed on Active Service 10.12.1941, aged 28 years. The Hamiltons lived at Satwell Barton. John, known as 'Jack', was in the RAF but his name is not on the brass plaque in the Church.

Quite a number of men in both villages also were captured and spent years in concentration camps, both in Europe and in the Far East. Their very moving stories were told when they returned home, sometimes months or even years after the war in both spheres had ended.

Of the men who stayed at home, many were too young or too old to serve. Others, such as farmers or woodmen, were classed as being in a Reserved Occupation because their jobs were seen as vital to the war effort. Several of the farmers were helped by young women who joined the Women's Land Army and came from all over the country to replace the men who had been drafted into the armed forces.

However, the men left at home too, were keen to 'do their bit'. The day after Mr Anthony Eden broadcast for volunteers for the defence of the country in the event of invasion, the Checkendon LDV [Local Defence Volunteers] was formed and, combined with Stoke Row, became the Checkendon Home Guard Platoon. It soon reached a total of almost a hundred men, all of who kept watch over the villages throughout the war.

One of the most important matters to be dealt with as soon as the war started was the transport of children from London to places of safety in the countryside. Some children were well received and made happy. Others were resented, their surrogate parents finding them difficult to deal with. This was not surprising as many of them were homesick and afraid of the countryside that was so different from the town they had left. Those that came to Highmore fared well. Mr John Gilbert from Monmouth remembered staying for two years at Satwells Barton, a very large house, and how the owner, Captain Hamilton came to the Village Hall, saw the six remaining children and promptly said: "I'll take the lot!"

******

Don Shelswell and Ron Taylor were both aged seven and already close friends when they came down from London to Highmore on Friday 1st September 1939. Having been assembled early in the morning with their classmates at Northfield School, Ealing, they were sorted into groups according to their destinations. Everyone, fathers, mothers and children were trying not to cry as, one by one, the children mounted the steps of the coach, each wearing a label and with their satchels and gas-masks in cardboard boxes, all name tagged, strung across their shoulders.

The Women's Voluntary Service and other volunteers met the coaches in Henley at about eleven o'clock in the morning and allocated the children to families around the area. Most seemed quite happy and, once they were settled in, many of them regarded the whole thing as a great adventure!

Don was sent to Mr and Mrs Clements at 'Rose Cottage' at the foot of Stoke Row Hill. This was just along from the little old cottage at the foot of Witheridge Hill, where generations of the Blackalls, the Franklin family and the Blows had lived. The present owners of the cottage, Mr and Mrs Stewart-Anderson, had erected a small board outside it, bearing the name Old Place, but they rarely came down to their 'summer home' now. Upon hearing that war might be declared, they had spent the summer stocking the little garage, which normally housed their Austin Seven, with tins of food and other necessities. Now they were obeying the government's command not to make unnecessary journeys and had decided to 'stick it out' in their London flat.

Along the road at Rose Cottage, the Clements were very kind to

Don Shelswell, the London boy, and he also became great friends with their nephew, Eric Edwards, who lived up in the village of Stoke Row, for they were about the same age.

Don's pal, Ron Taylor, who bore the nickname 'Golly' because of his hairstyle, was exceptionally fortunate as he was allocated to Fred and Edie Stallwood at The Woodman public house at Highmore. They took to this little boy at once, especially as Edie had recently come home from hospital having lost her only baby in childbirth and had been told that she was not likely to have another. Suddenly, Ron was her little boy and she cared for him as she would have her own son.

As soon as they arrived at The Woodman he was taken into the Tap Room for some lunch. He thought it was the lounge of the house, having never been into a pub before. At first he found the whole arrangement of a home within a pub to be very strange, but Mrs Stallwood was very kind and soon took him up to his own bedroom which she and her husband had quickly converted into one which they thought would be suitable for a young boy.

Later that day, Mrs Clements brought Don along to meet his pal again and with them she brought her nephew, Eric. She did this not only to show the boys the way, but also to see Edie Stallwood, who she had known for many years.

"As you know, Edie," Marge Clements said quietly. "Eric goes to Stoke Row School, but the WVS lady told me I'd have to take Don up to Highmore School to get him registered. Did she say the same to you about Ron?"

"Yes, she did. It's a pity they can't go to Stoke Row School with Eric, but I hear Miss Varley's a very good teacher. Shall we meet at the foot of the hill on Monday then, say about half-past eight?" Edie Stallwood nodded, smiling.

Marge continued: "It's funny, isn't it, them both having such similar names, Don and Ron? Edie again nodded her assent. "It seems they've always been friends, so it's good that they can go on being together, especially as they're so far from their homes. I don't know where Ealing is exactly, but George says it's this side of London."

Edie seemed just as unsure. "Fred says you'd have to take a bus to Reading and then a train up to Paddington and out again to Ealing, so it would take you a long time, even if you was able to go." Then, rising quickly from her chair, she said with a smile: "Let's go out and see what the boys are up to out in the yard. I must get them in for their tea. It'll be time to open the bar up before we know where we are!"

When Marge Clements and the boys got back to Rose Cottage, she confided to her husband, George: "It's an ill wind that blows nobody any good and that's a fact. I've not seen Edie smile so much since she lost the baby. Having this boy here's put new life into her. He's like a substitute son for both her and Fred."

Just as the WVS lady had explained, Don and his pal Ron were immediately allocated to Highmore School on Witheridge Hill, where Miss Eleanor Varley had been Headmistress for eleven years, ever since Mr John H Baker had left in 1924. She was a dedicated teacher who took a personal interest in each and every child. In fact, the newcomers from the city were welcomed with warmth and kindness by both Miss Varley and her assistant, Miss Hall.

In the autumn days Don accompanied Ron back to The Woodman every afternoon after school, and sometimes they played 'conkers' with the fruits of the horse chestnut tree on their way. However, as the evenings drew in, he obeyed Mrs Clements instructions to go straight home, "because it's so dark here. We don't have street lights like you do in London."

As soon as Ron reached the pub, Fred Stallwood would light the fire in the lounge on winter evenings. Edie would come in with a cup of tea for them all and they would sit by the fire and make marks with sticks in the soot and see whose sparks would go out the last. It was typical of the many simple games that Fred and Edie devised, because they had very few toys suitable for a young boy.

Like Don's mother, Ron's wrote to him regularly, of course, as did his sister. His mother also wrote lovely letters to Edie Stallwood including one written on 23 June 1940, which said, in a depressed, downward-sloping handwriting:

    . . . I do hope he is a good boy and not getting too rude,

especially as there are some terrible children down there [i.e. other evacuees]. Will you please give him a big hug from me, his Dad and his sister, as we are always thinking of him and hope he will keep safe.

Don't things look black for us now? I wonder sometimes if we will be invaded, I do hope not...

Yours sincerely,

Mrs Taylor

From time to time Ron's parents also visited him in his new home, although Highmore seemed very far from Ealing, London. It meant a journey by train to Reading and a bus to the village. At that time some people in London never went out into the country and looked upon Oxfordshire as being rather remote and a bit 'different'.

During one of the visits from his parents on a bright Saturday afternoon, his father said to Ron, just as they were going, "I dropped a half-crown in the wood store, lad, can you find it for me?" Ron went into the store and found there a beautiful bicycle, all black and chrome, a wonderful gift. They didn't see much of him after that, so soon was he off on his new 'bike'. The first place he went to was, of course, Rose Cottage, the home of his friend Don Shelswell. Eric was there too and they all took it in turns to ride. Eric had never tried riding a bicycle before but the London boys soon taught him.

One day, when Ron was visiting his friend at Rose Cottage, he wanted to go to the toilet. He hated going down at Rose Cottage because, unlike the pub, it did not have one just outside the house. Instead the 'privvy' was way down at the north end of the garden, where it stood on a small mound.

Don confided to his friend one winter's day: "Although Mr and Mrs Clements are so kind, this is when I miss home, having a toilet inside, I mean. The slop bucket sometimes overflows in there and now and again it freezes. I can't possibly get up that slope, so when I just need a pee, I go over there to the woods instead!"

George Clements was a tent-peg maker and it had been the custom for many, many years for the wives of these men to go out to them and take them their tea. They knew their way around the woods as much as their menfolk and they also took their children with them after school.

One day in the autumn of 1940, as the beech leaves began to fall in copper showers around them, Marge Clements, closely followed by her nephew Eric and his friends, Don and Ron, soon located the 'shelter' in Highmore woods that George and his mate, young Will Bakewell, were working under that week. The woman and the boys soon set about stacking the tent-pegs into piles. The London lads loved the freedom of the woods and as soon as the tent-pegs were all stacked, they started to have a leaf fight, picking up great handfuls and throwing them at one another. George, Will and Marge watched them for some time, laughing as they drank hot tea from the Thermos flasks that the tent-pegger's wife had brought for her husband and his mate.

Marge and the boys continued to come every working day, even after dark in the winter, when Marge held her electric torch low, so it could not be seen from the air. The men worked in 'shelters', made from corrugated iron supported on thin tree trunks knocked into the ground. Around the lower half was a wall, made from sacks filled with sawdust to keep out the wind. In the coldest weather they raised the height of the sack wall and hung empty sacks from the iron roof to try and keep out the draught. It was usually effective unless the wind was in the north.

The men found they needed minimal light for the task, as they knew it so well. This form of illumination was usually by means of a candle in a large glass jam jar. It gave a circular light and cast no shadows. A piece of wire gripped the neck of the jar and was extended to make a loop so that it could be suspended from the roof and held over the 'collar' of the 'tent pegger's horse' for the worker to see what he was doing. If he moved away from the 'horse' he had to take the candle jar with him.

Once the boys had had some hot tea and had had their fill of 'larkin' about', as Marge Clements put it, George showed the boys how the tent-pegs were made. Holding one up for the boys to see more clearly. "The method for making tent-pegs has always been the same. My father and my grandfather before him were 'tent-peggers'; that's what they call us. In the Great War they had orders for millions

373

and millions of these pegs which were sent to the Royal Army Ordnance Depot at Didcot, that's about ten miles to the west of here. There's a big railway junction there and they were sent by train all over the country and to other countries, too, especially France, or wherever our troops were fighting. Now it's happening all over again."

Putting on his jacket, as the wind was beginning to blow harder, George Clements continued: "Now, with another war on, we're getting more orders than we can cope with. Still I promised to show you slowly how it's done." He took a bite from a sandwich and went on: "First of all, the trees are felled. It's done by the wood fellers, cutting at the base of the trunk with an axe, like those over there. Then they're sawn by two men, called sawyers, with a cross-cut saw. After that they cut the wood into lengths. Then that's where we come in. We split the lengths into halves, with one of these." He picked up a type of hammer. "It's called a 'beetle' and one of these metal things, called a 'wedge'." He took a 'swig' of tea and a mouthful of cake and continued:

"Then we split the half-logs into sections using this round wooden hammer, we call it a 'molly' and this L-shaped axe, which we call a 'flammer'. Once the wood for the tent pegs has been split and the 'pairs' of pieces are made ready, it still needs twenty-four movements to make a peg, including the notch and the edges. All this work we do on these 'tent-pegger's horses'. You've often seen me do it now."

"Yes, but you do it so fast!" exclaimed Ron. "You seem to just flash it around and bingo! There it is being thrown on top of the pile with the others."

"Yes, my lad, and we'd better be quick, too. We reckon to make about six hundred a day each of these nine inch long ones. I often wonder where they'll finish up and of the poor blighters that'll have to sleep in the tents out in the fields. I only have to work in a shelter, at least I sleep in my own bed in my own home every night."

One day, in the spring of 1942, George Clements told the boys: "We've got men coming from the War Department in London to inspect this lot the day after tomorrow!"

"Men from London, phew!" Don was suddenly reminded of the town he had almost forgotten. "What will they be doing down here?"

374

"Well, my lads, it's the job of these inspectors to pass or reject the pegs and they come down when an order's near completion. Of course, they don't know anything at all about tent peg making!" he laughed. "Anyway, it's their job, so what they do is to pass almost every pile and then choose one which they knock over with a kick of their foot and then they mark a few with a black arrow. That means they're rejected. We then gather them up, take them back to our shelters and shave off the offending mark ready for the next batch. Needless to say they will pass the test next time because every one is exactly the same as the next one. Look, pick up half a dozen and put them beside each other and you'll see!"

The boys did so and were very impressed. They stood for a while longer watching the tent-peggers at their work. "You should take them up to the Cherry Tree in Stoke Row, Marge. Ask Bert Carter to show them how he makes the chair legs. I reckon they'd find that interesting, too," George suggested. "We can manage the stacking by ourselves the day after tomorrow, we won't have made too many pegs, what with having to look after these time-wasters down from London," he concluded in a whisper.

Marge decided to take Ron home and then she, Don and Eric walked up Stoke Row Hill. As they came up to the front of the Cherry Tree, Marge stopped for a moment and said: "Eric, you can run off home now if you like. Your Mum will be wondering where you've got to. It all took longer than I thought." Turning to Don, she said: "We've just got enough time to pop over to the London House Stores. Fortunately I've got our ration books in my handbag. I might be lucky and find that Mr Page has been able to save me a bit of cheese. He did say he would try. I find it so hard managing on the rations, though we're better off than your parents. At least my husband can shoot a rabbit or a pigeon from time to time and we're able to grow our own vegetables."

"My dad said he's growing vegetables, too." Don piped up. "He's taken up turf off our lawn and made a veggie patch - he says it's called 'Digging for Victory'."

Inside they found several ladies, all trying to persuade the owner to let them have 'a bit of this" or 'a bit of that'. When the weekly food ration for one person was one pound of meat, three ounces of bacon, two ounces of cheese, three pints of milk, two ounces of tea, nine ounces of cooking fat or margarine, eight ounces of sugar and only four ounces of sweets, the poor man was at his wits end to try and satisfy his customers.

Once the subject of food had been sorted out, the women's conversation turned to what was happening in the village. Several of them had just left their workplace and were buying a few items on their way home. Mrs Louisa Stevens of Highmore and Mrs Ivy Church of Stoke Row were both still wearing their overalls and the net 'snoods' that protected their hair. "I see you've embroidered the initials C.W. on yours. Are you sure that's not giving away war secrets?!" she laughed as she made this remark to Louie Stevens, who she had known since their childhood.

"Now you know as well as I do," reproved Louie. "I can't talk about our work. We're sworn to the Official Secrets Act, so don't you go asking me about anything to do with...well, you know what." she concluded, nodding her head towards the poster on the inside of the glass panel in the door. It bore the legend: 'Careless Talk Costs Lives!'

Marge was lucky that day, as Mr Page had saved a small portion of cheese for her and once they had paid for this and a few other items, they walked down the hill again to their home at Rose Cottage.

During the Second World War there were a number of mobile transport repair units (MTRU) hidden in the woods around Stoke Row. These were used for the repair of army vehicles, and there were at least two 'secret factories' in the village. The largest one was in Busgrove Lane and had been built on the site of the old brick kilns.

There was also a firm of engineers in Reading called Hawkins who did sheet metal work. At the start of the War they became very busy doing work for the Air Ministry and they needed to expand quickly into a place that was safer than Reading. Stoke Row, set as it was in thick woodland, seemed ideal. As soon as Mr Hawkins learned about the old brick-built warehouse on the former brick kiln site, he rushed up here to see it. At the time it was being used as a storage place for a Reading firm of car dealers who had many cars stored there, presumably waiting for the war to end! They had to clear them out quickly when Mr Hawkins commandeered it with the backing of the Air Ministry, as it was needed for urgent war work.

In this factory they made fuel tanks for aeroplanes, mostly Miles

Magisters that were being manufactured at Woodley, near Reading and used for training. Later, when other planes began to return from sorties full of holes, the workers had to repair these too, and test the tanks to make sure they were leak-proof.

Mr Hawkins brought Mrs Kettlewhite up from Reading as his Forewoman and Inspector to supervise the work as she had been employed by him for many years and had very high standards. Together with staff from the Air Ministry in London, they had more or less to start from scratch.

Most of the women they employed came by bus from Reading every day but quite a few were recruited in Stoke Row and Highmore. Two of them, Mrs Louie Stevens and Mrs Ada Britnell were sisters and lived opposite each other at Highmore Cross. Every day they cycled down the New Road together to the bottom of Witheridge Hill, where they came to the little cottage, with its Old Place name board outside. Although it was looking much smarter than it had been in the 1920s, somehow it had a slightly sad appearance. One Monday morning as they were on their usual journey, Louie slowed down and Ada came to a halt beside her sister. "It does look a bit unloved, doesn't it, Ada?" commented Louie. "Those London people never come down here now!"

"I'm not surprised," replied her sister. "It's not as restful here as it used to be, what with the bombers coming over at nights and dropping their 'unwanteds' over us!"

"Well, at least, they do seem to drop them on the fields, rather than on the village, thank the Lord!" Ada said.

As they cycled on up Stoke Row Hill, they fell to talking about their work and the strict regime imposed by Mrs Kettlewhite. "We'd better get a move on," said Louie, glancing at her watch. "It's a quarter to eight. Our Mrs K will dock us a quarter of an hour's money if we're late. I bet Miss Kitty never gets fined; she's always on time!"

"Yes, but doesn't she hate it when she gets there!" remarked Ada. "Miss Kitty is so very ladylike, being a spinster, too. I don't think she's ever had to rough it in her life!"

"Yes, and as sister of the Vicar, she's always held a very high position in the village. A sort of Lady Bountiful, but she's doing good work now, in a way, helping the war effort. I think she tries to see it that way. It must be hard for her, really." Louie agreed and then, puffing a bit with the exertion, she continued: "I wonder what work we'll have to do today. Last week I was mending and patching fuselages with aluminium after they had been through the panel beaters' workshop - that's really dirty work. I still haven't got my hands clean, even though I keep washing them."

"I suppose I'll be cleaning up the pigeon holes, as usual. Mrs K say's it's because I've got small hands. Those holes in the petrol tanks are only about three inches across, you know, and there's two rows of a hundred of them in every tank. I prefer to clean the oil lamp glasses, though they're even smaller. I have to do them perfectly, though. Mrs K sent some of them back to me a couple of weeks ago, said they weren't 'up to scratch'. Still, I quite like going out to work. This is more interesting than house cleaning, and better paid, too!"

As they neared the top of Stoke Row hill and started to pass the houses, Louie put her finger to her lips and Ada knew her older sister was intimating that 'walls have ears'. Instead they turned their conversation to wondering what they would be having for lunch. "That's another good thing about working up here," Louie whispered. "Getting a cooked dinner mid-day. Mrs Welsford's a good cook. I don't know how she feeds us all with the little she gets allowed her."

Alf Turner came out of his house, No 2 Rosetree Cottages, at that point. He waved goodbye to his wife and bade a cheery "Good morning!" to the two ladies, as he stood his bike by the gate of the adjacent house. "I'm just going in for Gracie, she's left school now and is coming up to work at the Crest with me."

Mr Greener, who, with Roland Page owned the Stoke Row Garage, had a small workshop on the Crest Estate up at the Checkendon end of the village. It was in a large shed which belonged to Tommy Cox and which had formerly been used for raising chickens. Greener and Page had been machining spindles for pulsometers, but they dropped this work in favour of subcontracting to Hawkins – drilling, tapping and turning cast parts to go on the fuel tanks being made in the Busgrove Lane factory. Very soon after the outbreak of war they asked Alf Turner to join them and the firm became known as The Crest Works.

Gracie was only fourteen years old but she, too, enjoyed working in the village. "The money's good and I don't have the expense or the effort of going into Reading. Not only that, but I'm glad to help the

378

war effort, even though I have only just left school. Otherwise, before the war, I'd have had to go into service. This is much more interesting; thanks for getting me the job." she said to Alf as they cycled through Stoke Row, past the London House Stores, the Village Hall, the Well and the Church on their way up to the Crest Estate.

The next day, Marge Clements kept to her word and that afternoon she walked up Witheridge Hill at three o'clock and collected the two boys outside Highmore School. It seemed strange to her to hear so many London accents among the Oxfordshire 'burrs' as the children came out of the building. The three of them walked up Stoke Row Hill and met Eric outside The Cherry Tree. It had only taken him a few minutes to walk along from the school and while he waited he had been idling his time away on the Alma Field, opposite the old inn, skimming stones across the clay-lined pond   In the middle of the field stood an old cottage named after the famous battle of Alma, which had taken place in 1854, during the Crimean War.

It was one of many ponds to be found around the village, where years before men had dug clay out for the brickyards. "The brick making here all came to an end in about 1925. That's when they started to make bricks up in Bedfordshire with big machines," his father had told him.

Luckily, Bert Carter was in his workshop behind the Cherry Tree, where he was publican in the evenings. His wife served the few lunchtime customers. Before the war she had run a small shop at the side, but as she explained to her sister, a few months after the war began: "I can't be bothered with all these ration cards and coupons, so I've left it all to the London House shop to do now."

Bert was not under so much pressure to complete his chair-legs as the tent-peggers were to complete their orders. As he explained to Marge and the boys: "I'm what's known as a 'bodger'. I suppose that, of all the crafts and trades practised in Stoke Row and Highmore over the years, 'bodging' must have the most intriguing name. Most people in these villages know that the term has nothing to do with a 'bodged' job, because this work calls for great skill and experience. The word actually comes from the Dutch word a 'botcher'. That means a man who only makes parts of things, but the meaning of it has become changed over the years."

He slipped off his stool where he had been sitting in front of his pole-lathe, a turning tool, driven by foot-power and a flexible pole, bent under tension. "As you can see," he explained. "This is a very simple design and goes back hundreds and hundreds of years. The spindle is attached to the foot pedal by a string and it's how you hold the chisel that sets the standard of the work. We bodgers make the beechwood legs and spars for chairs, which are finished in High Wycombe. In fact, we make a large variety of turned parts for all sorts of chairs. Some of them," he said, as he smiled at the boys: "have very strange names like 'Wheelbacks', 'Giant Arms', 'Windsors' and so on."

And then we also make plain chairs like this for kitchens. We put a box on the back of them to hold hymn books and bibles for chapels and churches." He moved over to the side of his workshop where a chair with straight legs, stretchers and back stood thick in sawdust. He picked it up, blew off the cream-coloured dust and showed his small audience an example of a locally made chair.

Bert then relit his pipe, which rarely left his mouth unless he was in bed, and returned to his treadle lathe where he continued: "Our work is very badly paid. If I wasn't a publican as well, I doubt if I could afford to do just this job. Especially now that not many people want furniture, most men are away in the war and families haven't the money." He sucked on his pipe thoughtfully.

"When did you first start making chair legs and stretchers?" Marge asked the old woodworker.

"I left school when I was fourteen," said Bert. "Old Bill Saunders taught me the trade. Like I am now, he was a publican, he ran the Crooked Billet and was a well-known local bodger. He started work at the age of 10, joining his father in the wood trade. His uncle originally provided the timber, but after the Great War, when Bill started on his own, timber became scarce and he had to buy it mainly from the Wyfold Estate and Checkendon.

Bert finished his tea and set the enamel mug down on the ground. "In 1913, when Bill's brother was taken ill, he often took the 'pimps', that's what they used to call bundles of kindling wood, into Wallingford before he started his day's wood turning. He produced for only three firms, Mealings, Allens and Holts and at first took the legs to Wycombe himself by horse and cart. Later he hired a lorry and eventually the firms collected them. Bill's stools and rolling pins were also in great demand. He was seventy-eight when he finished working as a bodger. My wife still has a rolling pin and a chopping board made from local wood by old Bill. He also taught me how to turn cricket sets, too, but I don't make many of them. They don't pay at all well."

"So where do you start?" asked Eric. "Do you go out and cut the wood yourself?"

"Why, no lad! I haven't got the time to do that. I buy timber at £1 per cartload of twenty-five cubic feet, cross cut it according to what sort of leg is required, and then split it with a beetle and wedge, like you say you saw George Clements use yesterday. I have to rough the wood out first with a hatchet. Our blacksmith makes them for me and then I shape them with a draw shave on a shaving horse like that one over there. It's what you might call a sort of combined seat-cum-bench-cum-clamp."

His pipe appeared to have gone out again at this point, so he stopped talking and knocked it out not far from a pile of sawdust and shavings. Marge Clements was astonished that they didn't catch light, but she didn't like to even mention the thought. Bert Carter refilled his pipe from an old oilskin bag in his pocket, clamped the pipe between his clenched teeth again, relit the bowl and went on with his explanation.

"Then I shape the billets on this lathe, shaping them with a gouge and marking out the pattern with this V-shaped tool, it's called a 'buzz'. When that's all done, I finish it with a flat chisel. Once the chair legs and 'stretchers' are finished, I stack them between wooden rails out in the yard for them to 'season', that is to get the weather to them, so they don't warp when they get in the warm. I say 'stretchers', that's the High Wycombe firm's name for them, we call them 'spars'. They're the bits of wood that join the legs together, or perhaps keep them apart, it depends on which way you look at it!" he laughed.

"Thank you very much, Mr Carter. Even I had no idea there was so much to making chair legs and spars. You'll never see anything like this in London, my lads!" Marge said, smiling.

Once out at the front of the pub again, she asked Eric whether he and his mother would be coming to the 'Social' at the Village Hall that evening. "Rather!" smiled Eric. "It's always such fun. We wouldn't miss it for the world!"

"Yes, and I hear someone's given a bottle of whisky for the raffle!" Marge replied. "There's going to be a singing competition tonight, as well. I've been practising and I hope to win some of those War Savings Stamps the Committee give as prizes now. They're talking about having a Mock Auction next month and a Fancy Dress Competition in the summer. They should bring in more money for the War Savings Campaign!" she concluded with a smile.

******

The stories of the evacuees in this chapter are taken from the 'Memories' of the people concerned and were published in the Stoke Row News in the 1980s and 1990s.

The Old Place

Chapter 19. The American and the Return: 1944 - 1948

Life in Stoke Row and Highmore continued much along the same lines throughout the remainder of the war. Some of the evacuees stayed on, though many of them had returned to London after the first year, when almost nothing happened. This period was often referred to as the 'Phoney War'.

Rationing became stricter and women, while often working in the 'secret factories' in the woods, continued to worry about their menfolk overseas, but gradually the news from the front got better. This was especially so after D-Day on 6th June 1944, when the Allies landed in Northern France and began to push the Germans back to their own frontiers.

For about six months before the Longest Day, as it became known, the American troops had come over to England in very large numbers to share in this onslaught and were stationed in Britain for training. It was a popular saying at the time that the 'GI's [General Infantrymen], or 'Yanks', as they were often affectionately called, were 'over-paid, over-sexed and over here!'

* * * * * *

The boys in Unit 4, Battery B of the 794 AAA, [Anti Aircraft Artillery] a 40 mm gun Battalion, had come over from America on the Dominion Monarch, a converted passenger liner, with a total of 7500 soldiers on board, following a period of training in various parts of the States. They tied up in Liverpool on 9th January 1944 and from there were taken by train to Blandford Camp in Dorset.

Among them was Sgt John Miller, who hailed from Easton, Pennsylvania and whose hobby was playing the horn, the trumpet and bugle. He also loved riding on trains and wrote to his mother and father to tell them of his experiences on his first day in England:

Once we left the ship we were marched to some sheds and eventually allowed to board the train. I was really looking forward to my first train ride in England and needed no push to board it. But what type of cars [carriages] were these? We thought they must have dated from the turn of the century! Everything here is so old and worn-out. I guess the British haven't had the opportunity to upgrade things like we have.

The windows were all blacked out, so no-one could read but everyone was tired, so we soon settled into every kind of position you could think of in order to get a little sleep, some of the guys even climbed up on to the luggage racks!

On the way down the train stopped and we were given Spam sandwiches and hot coffee by ladies from the Red Cross. The taste wasn't up to much but this was it, so we made the best of it...

They arrived at Blandford Camp, which they immediately called Camp Blandford. They were there to get their equipment, 40 mm guns, half-tracks, 0.50 calibre machine guns and so on. Most of all they were there to get trucks for loading all this equipment on to and to move it.

Their large barracks held about forty men each, in double-tiered bunks. John was in the one at the bottom and his pal, Sgt Tony Felini from New York, which he pronounced 'Noo Yoik', was in the one above. Every night, before lights out, they exchanged their experiences of the day.

"Gee, but it's cold in here, Tony!" John exclaimed. "I guess it's because the British are so short of coal. One of the guys told me that it, too, is rationed here."

"Seems that's right." Tony replied, his strong Italian accent still audible, even though he was a second-generation immigrant. "Say, you looked at that Instruction Book, yet?"

"Which one?" John asked. "We have had so many given us in the last few days, I'm overloaded!"

"Aw, shucks! I mean the one about how to deal with the British. It makes interesting reading. I wish my Mom and Pop had been given something like that when they came over to the States from Naples all those years ago. It does give you an insight into how these British have stood up to all their hardships since this war began."

"O.K, I'll look at it in the morning, must get some kip now." John answered, knowing that he would be lucky if he got a complete night's sleep, what with some men snoring and others talking in their sleep. He liked to think that some of them had smiles on their faces as they dreamt of wives and sweethearts back home.

The next evening he found a few free minutes to look at the thin pamphlet, which was entitled *Instructions for American Servicemen in Britain*. It consisted of seven pages of typescript, printed on poor quality foolscap size paper and had been distributed since 1942 by the United States War Department to American servicemen who were going to Britain.

"Gee whizz!" John thought to himself. "This is amazing! I had no idea we were so different from them, even given our accents." In fact, with remarkable succinctness this pamphlet represented a snapshot of Britain in wartime, as seen by a sympathetic outsider. It emphasised the British virtues of fair play and tolerance and showed Americans how to deal with everyday situations in places like public houses and on public transport.

He started to read each short chapter in his usual, slow, careful manner. The first one was entitled 'No Time to Fight Old Wars' and warned that Adolf Hitler hoped that these children of former immigrants, many of them coming from old Irish families, for instance, would once again see themselves as enemies of the British instead of Allies and that he would gladly make propaganda out of that situation.

He read on with interest, finding that the next chapter was to explain that 'The British are Reserved, not Unfriendly' and explained that on a small crowded island, where forty-five million people live, each man learns to guard his privacy carefully. John found the pamphlet absorbing and read it avidly. He was fascinated by the chapter 'Don't be a Show-Off', which fitted in with his own modest way of thinking. He could appreciate that the 'Tommies' [British soldiers] might resent the American manner of flashing their money around.

However, before long it was time for the men to leave the small hall in which they could get hot tea to try and warm themselves in the evening before returning to their barracks and go to bed. Once again the two men fell to discussing their experiences of the day before they went to sleep.

John said: "Thanks Tony, for suggesting I read that paper on the British way of life. I'm finding it quite amazing. I had no idea they were quite so different from us, since we speak the same language and many of us, well, perhaps not you," he added tactfully, "have ancestors who came from here in the first place. It's not only that we have a common language, but our laws are much the same as theirs and they have freedom of religion, the same as we do."

"Yeah! Okay, but don't go on and on about it!" Tony exclaimed. "I'm already finding the strangest things over here myself. We went out today and saw something I'll never forget. There were some guys digging a ditch and they were all stopped to drink tea. The driver told us that at ten o'clock in the morning and at four o'clock in the afternoon the British stop everything to have a break and drink tea. He said British soldiers do that too, except if they're fighting, I suppose."

He offered John a strip of gum, but his companion refused. "I'm just going out to look up at the stars. You, know, they're the same stars we see at home, but just at a different time of day!"

"Before you do, I'll tell you another thing I saw. Outside the kitchen door there was a large skid of potatoes and on top of them a pile of very strange-looking vegetables. Our cooks said they're called 'leeks', seems they're a bit like large scallions. Cookie uses them to flavour our meals."

"Well, we won't be here long. I heard today that we're moving again next week." John whispered to his pal.

"Aw, Jeez, just another rumour. You can't believe all you hear!" his friend replied. "Anyway, I gotta get some sleep, I'm dead beat!"

In fact, what John had overheard was true and the following week they were on the move, this time in a northerly direction. To John the countryside was beautiful, even though it was still winter. He was sensible enough to realise that if he survived all this he would have wonderful memories to take back home. "I'd never be able to go to England on my own and this is one way to do it," he thought. John Miller was nothing if not a philosophical man.

They finally arrived at their destination. It was a small camp hastily constructed some months beforehand under the cover of dense woodland. They were quartered in metal roofed huts which most of the men felt were 'not too bad'. All they were told at the time was that they were in Oxfordshire.

They had a tiled latrine that was kept clean by one of the older guys in the Battery and he seemed well suited for the job, having been a janitor in civilian life.

John wrote to his parents again, telling them as much as he could that would not be struck out by the blue pencil of the Censor, whose job it was to ensure that no military secrets, particularly indications of the whereabouts of the 794 Battalion, should fall into the hands of the enemy. He wrote slowly and carefully, trying to think of some story to write and amuse his folks:

> *I can't tell you where we are, but you must not worry, we are being well cared for. We have comfortable huts and our own latrine that is looked after by a former janitor. It'll make you laugh when I tell you how crazy this guy is. Every morning, from nine o'clock to ten o'clock, he locks the doors of the latrine and cleans the place thoroughly. OK, we don't find fault with that. But what gets our fellows, and especially those with a real need, is that he won't open the doors until it is exactly ten o'clock. Not only that but he looks out of the window with a big grin on his face and, no matter how much the guys scream and yell, he will not budge.*
>
> *Now you would think they'd get him when he came out, but he keeps a bike just inside the door and all of a sudden he jumps on it and comes racing out! As he's an older man with this 'special job' as he calls it, he is not required to do much training and then he's free for the rest of the day. I should have been a janitor!*

The men trained and trained. They watched movies about training and then they trained some more. They hooked up the big 40 mm gun and unhooked it. They loaded the 0.50 calibre machine guns on to the truck and then they took them off again. They marched and marched. They cleared out spaces in the woods and, with posts and ropes, they laid out the outline of the landing crafts that they would be crossing the Channel in, although they were not told that at the time. Eventually all this training wearied the men, but it also gave them a common purpose and they started to feel themselves as part of a family unit.

As they became more proficient and the weather got warmer, they were more and more often allowed to go into the nearby town of Reading. John was a quiet man, though and preferred to cycle around the local villages. The men had discovered by this time that they were in a place called Checkendon in the south-east of the county of Oxfordshire. The next village was Stoke Row and, after a week or two, John Miller of Boston met a couple called Roland and Edna Page. It transpired that Roland had a small four-piece group that played in the Village Hall on Saturday nights for dancing.

"Why don't you come and join us?" Roland suggested as soon as he learned that John was also a musician. "I play the saxophone and you could play your trumpet."

"Now that sounds like a good idea!" John returned. "We could really get the joint swinging!" Upon reaching the camp again he asked for and received the Captain's blessing to spend every Saturday night over in Stoke Row.

That night he confided in his Italian companion: "I've got it made for something to do on a Saturday evening and the Cap'n's actually given me permission to stay out until midnight. You should come over."

"No, not me." returned the Italian. "I prefer to stay here with Mario and Bennie. We sure do enjoy our cards."

Roland Page ran the local garage in Stoke Row and lent John three bicycles so that he and some of his other friends could use them to go into Reading during the other evenings. There they would go to concerts, dances or whatever was the highlight of the evening. Sometimes it was just having a drink with the British in one of the pubs.

One night he crept into his bunk, trying not to awake his Italian friend in the bed above, but he was not successful. "Where the hell have you been?" asked Tony.

"Ah well," answered John. "This evening the three of us were all returning from Reading and I pushed on ahead of the other two. I went to Roland's house to replace my bike in the place where he keeps it, but the others did not show up. I backtracked and found them in the hands of the local cops!"

"What had happened?" enquired Tony, wide-awake by now.

"They were riding a bike without lights." John whispered. "It seems that the little gadget that takes the power from the front wheel did not work. Luckily for them the 'Bobbies' let them go with just a warning and when we had finally put the bikes away we were able to come back here."

However, the offenders were lined up the next day in front of their officers and several British policemen. The American miscreants were then given a lecture on obeying the local laws and honouring the British way of life. The story of their misdeeds spread like wildfire through the small camp, losing nothing in the telling. Most of the guys had a good laugh at their expense, while some wondered at the pettiness of it all and others felt a twinge of conscience about upsetting their British hosts.

Once the GIs had been permitted into Reading for a few weeks and not much trouble had come out of it, they were allowed to go to London, just a forty-five minute trip from Reading train station. Eventually they were also given Overnight Passes. It was when he was on the train going 'up town' that John Miller found himself humming a familiar tune and eventually remembered the words to it. Instead of the word 'town' he substituted 'London'.

> *Yankee Doodle went to London*
> *Just to ride a pony*
> *Stuck a feather in his cap*
> *and called it macaroni!*

He looked over to his 'bunk buddy', Tony Felini, who had already had a few beers with his Italian friends in Reading before they had caught the train. They were singing Mediterranean songs, quite unabashed. "Eyeti's!" [Italians]" thought John to himself with some

389

amusement, "they sure do know how to enjoy themselves!"

He too, enjoyed himself in his own quiet way. Later that week he wrote to his parents back in Easton, Pennsylvania:

I sure had a good time last weekend. I got an overnight pass and went to London on the train. I was able to stay in lodgings recommended by the Red Cross for twenty-five cents a night and while I was up there I dropped into a British NAAFI canteen for a cup of tea and a biscuit. I also bought a chocolate bar for just a nickel!

I went to the movies and saw a British film called The Way Ahead. *It sure makes you admire these British and their plain common guts. There's no doubt about it, they're no panty-waists!*

I love the 'Tube', too. It's an underground train system and has quite a network. There's not only trains down there but shops as well. The Londoners have been sleeping down there nights, though not so many of them now that the Blitz, I mean the bombing, has largely stopped...

When he did not get a weekend pass to go to London, John was content to cycle around the local villages. One time he noticed that the 343rd US Army Engineers had erected a small castle-like building at the edge of the road just beyond Highmore on the Nettlebed road. It stood at the gates of their camp and they painted it red and cream. One of the guards on the gate told him that it was their company's insignia. Little did either of them imagine at the time that it would be preserved by the local people right into the twenty-first century as a mark of respect for these men.

He admired, too, many of the old-fashioned cottages and one day found himself cycling along the bottom of Witheridge Hill, though he didn't know that because all signposts had been removed, for fear of allowing spies to find their way around. There he noticed a little cottage, standing all on its own, looking rather neglected. Outside there was a name board, proclaiming it to be 'Old Place', but there was no sign of life. John thought how pretty it was and how he'd love to be able to come back some day and buy it.

He also went into the little shops and bought whatever was available, chatting quietly to the local people and noting their country accents. This also gave them a chance to see that not all 'Yanks' were the loud, noisy type like Tony Felini.

On Saturday nights he played with Roland Page and his friends in the Stoke Row Village Hall. Young Mabel Cox, who had recently started work on the Crest Estate, was a talented pianist and she, too, formed part of the band. John was surprised to hear that she had been playing the organ in the little local Chapel since she was fourteen years old. Sometimes, on a Sunday afternoon, he quietly slipped into the back of the Chapel and participated in the simple services there.

Later, also on a Sunday afternoon he was invited to tea with Roland and Edna Page in their comfortable home, Highview, in Stoke Row. They were very happy when, after a few weeks, he asked if he could bring a 'buddy' along. This turned out to be 'Louie' [Lieutenant] Jim Davis, a man from Wisconsin who had been born in England, but whose parents had gone out to the States in search of work in 1936.

"Jim's our 'Battalion Clerk'," explained John. "He's got influence. He puts down the names of the guys who would like to have tea with an English family. I think you say 'take tea'?" Edna nodded. "We're lucky, because you've been kind enough to invite us, but many don't know anyone and we're not all pushy you know!" John continued, with a laugh.

"You can put us down on your list as people who would like to entertain you on a Sunday afternoon." Roland offered.

"Well, that sure is kind of you, sir," said Jim. "Actually, I had a bit of a run in with our Captain a few weeks back. I wanted to make sure I got on the list, so I put my name down at the head of it. Cap' saw this and now my name is at the bottom!"

"Why don't you bring the Captain along with you next week?" suggested Edna, smiling.

"Thank you, Ma'am. I'll put it to him. I think he gets a bit lonesome, too. We're most of us not used to being away from home even and certainly not in a strange country." Jim 's face turned bright red at his inadvertent mistake. "I mean, not that you are strange, just different from us!"

Roland and Edna both laughed. "Don't worry, we don't take offence. You are as interesting to us as we are to you. What was it Winston Churchill said on the radio last week, something about us being a common people divided only by a language!"

Eventually several of the officers came to tea with the Pages, even the Colonel came on one occasion. "Just to thank you people for your kindness." was his explanation.

From this time on, Jim and John often went on cycle rides together, while the other men went to the pubs or to the movies. One Saturday afternoon when they were in Reading, a local newspaper photographer came up to John, just as he was giving some gum and Hershey bars to four little boys. The photograph came out in the *Reading Chronicle* the following week and was entitled 'Got any gum, chum?' John sent a copy of it to his parents, who proudly framed it and displayed it in their parlour.

At the end of April, the boys in Unit 4, Battery B of the 794 AAA 40 mm Gun Battalion were sent to the Welsh coast to practise firing their guns. John wrote to his parents that weekend. He wanted to tell them it was Wales but the Censor would not have allowed it:

We've been away for a few days. I can't tell you where we went to but it was just the type of trip I like more than any other. We packed up and away we went. It was a great way to see the country. My assigned seat in the back of the truck was the very last one on the left hand side. It was a tough place to be in stormy weather but otherwise OK.

I remember passing fields of what was left of a vegetable called 'Brussels Sprouts'. It appears that the farmers have portable fences that they place around a portion of these fields. They then let the sheep go in to eat both the leaves and the stalks. When the sheep have had their fill, the farmers just move the fences on. I was also interested, too, in the way that the farmers stack up the bales of straw. They make a rectangular shape and then put more on to form a sloping roof. This allows the rain to run off and cuts down the damage to the straw.
It was all very interesting, but we kept on the move and finally

reached some mountains. At first it was all very beautiful and the weather was good but then bit by bit, it changed. Up and down we went, then around and around these mountains. There was nothing to see, it all seemed to be wasteland. To add to the boredom, it rained and rained and rained. To tell you the truth, folks, it was dreary, dreary, dreary! At last we reached our camp and it's not too bad. Now the sun has come out, so things are looking up...

John found the most interesting part of his stay in Wales was the town of Aberayon. It was a small place and there was nothing to do but go to the local pub. Some of the American guys, feeling life was too quiet, started to make remarks about the British soldier being better than the Welsh soldier, just loud enough for the local folk to hear. Once they had started a fight, the Americans would leave, laughing. John observed all this and decided this type of evening was not for him.

Instead he volunteered to be a waiter in the English Officers' Mess Hall. He knew he would eat well there and as it transpired all he had to do was to clear the tables. As he remarked to his pal, Jim, later that evening: "I guess they didn't want me pouring hot soup down on an officer. It wasn't hard work and we sure did eat good afterwards."

Back in the Checkendon Camp in mid-May, the bluebells had just begun to carpet the woods around Checkendon, Stoke Row and Highmore but still the training went on. One of the tests was 'getting around in the dark'. The Captain led the men and their officers into the woods at about ten o'clock, just after dusk. They then walked for a while and stopped at a point where the Captain gave them a talk on how to find their way back quickly and quietly to the Camp, just as if they were in enemy territory. He and the officers then got in their Jeeps and returned to the Camp, expecting some of the men to get stranded, lost and tired in these dense English woods.

What the officers did not know was that most of the men already knew the area and even had girlfriends in the nearby villages. These night sorties just gave them the opportunity of spending a night in perfect bliss. Since no one was expected back before dawn, no check was made to see who was in and who was out. John and Jim were not among them, but they enjoyed seeing how much the others benefited from these minor misdemeanours.

As the weeks went by, Sargeant John Miller and his close buddy 'Louie' Jim Davis, who were no fools, realised that 'things were hotting up' and that they were in sight of the end of their 'vacation in England'. This made life all the more sweet and they took advantage of every chance to see something of their host country. One day a trip to Portsmouth was laid on. Soon they met some English girl sailors [WRNS] and were taking pictures of them, the Americans having camera film to which few British soldiers had access. At this Naval Base they were able to go on board the famous wooden warship, HMS *Victory*. Somehow the stories of the battles of long ago fired their enthusiasm to 'get this war over and done with!'

At the end of May, John wrote to his parents again. Although he was not to know, it was to be his last letter before they took part in the Normandy Landings. Like all the others they had received from their son, this one was shown to all the members of their family as well as to everyone in the neighbourhood in Easton.

I went yesterday on a trip to Oxford, where the schools [colleges] are. Jim and I went for the whole day. In the morning, we walked around the town, looking at those beautiful schools [university colleges]. Most of them are built of cream stone and are truly ancient.

At mid-day we stopped by a Fish and Chip Shop. You just go in and order a portion and wait a few minutes. Then up it comes, all hot and greasy, wrapped in a sheet of yesterday's newspaper. On the counter are bottles of salt and vinegar. We were told to sprinkle these on liberally as they help to counteract the grease. It seems that fat is very short here, like everything else and so it is used over and over, much more often than it would have been before the war.

We sat outside on the curbstone [kerbstone] to eat our food but were hardly started when a couple of 'Tommies' came and sat next to us. We had seen them standing in line behind us in the Fish and Chip Shop. Like most, British people, they started the conversation with remarks about the weather. It really is warm at the moment! Then, of course we got around to talking about the differences between us. It's a subject that seems to fascinate them as well as us. One point did emerge from this and that is that in Britain old is better than big or something that costs more money. As one of these Tommies explained to us, 'the older it is, the better it is, especially houses and furniture.'

We went off looking at more schools and in the late afternoon we stopped off at a Tea Room to get some tea. It's a great thing over here is tea. You get a small pot of tea, with milk and a little sugar. You also get a plate of sandwiches, made with cucumbers or watercress, plus a small cake or a biscuit, though these are smaller than our cookies. All this cost only fifty cents!

In the Tea Room Jim and I met a couple of young ladies who were students at the University here. Jim took his off to the movies but I took mine, her name was Linda, out to dinner. We went to a fine hotel, called the Randolph. It was real classy, with waiters in tuxedos [dinner jackets], polished dishes, glistening glasses, shining silverware and even an orchestra for dancing. I couldn't believe how low the price of the dinner was - just one dollar! It is set by law; specially imposed because of the war. The meal was sparse though, on account of the rationing here. Another dollar was charged for the music and even though I left a dollar tip, the evening was very cheap and Linda was great company. I hope to see her again soon. Maybe I'll take her out one day on a punt down the River Thames . . .

Actually, he never did take Linda out and it was several weeks before Sgt John Miller was able to resume writing to his parents once more, because the following day they began to get ready to go down to the south coast of England in preparation for what transpired to be the Normandy Landings and the great battles that followed.

Happily, Sgt John Miller survived the remainder of the war and returned home safe and sound to his delighted parents. He went to Engineering School and got qualified. Eventually, he married a lovely local girl and settled down. Several times in the coming decades he took his wife to England and Europe to show her the places he had visited during the war.

******

Thanks to the bravery of Sgt John Miller and the hundreds and thousands of men like him, both in the British and American armies, to say nothing of the thousands of Poles, French and many other nationalities which comprised the Allied Forces, the Second World War gradually came to a successful conclusion when the Germans agreed to an unconditional surrender on 8th May 1945.

After almost six years of war, Britain and Europe were finally free and celebrations were held all over the country in the form of street parties, dances and other social events.

However, it was only the beginning of a long struggle to return to anything resembling the old way of life, even in country districts like Stoke Row and Highmore. Rationing continued for many things until the mid-1950s. Even as late as 1953 fats, sugar and sweets were still rationed, but it did mean that most of the population had some food. The people were often asked to 'tighten their belts' as the government tried to maintain a fair regime.

With all the men returning from the services, the women who had worked in the 'secret factories' had to go back to their old way of life, just looking after their homes and children. Large numbers of children, who were later to be known as the 'Baby Boomers', were born within the first years after the end of the war, once the men had come home to their wives.

The men themselves often found it hard to go back to civilian life following years of travel and fighting throughout Europe and the Middle East. Suddenly it was difficult to find a job and even harder to find a house.

Also the men had to live with their memories of the previous five or more years. Some never spoke of the war again, some broke down and cried, most just tried their best to adjust to their new way of life.

******

George Stevens was born in Highmore in 1917 and stayed at

Witheridge Hill School until he was fourteen years old. On leaving school he got a job as a Keeper for Mr Commins at Highmore Farm, under the Head Keeper, Ernie Want, who lived in one of the Church Cottages. His pay was minimal, even for a lad, just ten shillings a week. However, after a year he found himself unemployed and the only work he could get was stone-picking at one shilling and sixpence a cubic yard. He had helped his mother do this work when he was a child, but found it harder still when the ground was further away from his adult arms!

This extremely arduous labour performed two functions; it cleared the fields of stones and provided material for the basis of road making and mending. The labourer would make piles of stones all over the field, sometimes as many as forty, and they would often stay there for up to three months, when the road menders would come with a cart and take them away. The Area Surveyor was very careful to check every pile and this was done with a piece of string, applied from the base, over the top down to the other side, making an amount equal to the contents of a box measuring a cubic yard. Woe betide any stone picker who the Area Surveyor thought was trying to short-sell him!

In the early twentieth century, the roads were made by laying the stones down and covering them with a mud slurry.

In 1926, the 'New Road' that ran down the south side of Witheridge Hill (as opposed to the 'Hard Hill' on the north side) was made. Before the creation of this new carriageway, the track was so narrow that if a cart went up it, a child could not pass on either side because the banks were so steep. This new road became very useful to Capt. Wells, the 1930s owner of the little old cottage at the foot of Witheridge Hill, as he was able to drive his car down this to the front entrance.

By the time George was sixteen he tired of stone-picking and his father managed to get him a job with the Oxfordshire County Council, as his assistant. In fact, on the quiet, he had been driving a steam-roller since he was ten years old. His work involved care of a Fowler and sometimes an Invicta. This gave him a love of these great machines that, unbeknown to him, at the time, was to be of great help to him some ten years later. As a young assistant, he had to clean and oil the engine and make sure there was enough coal. Most of the mechanism was steel, just a few parts were brass and copper and George was under strict instructions from his father to "keep the whole lot gleaming bright!"

One of his functions was 'sheeting up' in the morning and 'sheeting down' at night. This meant he had to raise the green canvas sheets around the sides of the driver's area and roll them up tight, securing them with ties of a similar material. The purpose of these sheets was to protect the steamroller engine from rust when it was not in use.

He started work at 7.00 am in order to light the fire to raise the steam for the engine and worked on until 5.00 pm. It was hard work but he enjoyed the companionship of his fellow-workers, and travelled about Oxfordshire, renewing acquaintances wherever he went. In the evenings he helped his father on their allotment at Highmore and to keep the pigs. Both of these spare-time occupations helped with the family budget and they also were of use to him later on.

In 1937, George Stevens joined the Territorial Army, and spent many weekends away at camp. He continued with his work for the Council during the week until 1939 when the Second World War broke out. Having been in the 'Terriers' George was immediately drafted into the 'Ox & Bucks' [Oxfordshire and Buckinghamshire] Regiment and trained for going over to fight in France.

In 1940 he was part of the disastrous landing in France and in a town called Watteau, not far from the beaches, he was wounded in the thigh. He spent some time in an army hospital but soon afterwards he and his compatriots were captured by the Germans and became Prisoners of War. From that time onwards he and his pals were moved from place to place. Often the camps were very poor and at one such place they were just given old barns to live in. Because of this the dozen or so British prisoners began to get demoralised, but Sergeant George Stevens would have none of it. He contacted the Red Cross, got them new uniforms and ensured they kept smart. This was good for their morale and for their esteem in the eyes of their captors. In his occasional letters home he often said they would never have survived had it not been for the goodness of the Red Cross and the Salvation Army.

Gradually, as the Allies began to drive the Germans back, the men were moved further and further east. Eventually this group, which had managed to stick together, found themselves in a 'farming camp' in German occupied Poland. It was here that George spent most of his last wartime days.

It was then that his former life on the farm and operating steam engines and steamrollers on the roads of Oxfordshire came in useful. He and his fellow prisoners had a very hard time on these farms but at least they fared better than many who were just locked into huge camps.

The months and years seemed to drag by endlessly, but at last, whilst he was working with about 500 other prisoners, clearing the local railway lines of bomb damage, they were released by the Americans. In late 1945, Sergeant George Stevens was finally enabled to return home.

For much of his first year back with his parents he tried to put on the weight that he had lost and to recover some of the sense of well-being that he had enjoyed before the War. He hardly ever spoke of his wartime experiences.

In 1946 he met and married a beautiful girl called Mavis Armstrong, who came from Mansfield, Nottinghamshire, and who had been working in Highmore with the Land Army. Luckily, when he had recovered his health, George was able to return to working for the Council, as mechanic, blacksmith, carpenter, grass-cutter and, of course, steam-engine driver.

Gradually, as he and his new wife began to settle down to married life, George started to tell Mavis just a few of the stories that had been in his head ever since he had left Poland, but about which he had not been able to speak before.

One evening, over a cup of tea, he recalled some of his wartime memories: "The last farming camp I was at in the Danzig was part of a very large one, employing up to a hundred prisoners at the height of the season. They were Russian, English, and Polish. All of us learned a smattering of German. Between ourselves we conferred in sign language as well as 'pidgin English'. Perhaps because we had a common enemy, we all got along together very well.

After a few months, we English rose to being in charge of all the key jobs on the farm. Doug Jenkins was the Chief Pigman, Bill Stocks was the Head Shepherd and John Seymour had charge of the Dairy, so between us all we did quite well for food, really."

Pouring himself another cup of tea, George continued: "I'll never forget it, on one occasion, when a flock of geese was being driven to the local railway station, one of the prisoners saw to it that one goose went missing. He had the bright idea as to how to conceal it from the guards. Believe it or not, he sliced vertically across a pile of frozen manure and made a hole for it in the middle!"

"Good heavens!" said Mavis. She was used to farm life, having been a Land Girl for five years, but nevertheless she was astonished. "Didn't it smell when he got it out?"

"No, it didn't. You see, the manure was frozen and anyway we plucked it and roasted it, so none of us came to any harm. We were so hungry by then, we'd have eaten anything!"

"We used to do anything to get food," he continued. "And coal. We needed coal and wood to make fires to cook on as well as to keep ourselves warm. The winter was bitter out there but luckily there was plenty of wood around the farm."

"What else happened? Now you've started, you might as well tell me a bit more." Mavis encouraged him.

"No, love." George said, with a tired smile. "I've said enough for now. Maybe I'll tell you some more another time. I've got to go out and water the vegetables before it gets dark."

Mavis did not like to press her husband on the matter of his wartime memories, but a few weeks later, when they were walking up on Witheridge Hill, she broached the subject again, but he dismissed it, saying: "Now I'm home, I don't want to think about things like that. It's wonderful to be back in England and especially here in Highmore. Let's sit under this big old oak tree in the shade. I remember this tree from when I was a boy and lived over there. We often tried climbing it when I was up here at school. My, it's good to be back."

However, one day, a few months later, they spotted a hare running across the field behind their new Council house in Holly Close. George became thoughtful and then said:

"That reminds me of the time when we were sent out on a hare hunt from the farm camp. We killed over a hundred. Afterwards the guards watched over us as we hung them up in one of the outhouses, so even if we'd wanted to, there was no filching one then. Luckily one of our lads had been a blacksmith in 'civvy' life and so he did this sort of work on the farm. Soon enough he managed to make a spare key and before long we got an opportunity to use it."

"How did you manage to cook it without the guards smelling it?" Mavis enquired. "Hare has a very strong smell. I know, because we often had hare when I was up at Highmore Farm. It's delicious!"

"Ah well, I'm coming to that, love." George replied. "Later that day, when we were cooking this hare our guard lifted his nose and said "Ich rieche hasen!" We thought we were done for then, but Doug Jenkins took a big chance and decided to give him some.

You probably don't think of them that way, but most of the guards were only working men like us and the Germans didn't have much food either. As Doug said wittily later that evening: 'Fed men tell no tales!'"

"But you got food parcels from the Red Cross, didn't you?" Mavis asked.

"Yes we did." replied George. "In fact we were so pleased to receive those Red Cross parcels that we used to dance around before we dared to open it. One thing we could be pretty sure of, though, was that it would contain a tin of salmon, tinned in Alaska. Do you know, love, I couldn't touch tinned salmon today, even if you were able to find one!" he concluded.

Bit by bit, George told his wife just a few more interesting or amusing stories, but after a while he decided to put the war behind him.

In 1947 Mavis presented her husband with a son who they named Anthony and in 1956, their pretty, little daughter, Hazel, was born.

George continued to work for the Oxfordshire County Council and by the time he retired he had thirty men working under him. However, he rarely mentioned any of his war experiences to any of them or to his family again.

******

Late in 1944, the wooden huts, so hastily erected by the Americans in the months before D-Day, were requisitioned by the War Department as housing for German and Italian prisoners-of-war.

Many of these men worked on the local farms and some even stayed on and settled down in the villages when the War ended.

The Polish Army found themselves in a difficult position at the end of the War. Most of the Poles were reluctant to return to their homeland, now occupied by the Russians who they feared as much, if not more than the Germans. While their problems were being sorted out they made further use of the wooden hutted camps. Some of the men were joined by their families and local people were astonished to see the women, wearing headscarves in the Polish manner, gleaning firewood or corn in the fields. Some of these buildings at Peppard were also used to house other refugees and even some British homeless who had suffered from the London bombings. It was a time of much movement of peoples from place to place in an effort to sort out their needs and to find them permanent homes.

******

Although the War in Europe finished in May 1945, the fighting in the Far East continued until 15 August of that year when the Japanese finally surrendered, following the dropping of atomic bombs on Hiroshima and Nagasaki. Before this several regiments had been fighting for over three years in the Far East and Burma had been re-conquered by the Fourteenth Army, under General William Slim, between January and May 1945. While Britain and Europe were in the grip of euphoria, this group of extremely brave and persevering men thought of themselves as the 'Forgotten Army'. This was largely because few journalists were sent out to cover this aspect of the War and the troops in Europe always seemed to get priority for supplies of all kinds.

******

One of the first men to come back from the Far East was Jack Heath, who had been born in 1917 in Cane End and had attended Goring Heath School under Mr John H Baker, schoolmaster and author of several books about this area.

When he left school, Jack worked at the Star Brush Sawmill, at the far west end of Stoke Row. At the outbreak of the Second World War this work was classed as a 'reserved occupation', so it was not until

1942, when he was conscripted at the age of 25 that Jack entered the Armed Forces.

Just before he did so, he and his fiancee, Kathleen (Kitty), were married. He had wanted to go into the RAF, but when he applied he was told there were no vacancies, so he was drafted into the Bedfordshire & Hertfordshire Regiment and given the Army number 14317152. Jack stayed with the Beds and Herts, fighting the Japanese in Burma for one hundred and forty-nine days. When the War in the Far East finally ended, King George VIth gave the men of this brave regiment special dispensation to be awarded the Burma Star for which the criterion was that they had had to serve for one hundred and sixty days. Under their famous leader, General William Slim, they patrolled the Chindit Hills and earned themselves the nickname of 'The Chindits'.

Following the tremendous celebrations throughout May and June of 1945, there was no one to greet the Beds & Herts when they arrived back at Southampton in the September of that year and so the men made their way quietly back home. A photograph on the front of a daily paper showed the empty dockside and the caption bore the title: 'The Forgotten Army Returns".

However, on the fifth anniversary of 'V. J. Day' [Victory in Japan] a local paper decided to send a reporter out to cover the story of these unsung heroes. Jim Smithells was a bright young lad, with a ready smile and a slightly nonchalant way of speaking. It was with great difficulty that he located a number of the Burma Star men. At first they were all reluctant to relive those awful days out in the Far East, but gradually as the reporter asked the questions so they responded.

Jack Heath was the first one he located. He had to interview him in the evening as Jack was, by that time, working for a local builder in the daytime. First of all, Jim asked him brightly, as he had been trained to do: "What was the worst thing about being out there then?"

"Going through water in the jungle was one of the worst aspects of it all." Jack remembered. There were thousands of mosquitoes and often it was impossible to erect nets over ourselves. The leeches were the worst. We used to touch their bottoms with a lighted cigarette or a match. When they attached themselves to you they were tissue paper thin but they would finish up as thick as your finger, once they'd sucked your blood, but they did it very silently. You didn't feel anything until you felt the wet and realised on touching the spot that it was your own blood. They got into every part of your body, your ears, nostrils and so on."

"Ugh! It sounds horrid! Jim exclaimed, shivering as he did so. "There were a lot of diseases, too, weren't there?"

"Oh yes!" Jack recalled. "Malaria and cramp were a constant problem. We took quinine every day, it's made from the bark of a tree, and we had to take salt tablets against the risk of getting cramp. The main thing was you had to try and drink chlorinated water all the time. Actually, I had quite a time over that."

"What do you mean, tell me!" Jim was getting more interested in the older man now.

"Well, we had an officer called Lt Salazar. Before the war, he had been a ski-ing instructor in Switzerland. He was a hard man and maintained a rigid discipline. One day when he caught me drinking a small amount of unchlorinated water, he had me tied to a tree. I was released when we marched on, but each time they stopped, throughout the five day trek, I was tied to a tree again."

"Good heavens, how cruel!" Jim exclaimed. "It sounds more the sort of thing they said the Japs did!"

"Ah well!" the former soldier explained. "This was to punish me and teach me the dangers of drinking unchlorinated water as well as making me an example to the others. The dangers of catching any one of several diseases was very great, especially from contaminated water. Luckily, I suffered no ill effects from any of this treatment. Many other men did die, I reckon more died from disease than were killed by the Japanese."

"It sounds as if it was really dreadful. I hadn't really realised how bad it was." Jim admitted. "You must have longed to get home!"

"Well, actually, I tried never to think about going home." Jack said. "You just lived for yourself just for that day, hoping you'd get through it without getting ill, or shot. You hadn't really got time to think about anything else and as soon as you lay down, you were so tired, you fell asleep!"

At this point, Jack went to a drawer in his sideboard and took out a large photograph that showed a group of about thirty very thin men with beards. "When we were about half-way through the campaign we were all assembled and photographed. By then our beards had grown considerably. In order that the Japanese should think we were a new lot of fighting men who had just been brought in we were then ordered to shave ourselves clean. That's me there." Jack pointed to a particularly thin man with a big bushy beard.

"You must have felt much better after that!" Jim remarked.

"Yes, we did, but at the same time it was something of a danger," Jack explained, "because a freshly shaven pink face can be seen more clearly through the jungle than one partly covered with dark hair!"

"I suppose so, I hadn't thought of that." admitted the 'cub' reporter, "This is all so interesting to me because I was only born in 1931 and I was really just a child while the war was on."

Jack smiled at the fresh-faced young man with his earnest expression. "There were some advantages to me after that though," he went on to recall. "I became a Platoon Runner and, although that was dangerous, I didn't have to do guard duty and so usually got a good night's sleep. It helped you to keep alert during the day. You always had to be on your guard, the Japs were all around you most of the time."

"Were you fighting right up until the Japs surrendered?" asked Jim.

"No, not really. I was wounded in the arm but luckily it didn't turn gangrenous. I could have gone home then, but I decided to stick it out. In fact, all our Platoon were sent back to India for a fortnight's recuperation and it was whilst we were there that the Japs gave in and then we were sent home." Jack recalled.

"Thank you very much, sir." young Jim said, rising from his chair. "Do you know anyone else hereabouts who was out there at the same time?"

"Yes." Jack said. "You could ask Dennis Clark. He lives further down the village, near the church. Here you are, I'll write out his address for you."

Jim Smithells shook hands with the former soldier as he left, a little less flippant than when he had first come through the door.

The following evening he found his way to Dennis Clark. He lived in one of a circle of Council houses that had been erected only about five years before to accommodate men who were returning from the 'front' but who had no homes to go to.

Dennis was a big man, with broad shoulders and a broad smile.

"What do you want then?" he asked

"Mr Heath said you might be able to tell me about your experiences out in Burma." Jim said, with a slightly more respectful manner than he had first shown to Jack Heath.

"Well, I try not to think about it too much." Dennis explained. Nevertheless, he opened the door and took the young man into the front room. "What exactly do you want to know?"

"Perhaps we could start with the regiment you were in, sir." asked the young man.

"I was conscripted when I was twenty-one, that was in 1942. I started off in the Berkshires, but soon I was sent into the Sussex Regiment. They were a good lot, they were. They really looked after their men."

"Did you go out east straightway?" asked Jim as he started to take notes.

"Yes. We went out on the *Stirling Castle.* There were eighteen thousand of us on that ship. In peacetime she carried just two thousand passengers. The journey took us fifteen weeks, as we had to go across the Atlantic to Brazil and across again in order to avoid the German submarines. Eventually we landed in Bombay and were sent by train to Hyderabad."

Young Jim Smithells found he was becoming more and more interested in the foreign travels of these former soldiers. He had lived in Henley all his life and, largely because of the war, had never travelled further than London. "You certainly have seen the world!" he remarked.

"Yes, and I've never regretted it, even with all I saw and had to do." Dennis agreed. "As a farmer's lad I would never have seen all those countries otherwise. I've been to Brazil, India, Burma, Malaya, China and Ceylon. I could never have done that on my own."

Jim continued to make notes. "Did you have any narrow escapes?" he enquired.

"Yes, I did, several times. I reckon I lived a charmed life." He went on to explain: "Because I had worked on a farm, I was lucky enough to be very strong in the arm and could dig a trench in half the time of other men. Once I had to dig one four foot long by four feet deep and I had just done so but the other men had only got two feet down. Because I'd already finished the officer took me as an escort to another place about a mile away. It gets dark out there in less than five minutes and by the time we got back we could hardly see but we could see enough to realise that all six men had been attacked and killed in our absence, which was probably no more than half an hour."

"Hold on a minute." Jim requested. "My shorthand isn't all that good yet. Give me a second or two and I'll be there."

Dennis smiled and when he saw that the young man had finished making the funny signs in his notebook, he went on: "On another occasion, towards the end of the War, we met up with some American servicemen who asked me and some of my mates back to their camp for the evening. We got a pass, so that was alright. We had a wonderful time but when we got back to our own camp at one o'clock in the morning we were told that there had been a sudden emergency and that we should have been there to go on a plane with the others." Dennis paused for a moment reflectively and continued: "The strange thing is, you know, that plane was shot down and they were all killed."

Dennis went on to explain that when he was out in Burma he was still a young man and very fit from all his experience and life on the farm. However, he found that many of the older men and particularly those who had worked in offices in 'civvy street' [civilian life] were unable to carry all their kit in the heat of the sun. He therefore often carried as many as ten rifles or a machine gun in addition to his own kit.

"Did you ever have a good time or a break from all that hard life?" enquired Jim.

"Oh, yes, sometimes. One time I remember," Dennis said, "was when we had an Irish cook. We had some chocolate sent in with the rations and he was told to ensure everyone got some of it. We thought the corned beef tasted funny that night and were told that he had melted the chocolate in with the stew! Actually, it didn't taste that bad." he recalled.

"I often worked with mules, they're half donkey, half horse. Mules are less stubborn than donkeys and more nimble, better at climbing, more footsure, too." Dennis explained. "One time I was flown out with several other men to China to get thousands of these animals. When we finally acquired them, it took six hundred

407

Burmese, each responsible for six to eight mules, to drive them over the mountains to Burma. The column stretched for hundreds of miles. The mules were wonderful, they carried machine guns, water tanks, all sorts of things and hardly ever missed their footing in the hills."

"That sounds very risky. You could have been machine gunned from the air!" Jim exclaimed.

"Yes, it was risky, but we had to do it."

"It all sounds very exciting but also quite frightening. I suppose your family must have worried a lot about you being out in such a dangerous place?"

"Perhaps." Dennis answered. "But before I left home I made a pact with my mother and that was that neither of us would write to each other. "If you get a letter," I told her, "You'll know I'm dead. In fact I reckoned that my attitude saved me a lot of heartache. When the mail came, other men who received letters from home often broke down and cried and those who didn't get any post that day got worried and depressed."

"Did you get any medals?" asked Jim, recalling the last Remembrance Day in Henley when everyone had gathered in the Town Square and all the ex-servicemen had paraded wearing their shiny medals. He had been very impressed by that.

Dennis, who up until then had been quite forthcoming, became suddenly silent. "Yes, well," he said quietly and got up from his seat to rummage in a cupboard. "I got the usual medals of war, like we all got, but I did get the Military Medal as well." he said quietly.

"Why did you get that - it's a special one, isn't it?" the young reporter enquired.

"I suppose it was because I went back into the jungle after the war." Dennis replied, modestly.

"Why did you go back - even after the fighting was over?!" The cub reporter couldn't believe anyone would want to do that.

"Yes, I volunteered to go and dig up the bodies we'd buried, that is where we could find them." Dennis stated, simply.

"They must have been in an awful state, it's so hot and humid out there isn't it?"

"Yes, we usually couldn't bury them, you see we hadn't got the time, it was too dangerous to hang about, so we just scraped a shallow trench in the ground and covered them with their ground sheets. Often we couldn't find the bodies, or they would have changed in some way." Dennis recalled soberly. "I remember one lad I buried. His head was shaved, to keep it clean, and when we dug him up his hair had grown about four inches, even after he had died."

He blew his nose loudly and continued: "Another chap I recall was a very big man, a lovely chap, he had three or four children. I managed to bury him reasonably under a bridge. I had enough time to dig a grave about four feet deep for him, well above water level. When I got back to the bridge there was no sign of him. Other bodies had been turned to black jelly, we couldn't recover any of them, the heat does awful things to corpses."

The Burmese were better at this work than the British. "Many men were turned up by what they found." Dennis explained. "Sometimes all we discovered was part of a corpse, the rest had been eaten by animals, especially if there had not been time to dig the graves deep enough."

These groups from A, B, C, D and HQ companies found the bodies of over two hundred men which were then taken by Jeep and trailer to the official cemetery run by the War Graves Commission in Burma and buried with full honours.

When Dennis finally returned home his mother was, of course, delighted to see him although she was appalled to see how emaciated he was and contrasted his present condition with the photo that had been taken of the handsome fit young man who had left home some three years previously.

Gradually he returned to full health though and married a girl from Stoke-on-Trent. They had a daughter and two sons. Dennis worked for many years for a boiler-making company in Reading where he stayed until he retired.

* * * * * *

The reminiscences of the American, the late John Miller, were sent to the author in a series of letters in 1993. With one of them he enclosed a copy of that part of his Memoirs *that covered his time in Checkendon and Stoke Row and are published with his permission.*

The stories of the returning soldiers are all taken from the Memoirs *of the people concerned, collected by the author. Many of them were published in the* Stoke Row News *in the 1980s and 1990s.*

Chapter 20. The Fire, the Duke and the Haunting: 1949 - 1965

The little old cottage at the foot of Witheridge Hill, a hamlet of the village of Highmore, had seen many changes in the period after Ellen Franklin and her daughter, Dolly, had been made to move by George Page, their landlord in late 1930. This change was very distressing for Ellen and Dolly who had lived in the old house for twenty-four years. George Page arranged for them to rent equally cheaply another old and rather dilapidated cottage and Dolly went around the village telling everyone that they had 'muvved' up to the top of the hill. They would have liked to have rented one of the beautiful new Highmore Cottages that had just been built opposite the Village Green by the Henley Rural District Council but they could not afford the weekly payments.

George Page had, in fact, been made a very good offer for the little cottage at the foot of the hill by Sydney Blow and his actress wife, Hilda Trevelyan. The little old cottage had by then become very run-down, as George Page had only been able to do essential repairs for the three shillings a week that Ellen and Dolly still paid. Together with his architect brother, Detmar, Sydney made considerable improve-ments to the cottage, as they had already done with The Little Manor House and Witheridge Hill House.

The Blows redecorated the cottage throughout and landscaped the garden to some degree, laying down a large lawn and flowerbeds around the edge of it. They also made a path across the strip of Commons land at the rear to enable the owners to enter the house by the new back door. The old front door, which faced the main garden, was replaced with a pair of French doors. These, like the windows, were fenestrated with 'Crittall' steel frames that were popular in the 1920s and '30s.

When in 1931, the Blows moved on to their last house, which they built on Witheridge Hill and named 'Janes', they sold the little cottage at the foot of Witheridge Hill to a Captain Vincent Wells who had been lamed during the First World War. Captain Wells kept a manservant called, appropriately enough, Goodfellow. This man was very fond of gardening and also kept the cottage in excellent order. He planted two apple trees, a Bramley and a Newton Wonder at the bottom of the garden and took particular pride in planting the two old yew trees either side of the new front entrance. This gave Captain Wells the idea of naming the house 'Yew Tree Cottage'. A year later he moved to 'Bushwood House', near the Crooked Billet in Stoke Row.

The lady to whom he sold 'Yew Tree Cottage' was a Miss Adelaide Daisy Litten, who often brought her sister down from London and the two of them would stay for the weekend. However, these two Jewish ladies preferred to spend most of their time in town. According to the Register of Electors, Miss Litten owned 'Yew Tree Cottage' from 1932 to 1935.

In about 1936, Miss Litten sold the cottage to a Mrs Alicia Stevens, a widow whose husband had been out in India. When she bought the house, it was this lady who decided to change the name from 'Yew Tree Cottage' to 'Old Place', this being a translation from the Celtic 'Hanley' [Henley], meaning 'old place'. This lady continued to live at Old Place with her son, Anthony until 1942. He grew to love the old cottage so much that he took the name with him when he eventually married and bought a home of his own at Harspden, near Henley.

In 1942, Mrs Stevens sold Old Place to Mrs Cecily Stuart-Anderson, a charming, well-educated lady who had become a keen collector of antiques and had accumulated many valuable treasures, especially George III furniture and Hester Bateman silverware, most of which she kept in her London house but some she brought down to her new summer retreat at the foot of Witheridge Hill. In fact, she also brought some of her most valuable furniture to protect it from the possibility of it being destroyed in the bombing which had become a regular part of life in London.

Mrs Stuart-Anderson actually bought Old Place with the idea that she could use it as a 'bolt-hole' in the event of her needing to leave London if the bombing became intolerable. To this end she stocked the house with tins of food, candles, matches etc.

However, she gradually found the lack of a proper kitchen to be a disadvantage so, when the Second World War was over and a few building materials were at last available, she had a small extension built on the east side of the house. It was her intention to have an Aga cooker installed there. These domestic appliances of Swedish design served as both cooker and heater as they were made of cast iron and not only housed two ovens, with a couple of hot plates on top, but the heat emitted from this solid fuel device helped to warm the kitchen and that end of the house itself, twenty-four hours a day. An open fire heated the other end.

She had the work done on a Thursday and Friday in June 1948. The builder left the Aga lit and coming up to heat which it did all during the Saturday. On the Sunday morning, as was her custom, Cecily donned one of her exotic hats and went up to St Bartholomew's Church in Nettlebed which she preferred to the little church of St Paul at Highmore. St Bartholomew's is a most interesting church and at that time the priest was Canon Ball. Rebuilt in 1846, it is possibly the third building to stand on the same site. When Dorchester Abbey was founded in the twelfth century, Nettlebed was one of the twelve parishes that came under its jurisdiction.

Unfortunately, the builder she had employed to install the Aga had not set the flue properly and by eleven o'clock in the morning the chimney had heated sufficiently to catch fire. Luckily, Mrs Freda Fairbairn, her next-door neighbour at Beech Hollow, was in her garden and noticed smoke coming from the thatched roof of the little kitchen extension. She immediately realised with great consternation that the cottage was on fire. She had with her a friend to whom she was showing her beautiful herbaceous borders. The two of them and the gardener rushed over to the house with the chief idea of rescuing Mrs Stuart-Anderson's Pekinese and Corgi dogs, as well as her parrot!

As she did so Freda Fairbairn called to her husband to phone for the fire brigade and this he did immediately. It was a blessing that they had a telephone, only the larger houses did. It was connected to the manual exchange at Nettlebed and had the simple number Nettlebed 315. When he dialled 999 he was asked by the operator: "Police, Fire or Ambulance?" and when he replied "Fire" he was at once put on to the Head Office at Woodstock in North Oxfordshire. This operator then had to dial both Wallingford and Henley Fire Stations. As soon as the siren went, 'retained' men from all over both towns jumped on their bicycles and rode as fast as they could to their Fire Station. Within minutes of their arrival they were dressed and ready to go. They wasted no time but it still took them each about half an hour to make the journey, driving as fast as they dared, bells clanging loudly all the while.

As soon as he had finished on the telephone, Mr Fairbairn rushed to join the others. Meantime, Mrs Stuart-Anderson had, apparently, come out of the church and popped in to see a friend in Nettlebed to return some books. As she walked along the pavement, seeing the fire engine rushing past, she is recorded as having remarked casually to another worshipper, also on his way home: "I hope that's not my house!"

As he dashed along the road, the gardener, Tom Garlinge, noticed young Eric Bradford riding by on his bicycle and instructed him to "ride with all speed" up to Highmore to fetch George and Francis Stevens, Harold Treadwell and any other men and lads he could find to come and help. Soon there were about twenty men, women, boys and girls, forming a human chain to get as much out of the house as they could and put the items on the lawn. Fortunately it was a fine sunny day and they worked with great speed to get as much out before the blaze grew too hot.

In about half an hour a fire engine came from Henley, some six miles away and very soon afterwards another came from Wallingford. That had made a longer journey, about ten miles and both had to come up hills. The fire service was at that time the same organisation, the NFS [National Fire Service] that had served the country throughout the Second World War since it had been formed into a unified structure from the old brigades combined with the AFS [Auxiliary Fire Service] by Mr Herbert Morrison, the Home Secretary, at the outbreak of the hostilities.

This fire actually occurred one year before a massive reorganisation of the Fire Service. In 1949, Wallingford was still a part of

Berkshire; the boundary was not changed until 1974. Therefore the two engines that arrived at Old Place to deal with this fire were quite different and so was the command structure.

The differences between them were largely mechanical. For one thing, they had different makes of fire engines and some of their equipment was pre-war. Berkshire preferred the more modern scarlet Bedford, while Henley in Oxfordshire had an old red Commer as well as a grey Karrier, although the latter was only used if absolutely essential. The Rootes Group had manufactured both. They also had different types of couplings for the hoses to the pumps and there was no natural water supply up on these hills. The old garden well was inadequate for the job and mains water did not come to Highmore until 1950 so they were entirely reliant upon the five hundred gallon trailer that Henley's Commer had towed up the hill and the four hundred gallons that were contained in the tank of the newer Bedford that had come up from Wallingford.

There were five men from Henley under the command of the Station Officer but only four men could be found in time in Wallingford. They were led by a Senior Fireman. The two teams immediately agreed that the Station Officer should take charge and this he did at once. He could see that the fire had already taken a strong hold on the little old cottage and that the chimney-stack rising from the badly installed Aga was about to collapse. It fell only minutes later.

Station Officer Hawkins bellowed to the frantic people rushing in and out of the building. "Everybody away from the house!" So authoritative was his tone that everyone promptly rushed to the far end of the garden. At last they all realised that the roof was about to collapse and there was nothing anyone could do to save any more of Mrs Stuart-Anderson's precious possessions. As it was, antique china, glass, paintings, clocks, vases, silverware, mirrors, rugs, samplers, a fine George III barometer and even a pile of freshly ironed clothes lay in heaps, scattered all over the lawn.

One of the women had drawn a bucket of water from the well and this was drunk thirstily and used to wash blackened hands and faces. The men pulled away from their mouths the wetted handkerchiefs that they had quickly tied on before going in time and time again to the burning building. Some of the women, finding all the major activ-

415

ity to be at an end, broke down and wept to see the charred house being soaked with water from the firemen's tanks. Even as they sprayed it, according to an eyewitness: "the cans of food were popping like fireworks!"

It was at this point that Mrs Stuart-Anderson came back to her home, still wearing her beautiful hat, and accompanied by her friend. She was devastated at the sight of her beloved cottage a mass of blackened beams, shattered glass and all smoke-ridden and sodden with water. At the same time she became mindful of the heroic efforts that her neighbours and the village people had made to rescue what they could from the blaze and warmly thanked them all through her tears.

As soon as she could be persuaded to leave the site, Cecily Stuart-Anderson accompanied her next-door neighbour, Freda Fairbairn, and her husband back to their home, Beech Hollow. There she telephoned to her daughter, Mrs Anne Kelly, in London and was fortunate in finding her at home. Later that afternoon, accompanied by her daughter, Cecily returned to Old Place but was not allowed by the firemen to enter the building. By this time only the main chimney and part of the front wall stood testimony to the pretty little home it had once been.

Mrs Kelly persuaded her mother to return with her to London and there, the next day, Cecily Stuart-Anderson started to make a claim against her insurance company, the Guardian. She found the task very difficult as she began to list the items of furniture that had been too large for anyone to rescue in the short time available to them. One of the chief problems had been that the house was well secured by several sets of locks, against burglary. All the rescuers could do was to pass through smashed windows a number of smaller items. It is true they had little awareness of the value of the furniture and even if they had, they would not have been able to lift such heavy pieces, especially the ones on the first floor that would have had to be moved by way of a narrow and very steep staircase that led up from the living-room.

Cecily and her late husband had always been great lovers of George III furniture and she herself was something of an authority on Georgian silverware. Fortunately she had all the relevant paperwork, including all the provenanced invoices, in her London flat. The claim form for the house itself and its contents took her several hours to complete but it was not until she came to the antique items that she found tears rolling uncontrollably down her cheeks as she listed them:

1. A pair of George III mahogany Gainsborough-type armchairs, with padded back, seat and arms. Value £1,500 each.

2. George III mahogany drop-leaf table. Oval top with chamfered edge, supported on four club legs with pad feet. Value £850.

3. Set of four early George III-style mahogany chairs, including two carvers, drop-in seat and cabriole legs with claw-and-ball feet. Value £500 the set.

4. George III mahogany chest, top with moulded edge above a slide. Two short and three long drawers with brass handles on bracket feet. Value £785.

5. Two brass bedsteads, with duck and goose down mattresses and all linen. Value: bedsteads: £480 each. Mattresses and bedding: £250 each set.

6. Two antique patchwork bedspreads. Value approximately £250 each.

5. Two early George III mahogany corner cupboards. Under 'value' she wrote £350 each.   (Sadly, these had been screwed to the wall and locked. Inside them was all her most precious silverware).

6. Pair George III silver candlesticks by John Carter of London, 12.1/2" high. Value £925 pair.

7. One George III silver oval salt cellar, with pierced sides on claw and ball feet, by Hester Bateman. Value £785.

8. One silver swing-handle basket, 14.1/2" long, pierced foot with reeded rim, by Hester Bateman. Value £1,800.

She concluded her entries with a heavy sigh. She could hardly bear the thought of her beloved cottage, now just a charred and steaming ruin, and that for her, weekends in the country would never be the same again.

Some time later she was to try and explain to her ten-year old grand-daughter, Vicky, the importance of the work of the eighteenth century silver-smithing widow, Hester Bateman. "Now you are getting older, darling, I think you should learn something about the famous women silversmiths. You see, silver-smithing was a family business in the eighteenth century and when a man died his widow often took over the running of the family firm and registered her own mark. It was rare for women to work in the arts at that time, but there were a number of these widows who became well-known in their own right."

At this point she cleared her throat before continuing: "Although she was more or less illiterate she ran the company for thirty years and it became one of the most successful workshops in London. Eventually her sons and grandsons joined in the running of the family firm and although their standards were high their output was prodigious. They made all sorts of things like bon-bon dishes, cruets and small candlesticks."

She concluded with a promise: "One day, perhaps when you are twenty-one, I'll buy you a piece by Hester Bateman as a keepsake."

******

Having finally got her claim settled, Cecily Stuart-Anderson decided to take up the offer made by her kind next-door neighbours, Mr and Mrs Fairbairn of Beech Hollow, to buy the gutted wreck at the foot of Witheridge Hill and she then set about finding another home in the locality. She found a pleasant enough house, 'The Brawns' at nearby Bix, but she missed her old home in Highmore.

It was the intention of the Fairbairns to rebuild the cottage in its original form as a dwelling for their gardener, Mr Baldwin. Unfortunately this man began to have trouble with his leg, due to a war wound, so instead the couple employed the services of a local chartered architect, Mr Stephen Bertram, MBE, ARIBA, who had lost an arm during the Second World War, to design a larger residence which could then be sold. This gentleman was well-known for his love of vernacular architecture and proposed a house which would incorporate the original form in the centre, but have extensions on either side, with steps internally to allow for the rise of the land.

The Fairbairns were delighted with his proposed plans that were eventually accepted by the planning authorities and the house was built by Mr A E Nunn of Henley. Sad to say this man went bankrupt not long afterwards, a fairly common occurrence for small builders of that period. Mr Fairbairn was an extremely particular man who had very high ideals about the standards of workmanship. He insisted on many extras being put in, for instance, the cork flooring in the hall and the oak newel post and shelf at the foot of the stairs.

Mr Bertram was also very keen that this new cottage should be erected with the best possible materials that could be found, at a time when wartime building regulations were still in force. When Mr Fairbairn enquired from his architect what the difference was between a house and a cottage, Mr Bertram replied: "The dictionary definition is: 'Cottage: dwelling built from local materials'." So Mr Nunn had to source second-hand stock bricks and old timbers from a bomb-site but he also managed to use a few of the less charred beams and some of the glass, albeit somewhat distorted, from the ruin of the original Old Place. He kept to Mr Bertram's criterion by embedding panels of local flints in the exterior walls as well.

Through contacts who he knew in the trade, Stephen Bertram located a pair of arched timbers that Mr Nunn was able to use to support the central beam in the living-room as well as a little leaded small-paned window to provide light from the passage-way into this large room. Mr Bertram, who had mainly practised in the 1930s, decided that it would lend a 'cosy' atmosphere to this rather large room if it were not plastered. Thus the bricks and timbers provided a warm ambience and also saved a great deal of decorating for future owners of the property.

The outcome was a most attractive residence, a long, low brick and flint cottage, with three dormers upstairs and a chimney arising from the large inglenook fireplace at one end of the sitting-room and another from the now properly-flued Aga in the kitchen at the other end. The new dwelling also boasted a dining-room, a kitchen with view from the sink out to the garden, and a good-sized sitting-room with French doors, all on the ground floor.

To cope with the rise in the land, a couple of stairs led up to a second and third bedroom at which point one turned to go up the stairs where eight steps led to a very large storage attic and the rooms on the top floor. Up there was the master bedroom and bathroom with a dressing-room at the far end of the bedroom. Every window looked on to the garden and the Fairbairns were delighted with the result.

It did not take long for Simmons and Sons of Henley to sell the house for them at a price of £3,800 to a Mr and Mrs Cox who had recently returned from Kenya and South Africa. Mr Cox had been a director of Metal Box Ltd of Reading. They had a daughter called Margaret and another named Rosemary who played the grand piano that was kept at the far end of the sitting-room.

Both husband and wife were very keen on gardening and were delighted to find that their land comprised nearly an acre. Mrs Cox was especially fond of rose beds and planted many standard varieties in the lawn, as well. Each had a canopy frame over which it grew. Peggy Cox and her daughters were also much attached to their Scots terriers, Bill and Molly, as well as to their cat, Nancy of which photographs still survive.

The Coxes lived at Old Place for about six years. Mr Cox died soon after they moved in but Peggy was often to be seen driving around in her open Morris Oxford car, made at nearby Cowley, a suburb of Oxford. She had felt bound to buy one, since Viscount Morris of Nuffield, the famous car manufacturer and philanthropist lived at 'Nuffield Place', Huntercombe, just up the road.

When her daughters eventually left home she sold Old Place in 1958 to Cecily Stuart-Anderson who was glad to return to the bottom of Witheridge Hill and soon managed to adjust herself to the larger house.

Cecily was often visited by her daughter, Anne Kelly and her grand-daughter, Victoria, who loved to sleep in the little room beyond the master bedroom. Like her mother, Anne was passionate about antiques, particularly pictures and at the end of the sitting-room she hung an oil painting of a greyhound. Gradually the cottage was restored to a beautiful home, furnished in traditional style.

Later, Anne Kelly was to write to the author of this book: "For me Old Place always had a spirit of timelessness, of detachment and withdrawal, as though it is quietly dreaming its days away and remembering the past..."

In 1966, when she was 78 years of age, Cecily Stuart-Anderson collapsed and died suddenly. She was buried in the churchyard of St

Bartholomew in Nettlebed and on her grave were planted some of the roses that were growing in the front garden of Old Place.

The cottage was left to her daughter who continued to come down at weekends, often bringing Victoria with her. They, too, loved the house and were fortunate in finding Barbara Sedwell of Nettlebed, who, on receiving a phone call from Anne, would pop down to light the Aga and ensure all was ready for the weekend visitors.

The garden was always kept neat and tidy by Mr 'Skib' Webb of Highmore who had cared for it since the demise of Mr Baldwin, some fifteen years previously. Gardening was obviously a healthy life because Skib was over ninety when he died.

******

Another nonagenarian was Mr William Brazil who, in his earlier years had lived at Newnham Hill Farm at Stoke Row. When he died on 8th July 1955, aged 97, he left to Stoke Row Chapel a piece of land called Alma Green, after the famous Crimean battle. On this a row of houses was then built and given the same name. This generous bequest enabled the Chapel Trustees to add on a kitchen and toilets; a Meeting-room had already been erected for the thriving Sunday School late in the nineteenth century

Part of the endowment enabled substantial modernisation of the interior of the Chapel that had become rather dark and old fashioned. Light oak panelling and a dais were installed and the pews were stripped of their brown stain. A local craftsman and skilled wood turner, Mr Geoff Boyson, was commissioned to make a communion table and three Glastonbury- style chairs; all were dedicated to the memory of Mr William Brazil.

Later a pipe organ was installed and this was played by Mrs Mabel Cox until she retired in 1981 after 72 years' service. She died in 2002, aged 106; longetivity was one of the hallmarks of those people who had resided all their lives in Stoke Row.

Moreover there was also enough money for a house to be built for a resident Minister at the far eastern end of the Alma Green site and from that time onwards the Chapel was to have the great benefit of its own pastor at a time when the Church of England was finding it difficult to enrol new clergy.

******

By the early 1960s, the villagers of Stoke Row had become quite accustomed to their piped water supply, even those who had said in the early 1950s when it was laid on, "It's alright, but it's not as pure and sparkling as the Well water."

As the years went by they even began to take their tap water for granted and few people took an interest in the Maharajah's Well any more, save for the Townsend family who owned the horticultural nursery at the Grove, opposite the Well. They always kept the grass mown and the hedges cut, if for no other reason than their fondness for Miss Cecily Turner, who had grown up in the little octagonal Well House with her aunt and uncle, Mr and Mrs Whittick. Although photographs of the time showed that she had lost some height and gained a little weight, this formerly slender, willowy, young lady had become the much-loved Infant schoolteacher at Stoke Row School and was always treated with great respect.

In fact, it was when Queen Elizabeth II visited Varanasi [formerly Benares] in 1961 that the Maharajah mentioned the centenary year of his great-grandfather's benefaction to Stoke Row was only a few years away. At that time he asked the Duke of Edinburgh if he would be kind enough to visit the little Chiltern village when the occasion arose. The Duke readily agreed and the Maharajah presented Her Majesty with an ivory model of the Well.

The Well Trustees, under the Chairmanship of Mr Michael Reade, great-nephew of the original founder, Edward Anderdon Reade, kept in touch with the Maharajah and when the year of the centenary drew near, a committee was formed to plan the celebrations. They wrote to the Duke and he was kind enough to recall his promise made to the Maharajah three years earlier and accepted the invitation to attend in person.

For the village, Wednesday 8th April 1964 was probably the greatest highlight in its life since the opening of the Well one hundred years before. The Duke arrived on the Village Green in a red helicopter which he piloted himself from Windsor. This helicopter was part of the Queen's Flight that was based at Benson, near Wallingford. Fortunately the weather was beautiful for the occasion. The *Reading and Berkshire Chronicle* reported it thus: "Captured, single-handed, one village – by the Duke of Edinburgh. This is what happened to Stoke Row, the little Oxfordshire village which opened its heart to welcome the Duke when he attended the Maharajah's Well centenary celebration."

The 3rd USAAF Headquarters Band provided music for much of the day. At the Well the Duke met the Maharajah's envoy, Mr B Sahi, his wife and their fourteen-year old son. Mr Sahi then presented the Duke with a sealed urn of water from the Ganges and other gifts. A cable of good wishes from the Maharajah was read out aloud. The Duke brought with him the little ivory model of the Well that had been given to the Queen by the Maharajah some three years earlier.

Mr Michael Reade and other members of the committee watched with great interest as the Duke then drew a bucket of water from the Well under the supervision of Mr J H Wilder, the great-nephew of Richard Wilder whose Wallingford firm had made and installed the mechanism one hundred years previously.

This water was mixed with the Ganges water and put into an urn, to be carried by Janet Martin and Barry Carter to St John's Church for the service. The water was later bottled and one of the bottles given to Mr Percy Stallwood, landlord of the Cherry Tree public house, where the Duke partook of lunch in the little parlour.

The commemorative service was conducted by Revd Cyril Isherwood. He had been Vicar of the church of St John the Evangelist at Stoke Row for as long as anyone could remember. By then it was almost twenty-five years and, in fact, he went on to serve for another fifteen. After a short speech by the Bishop of Dorchester, the Duke planted a cherry tree in the Well Orchard. Later, he went to the Village Hall, where he met about seventy of the older residents, many of whom were able to tell him of the days when they drew water from the Well and were glad of it.

After the Duke departed, Stoke Row continued its celebrations with children's games and tea. A film about Varanasi [Benares] was then shown in the Village Hall. The day was rounded off with a dance and barbecue. Mr Percy Collis and his wife, Ivy, were awarded First Prize for the best decorated house in the village. They were inordinately proud of their efforts.

Heather Townsend, daughter of John Townsend, a member of the family that ran the horticultural nursery and had kept the gardens around the Well and the Cottage so carefully for many years, wrote an essay about the Centenary Celebrations. This concluded with the words: "Lastly, I asked Miss Turner of her recollections of the Centenary Celebrations. She told me that several glass jars of Purple Heart cherries from the Well Orchard were sent to Buckingham Palace and the name of *Purple Hearts* [at that time a form of illegal narcotic drug] caused the Duke much amusement."

This delightful schoolchild's discourse continued: "Also she said they decorated her cottage, but although it was nice when it was finished, it was rather a nuisance at the time. She said that it was a great honour to meet the Duke and the Indian guests; one of them was a cousin to the present Maharajah, who was unable to come himself. In the cottage, there are many documents. One is from the Maharajah, confirming that Miss Turner's uncle was Well Warden. There are also many pictures, one of which was signed by the Duke during the Centenary Celebrations."

Following the celebrations, the ORCC [Oxfordshire Rural Community Council] encouraged people in the village to start their own magazine and thus the Stoke Row News was born. The map on the front cover, designed by local artist Gundrada Sheridan, commemorated the event by including a helicopter in the top left hand corner. Ever since then this has been hand-coloured red on every copy in memory of Stoke Row's greatest day.

In 1979 an appeal was launched for £20,000 to restore the Well structure and the work was started in 1981. In March 1982 the whole edifice, having been refurbished by Wilders of Wallingford, the original makers, was reassembled. The little octagonal cottage was enlarged to include a bedroom and bathroom and since that time it has all been very carefully maintained, as have the surrounding gardens and Well Orchard. In time a tenant was taken on in lieu of a Well Keeper and the rent from the cottage financed the upkeep of the whole site, which is managed by the Well Trustees. The Trust comes under the auspices of the Stoke Row Parish Council and some of the Trustees are Parish Councillors.

******

Although the name of Highmore was spelled in many ways in earlier centuries, the ending 'more' was, on the whole, in use throughout records of the eighteenth and nineteenth centuries.

However, this village, which had hitherto been within the jurisdiction of Rotherfield Greys, both ecclesiastically and politically, broke away in 1952 and became a self governing Parish Council, under South Oxfordshire District Council and Oxfordshire County Council. Whether it was intentional or just a bureaucratic error at the time, the new Parish Council minutes were taken in the name of Highmoor and this spelling has been in use ever since. It would seem appropriate, therefore, to use this version in this book from now on.

******

Like several pubs in the Highmoor and Stoke Row area, the Lamb at Satwell was formed from a pair of cottages. It is said to have been built in 1520. Unfortunately there is no written evidence for it before 1804, when William Treadwell is quoted as Licensee and gave a surety of £10 for himself. John Tanner gave the other. The system of a landlord having to provide surety under the Victuallers Licensing laws started in the eighteenth century by which time many public houses had become 'dens of vice and sinks of iniquity'.

Thereafter, sad to say, all records for the Lamb are missing and it is not until August 1882 that the owners are stated as being Greys Brewery Ltd. Edward Aldridge was licensed to sell beer then and in 1919, George Whitfield, who had for many years previously been the publican of The Hope at Stoke Row, was also licensed to sell beer and did so until 1924. The next long-serving landlord was Arthur Baldwin who came in 1927 and stayed for ten years. When he left, a gentleman with the grand-sounding name of Samuel Walter de Voil (he was actually descended from a French Protestant Huguenot family) became licensee until 1946 when Phyllis Grace de Voil (probably his widow) was licensed to sell beer.

******

Mr H J Illing and his wife, Beryl, took over The Lamb at Satwell, a hamlet in the village of Highmoor, in February 1974. He was promptly given the nickname of 'Larry', taken from a well-known character in a BBC Radio Children's Hour play. This series had some easily recognisable figures, the Mayor, Mr Growser and several others. The real

425

hero, though, was one called 'Larry the Lamb' who spoke in a 'baa-ing' type of voice that was often imitated. The name seemed to the customers very apt for the new publican of The Lamb.

Between the February and July of that year Larry became totally convinced there was an inglenook fireplace behind the blocked up wall, partly because the oak beam was still in place. Until then there had only been a small stove, which stood against the wall.

Larry decided to excavate and found that there were four fireplaces in *situ*, all increasing in size as they were opened up. Finally he came to the ultimate inglenook where he found some bones buried within the rubble. They might have been those of either a cat or a rabbit, he didn't bother to find out, he was so pleased to find such a huge fireplace. It had been a custom in earlier times to put the body of a small animal into the chimney as the house was completed, a practice which was supposed to bring good luck to the residents of the dwelling!

At the base of the fourth one, Mr Illing found a pair of duelling pistols, which he gave to someone to value, but they were never returned. Subsequently the Illings had magnificent log fires and these were well received by the customers, especially in the winter. It seemed to be part of the publican's usual welcoming cheer, but it wasn't long afterwards that some haunting incidents started to happen!

First of all Beryl opened the door of the stairs and went up two of the steps to put on the light, and on so doing, saw a figure facing her. He had a well-proportioned paunch and an old cardigan with buttons down the front.

One night a few weeks later she awoke about three o'clock in the morning and swore that 'something white' rose from the end of the bed and disappeared. She claimed that it didn't scare her.

A couple of months later, early one evening, after they had opened the pub door and there were half a dozen customers in the bar, all of a sudden there was a noise above, in their bedroom, as if furniture was being dragged over a wooden floor, which was strange, as they had fitted carpet. All the customers heard this and some of them offered to investigate with Larry. When they got upstairs there was no sign of any disturbance.

The final episode was when Larry was in bed, nursing a bad

attack of 'flu' one Saturday afternoon in November. Beryl and their son were downstairs watching television. They took care not to disturb Larry until Beryl decided to take him a cup of tea about half past five. She asked him if he'd had a good sleep and he said: "I would have done if someone hadn't come along the landing and disturbed me!" She assured him that no one had been upstairs but he stuck to his story.

The Illings could only conclude at the end of that year that by dismantling the fireplace they had obviously disturbed their friendly ghost whom they dubbed 'George'. They did think that perhaps he had been a former publican at The Lamb and that he had bricked up the fireplace.

Many publicans have held The Lamb since then but there have been no further reports of sightings of this strange phenomenon. Perhaps the Illings (and their customers?) were unduly sensitive and when 'George' had made his displeasure known to them for what they had done to 'his' pub, he went back to where he came from, who knows?

******

All the people in the foregoing chapter are real and the facts are those presented by eye-witnesses of the time. Mr Charles Keevil of the Fire Brigades Society kindly supplied the details of the Fire Stations and their engines.

The history of Stoke Row Chapel is recorded in Dipping into the Wells. *The Chapel is still very active and well-attended today.*

The accounts of the visit of the Duke of Edinburgh were related in newspapers at the time and in the Memoirs *of many of the inhabitants, collected by the author and published in the* Stoke Row News *in the 1980s and 1990s.*

The story of the visitations of 'George' was related to the author in a series of letters from Mrs Beryl Illing, widow of the one-time landlord of The Lamb at Satwell.

Chapter 21. The Estate, the Historian and the Millennium: 1966 - 2000

A young couple, John and Betty Searby, who had only been married a few months before, came down from Yorkshire to Stoke Row in December 1948 and found there a shop where they could register their ration books for provisions, a post office, a garage, a small school, a church, a chapel, four pubs, a mobile hardware shop and a mobile greengrocer. In addition to this, the farmer at Church Farm, a Mr Oliver, who had two or three Jersey cows, delivered milk daily and there was also a Police House where lived a policeman by the name of PC Barrett, who kept law and order in the immediate area.

John was already familiar with Stoke Row, for he had preceded Betty several weeks before, in order to site a superb caravan which he had built himself with loving care and which was to become their home. This vehicle was of very high quality, made of aluminium, double-skinned and lined with leather. It had been fitted with every necessity to enable the couple to live in it during the winter as well as the summer. In a time when housing was extremely difficult to find, it fulfilled a dream for the newly-married couple and was the primary reason for John having built it.

He was a skilful panel beater by trade and had a flair for design as well. Whilst he was still in Yorkshire and a director of Aero Caravan Products Ltd, John had designed a luggage trailer, also made of aluminium and this proved to be extremely popular. Its size, 4 feet long by 3 feet 3 inches high and 3 feet wide, with a fold-back lid, made it ideal for many uses. During the first few years after the War no new motorcars were manufactured in Britain but those people who still owned vehicles that they had had 'laid up' throughout the War began to bring them out again and any accessory for them was very saleable. Salesrooms, which had no cars to sell, snapped up these trailers by the dozen and within a couple of years the company had sold nearly eight hundred.

It was whilst John was building the caravan in a rented garage during the weekends and after work that a colleague brought a man called Ivor Ratut along to see it. Envisualising the enormous potential, Ivor invited John to consider a business partnership. Eventually, in 1946, this partnership under the name of 'Aero Caravans', got under way, with one other director, in a premises in Batley, Yorkshire. Here John designed and supervised the building of the luggage trailers and also ice-cream kiosks, with Ivor acting as Marketing and Sales Director.

In 1948, there was a serious disagreement amongst the three Directors, causing John and Ivor to leave. John then gave his mind to designing another mobile kiosk and when the design was completed they looked around for somewhere to construct the prototype and it was Ronnie Hawkins of Stoke Row in Oxfordshire who provided the solution; his father, Fred Hawkins, had run the 'hidden factories' during the Second World War. In an advertisement that offered a corner of his factory at Stoke Row, as well as a team of experienced metal workers and the use of machinery, all John had to supply was the expertise.

The unit Ronnie was offering to let was a small part of a building that had been constructed in the last months of the War and was, in fact, a huge metal marquee, on high king poles, with strong metal cables, rather like ships' hawsers stretching out from the centre to concrete blocks sunk into the ground fifty feet on either side. The whole structure was covered with aluminium and perspex sheets, creating a factory unit of some 25,000 square feet. It became affectionately known in the village as the Big Top. It was believed to be one of only two of its kind in Europe.

It had been constructed in order to protect a number of small brick buildings that had originally been ovens for baking bricks, part of the Stoke Row Brick Works. The latter had thrived on top of the hill in the eighteenth and nineteenth centuries, but by the 1920s had almost ceased to exist.

These old buildings had, however, proved useful during the War as 'secret factories', hidden from view by the trees around them. Inside metal items for aeroplanes had been made and repairs carried out to damaged sections of aircraft.

Not only did Ronnie Hawkins let John and his partner make use of the small part of the factory, but he also allowed their caravan to be sited close by, with water and electricity laid on. It all seemed to be too good to be true!

The mobile kiosk, which John had designed in a basic form, had many possibilities. However he decided that the proto-type would be an ice-cream kiosk and, like the caravan, it was made of aluminium. Thirty gallons of ice-cream would be held in fitted insulated units as well as the provision of a hot and cold water supply and storage space for wafers and cornets. Sliding windows on both sides meant that the maximum number of people could be served at any one time. Finally the proto-type was ready for testing and it looked magnificent with its high gloss cream finish and chrome fittings.

The Vanguard Trailer Company was formed with John and Ivor as partners, Betty having no part whatsoever in the business, except to accompany John in his endeavours to try out the kiosk.

John and Ivor decided to put it on display at the Dairy Show in September 1949. Most of their potential customers were Italians who had been making ice-cream before the British had ever heard of it. Before September, however, they had to try out the kiosk, towing it behind their old Ford V8 car. They sold ice-cream around Reading and Wallingford, learning, sometimes bitterly, from their experiences, particularly about the difficulties of reversing a thirteen foot trailer!

Nevertheless, they did achieve their ambition and the Vanguard Trailer Company won a Bronze medal at the Dairy Show, where a famous London comedian of the time, Charlie Chester, was kind enough to help promote this product.

Eventually the company was making and selling kiosks and trailers that were adapted to sell not only ice-cream but also cakes, greengrocery and even fish and chips. There seemed no end to the permutations to which John's design could be adapted. Its uses to the florist, the bookseller, the tobacconist, etc were almost never-ending, since it was easy to tow, easy to use and easy to keep clean. In the days when motorcars were few and far between, it was an ideal trailer because the customer could take it to a site, leave the vendor with it, go back to his base get another and take it elsewhere.

Attractive striped awnings could be fixed on the sides of these vehicles and one of them was bought by J Lyons & Co and adapted as a refreshment kiosk, serving coffee, tea, cakes and biscuits. The well-known entertainments company Mecca, bought five of these hygienic trailers to use for selling refreshments in the Royal Parks. Several were also used as mobile offices in Scotland. The price for these vehicles which were 8 ft 6 inches long by 5 feet 7 inches wide and 7 feet 7 inches high, ranged from £328 to £375.

The directors decided to call their new business the Vanguard Trailer Co. Ltd., the idea being that *van* meant 'out in the forefront of the market' and *guard* implied taking care of the contents. Unfortunately, the Vanguard Motor Company took umbrage at this title and took the company to court over the matter. John was able to point out that the name Vanguard was actually German and had been in use before the War, so the motor company finally agreed to their using the name VANGUARD with the words Trailer Co. Ltd in small letters beneath. Once the prototypes were developed, the trailers were mass-produced, firstly ten in Paddington, London and then another hundred in Rochester, Kent and in this way Vanguard Trailers went on from success to success.

Very soon, however, the Oxfordshire Council planners had started to take an interest in the Stoke Row site and wanted to demolish the Big Top, for which no planning permission had been obtained when it had been erected under wartime conditions. The land on which it was constructed had originally belonged to a Mr Henry Brigham Douglas Vanderstegen, a local landowner who lived at nearby Cane End. This man was a passionate collector of farm vehicles and owned what was known locally as 'the mechanical cemetery'. It was said that he could never resist an auction of farm equipment.

When the old brickyard was converted into the 'secret factories' at the outbreak of the Second World War, Mr Fred Hawkins had purchased the land and the old brickworks from Mr Vanderstegen and later gave it to his son, Ronnie Hawkins. Soon after the war ended, the metal marquee was erected over the small brick workshops and Hawkins endeavoured to get the factory on to a peacetime basis, producing greenhouse frames to be exported to the Channel Islands.

Unfortunately this did not go well, so they closed the business down, leaving the factory empty but for a few greenhouse frames and Ronnie was obliged to sell his house and move his family into a small wooden building at the front of the Estate. At the same time, Morrisons, the large engineering firm in Rochester, Kent, where facilities had been provided to build the Vanguard kiosks, was now feeling the pinch, as were so many in the peace-time market. Sad to say, when John turned up for work one morning he found the firm had gone broke. Fortunately, though he and Ivor managed to retrieve the expensive metal extrusions that comprised the main structure of the kiosks and by offering Ronnie rent for his now empty factory, the Vanguard Trailer Co. Ltd was able to transfer to Stoke Row. Having salvaged the expensive extrusions and safely housed them in a corner of the building, the question was then, what to do with this vast covered space? First of all, Vanguard Trailers filled it with anything that could be stored and sold on, such as ex-government plywood, sisal paper, coffee, corn, indeed anything that was marketable at that time. However, as fast as they got the goods in they went out again, so great was the demand for anything at all saleable in the years following the War.

By 1953, with storage virtually at a standstill, Ivor found fresh interests and decided to leave. John's problem then was a lack of capital. John's money invested in Aero Caravans was still there, and is there to this day in fact, as the company simply ceased to trade. John's income from Vanguard, which was in the form of a salary, had now ceased. There were opportunities, opportunities a plenty in fact, but an opportunity without capital was nothing but a pipe dream!

One such opportunity appeared in the shape of the greenhouse frames that Ronnie had had on his hands, still stored in the hangar. His intention had been to sell them for scrap where he could retrieve a much-needed £70.

Now it so happened that Betty had some £67 in National Savings Certificates, which she laughingly referred to as her 'safeguard against destitution'! "I'll give you £67 for the frames here and now!" John volunteered to Ronnie, fully aware that he had a serious problem in persuading Betty to part with her Savings Certificates. She maintains to this day that the £67 has never been repaid!!

So John acquired the frames and sold a 2,500 square feet green-house to Woodcote Nursery. He erected it for them completely, save for the glazing and made enough profit to purchase some second-hand machinery. And so began the tiny start to the partnership; this time it was without any third parties. The Searbys named this company Vanalloys (from van meaning 'up front' and 'alloys' being the materials they were using).

The second opportunity lay in the shape of the kiosk extrusions. An enquiry was passed on to John by Ivor's secretary who was working in his London office. This was from a firm called Locomotors in Westerham, Kent, for a kiosk, fully fitted for catering, to be completed by Christmas. It was then September. Would it be possible for John, with no capital, and no labour to produce such an order within three months?

"Well", he thought to himself, "I built the caravan on my own and I am now in possession of the main extrusions." This was because Ivor, feeling slightly guilty about withdrawing from the partnership, had offered them to John. It would mean acquiring monthly trade accounts, probably taking anything up to three weeks, then ordering the required materials, sheet metal, window frames and windows, a suitable chassis, a hot water heater and cold water storage tank, as well as suitable internal fittings, all to be delivered by early November. That way payment would not be required until the end of December, by which time the work would be finished, hopefully, and payment received.

It was an enormous gamble. The slightest thing going wrong with the delivery of materials and the whole project could turn out to be a catastrophe but, 'nothing ventured, nothing gained!' Come November, materials were arriving daily and John launched into a six-week period of working from dawn each and every day until late at night.

It was Betty's little business, selling ice-cream from her blue motor-bike and side-car that put food on the table and paid the rent to Hawkins for the use of one of the original buildings, leaving John free of all burdens but that of finishing the kiosk by late December.

They realised that Christmas would be pretty basic, for there was no money to be spared for anything but the bare essentials. It was well into the third week of December when John was applying the final coat of cellulose to the finished vehicle that he was able to ring Locomotors to announce that the vehicle would be ready for collection on the 20th December and to ask for the cheque to be sent on.

By 21st December the kiosk, with its high gloss cream finish and sparkling chrome interior stood majestically outside the workshop, awaiting collection and the Searbys surveyed what was Vanalloys' first brave venture! Perhaps they could be excused for the enormous sense of achievement they felt.

There was a slight feeling of apprehension that the cheque had not yet arrived, but the Christmas mail being what it was, they concluded that the driver would, no doubt, be bringing it with him. Their worst fears were realised when this proved not to be the case and the driver, anxious to get towing such an expensive vehicle all the way to Kent, was even reluctant to wait while John anxiously telephoned Locomotors. It was even more alarming that the Manager was not there and they were faced with the unenviable decision about letting their precious kiosk go.

With hindsight, of course (always a wonderful thing!) they should have secured a deposit, but as the kiosk disappeared out of the factory premises they could only cling to the faint hope that it was indeed the Christmas mail that was causing the hold-up. The rest of the day was spent ringing Locomotors and trying in vain to contact the Manager. When morning came and there was still no cheque in the post, things started to look desperate.

The next day the Manager was there, 'with a client' they were told and their urgent request that he should ring them back yielded nothing. As hope began to fade, John, ever the optimist, suggested that the smart pen, which the Manager had left behind when the original order was signed and which had Locomotors in gold letters emblazoned on the side, was surely proof of the firm's authenticity. But Betty promptly pointed out that a few pens to 'con' suppliers out of thousands of pounds was cheap at the price!

Seeking assurance from any avenue he could think of, John contacted a friend in the motor trade and outlined the problem. "Don't worry, John!" his friend replied. "I'll check in the Red Book. Anyone remotely connected with the motor trade is listed in that!"

When the call came back from John's colleague informing him that the Red Book contained no such name as Locomotors, their worst fears were realised.

It was 23rd December, the cost of the materials incurred, including the expensive catering equipment, amounted in all to nearly £500. This was mostly on new accounts that needed to be paid in a matter of seven days. At that time a small house could be purchased for under £1000. There was no way that the money could be raised unless the kiosk was paid for. Thoughts of bankruptcy, or worse, seemed to be staring them in the face. Vanalloys was not a limited company, so they could lose their caravan and be rendered homeless!

Then, like a light from above came the reply from the persistent calls to Locomotors. The Manager said he was sorry and was surprised that the cheque hadn't arrived. He suggested John ring Head Office. "Never mind ringing!" John exclaimed, "Just give me the address."

And so it was next morning, 24th December, with a bare ten shillings in his pocket, John caught the workman's train to London. With insufficient funds for the tube or tram, he set off on foot from Paddington to Locomotors' Head Office near Vauxhall Bridge. There was now a ray of hope on the horizon. It seemed far more of a certainty to be dealing with a Head Office, a place where cheques could be made out so monies that were due could be paid. With that in mind, the three-mile trek from Paddington on a cold winter's morning seemed no hardship at all.

It was late morning when John found his destination and even before he arrived at Vauxhall Bridge he was scanning the buildings opposite in search of the one name 'Locomotors'! There was indeed one name on the big, tall building in the place of where Locomotors should have been. With its name in large, gold letters clearly showing across the front of the building was 'HOVIS'. John stared long and hard at the red brick building, he even walked on to the bridge to view it from another angle but sadly, where Locomotors was reputed to be was the massive Hovis building and nothing else!

Back came the desolate feeling and the thought that the tiny fledgling business, which had barely got off the ground, was in dire trouble. Into his mind came the feeling that they had, indeed, been 'taken for a ride' and as he peered into the grey waters of the Thames, it was difficult to assess which was the better option, jumping in or facing Betty on Christmas Eve with the news that they were finished!

As if willing the building to change before his very eyes, John left the bridge, approached the Hovis building and walked up the steps to the imposing glass doors and there, wonder of wonders, before him on the wall just outside the doors was a tiny metal plaque inscribed with the magic word: Locomotors. John burst through the doors and addressed the Commissionaire with just one word: "Locomotors?" The man replied in a matter-of-fact tone: "Second floor."

John leapt up the steps two at a time and found the office at the end of the corridor with the one word on the door that he wanted to see. He knocked, was bidden to 'Enter!' and breathlessly introduced himself to an impressive looking gentleman seated behind a huge oak desk. "I'm more than sorry you've had all this trouble, Mr Searby," he volunteered. "The cheque was sent in very good time, it must have gone astray. No matter, we will cancel it forthwith and make out another one!"

John extended the appropriate "Thank you!" and, with the cheque safely in his pocket, set off for Paddington with a light heart and an even lighter step. It was unfortunate that he arrived home after the banks had closed and perhaps somewhat ironic that as the Searbys shared a six-ounce tin of corned beef for their Christmas dinner on the morrow, there, grinning at them from the sideboard, sat the cheque for nearly £1000.

Two weeks after Christmas, with the money safely banked, and cheques made out to honour the debts incurred, came the day when Cecil Lambourne, the local baker who had been baking bread for Stoke Row and nearby villages for many years, turned up to deliver his usual supply of bread in a brand new van, with the Hovis logo strikingly obvious on the side. When John stopped to admire the new vehicle he noticed a tiny inscription on the bottom corner: Locomotors. And so the mystery was solved. It appeared that Locomotors was actually owned by Hovis and supplied vehicles to bakers who sold their products countrywide.

Vanalloys also did much work in conjunction with Kinghams, who were the biggest wholesale provision merchants in the Reading area and who, in order to promote their products, renovated almost every small shop in villages within a fifty mile radius around. It all started one day when they came to John and asked him to design a *Fruit Vendor* [a mobile display unit] so that shopkeepers could put their produce outside their shops every morning and take them in at the end of the day. This also gave them more space inside the shop, though if they closed for lunch, it meant them moving the units as many as four times a day!

In the end Vanalloys were also producing shopfitting frames for Kinghams and went on to make them for such well-known companies as Marshall, which sold cigarettes and confectionery, Beechams Medical Products and even British Airways for their offices all over Europe. Quantas Airways in Piccadilly and West Indian Airways ordered John's metal shop fronts, too, so he and Betty were able to joke about their small company in Stoke Row having connections all over the world!

A son, who they named Anthony ('Tony') was born to them in December 1958 and brought them great joy for the remainder of their lives.

The following year, the Searbys were fortunate enough to be able to buy the five acres of industrial land, although it was a precarious and risky thing to do, as they had no planning permission. Also they were able to purchase five more acres at the side on which John and Betty built their lovely home, Tanglewood. At last, in 1961, following thirteen years of living in a caravan, they had a brick-built home of their own, with a large garden and big piece of woodland behind it. After more than a decade of toil, all their hard work had started to pay off.

Vanalloys let half of the Big Top to a firm called Marshalls, in 1962. They dealt in government surplus. The Searbys kept a quarter of the space under the Big Top, which they had been using as a workshop and a plot of land at the rear of the site was sold to Toga, a firm that made furniture, toys and fancy goods for mail orders. On this site Toga built two units, each of some five to six thousand square feet.

In 1963, Marshalls and Toga decided to move out, so that left three-quarters of the Big Top empty. The Searbys then commissioned local builder Alan Cox to construct a number of workshops, made from concrete blocks, each with its own office and toilet under this vast roof. They were soon able to let them to small businesses, self-employed people including a professional photographer, a delivery service, a tester of building materials, a couple of sheet metal workers and even a professional horologist named John Sargeant who repaired long case and other antique clocks.

In September 1967, disaster struck the Big Top when severe snowstorms produced a foot of snow and ice on the roof. This caused it to bow considerably on one side and threatened its stability. John and one of his employees had to climb on to the roof and cut the frozen snow off the aluminium in large blocks and then place them on the perspex sheets on which the snow had not frozen. This allowed the snow to slide down to the ground. Altogether it was a dangerous and worrying task. Fortunately, they succeeded without any permanent damage to the structure or themselves!

In 1985, a fire broke out and this proved to be very serious. The Fire Brigade could not decide on the origin of the blaze, but it was thought to have started in a section that was used as a warehouse for foam-filled furniture. This produced a great deal of acrid and dangerous smoke and in the end about a quarter of the factory was destroyed.

The curious thing about this fire was that John and Betty Searby were enjoying a meal in Antico's Restaurant in Henley at the time and they actually saw the fire engine leave its station on the other side of the road. Betty's intuition made her persuade John to leave their meal and follow this engine which was heading up Gravel Hill, Henley in a westerly direction. Her fears were well-founded for, as they followed the big red vehicle it drove ahead through Rotherfield Greys and Highmoor, bells clanging all the time, it continued on to Stoke Row. There the Searbys found their beloved Vanalloys Industrial Estate a mass of smoke and flames, with fire engines, not only from Henley but also from Wallingford, pouring water on to the blaze.

Unfortunately, at first the Sun Insurance would not pay out for the Big Top to be repaired, as the cost would be in the order of a hundred thousand pounds. Finally, through one of John's many friends in the Rotary Club, they found an agent who fought their case for them and they managed to get enough compensation to restore the big hangar.

Yet another disaster struck the Estate in 1987 when record gales took two sheets of aluminium off the roof and, six months later, whilst John was recovering from major surgery, another gale took off parts of the roof and spread sheets of aluminium and plastic all over Stoke Row! Lying in his sickbed John decided to sell up. It all seemed to be so much worry, as he was now without part of the huge building which had kept intact and watertight for over forty-five years.

The sad part was, of course, that by selling the site, it was a foregone conclusion that any would-be developer would want to clear the area first and rebuild from scratch, thus rendering Vanalloys' tenants without working accommodation. There was no way the Searbys would do this, so a most adventurous scheme was devised with the assistance of their architect, having first acquired outline planning permission for twenty-five new units to be built on the site.

The plan was to build the first eight units on the car park at the far side of the Big Top and so provide working space for the tenants from the units on the front of the hangar. Then, 'with a fair wind', they aimed to take down the front of the hangar entirely and so make space to erect a further seven units. It was a risky undertaking with such an unusual building but it was to be hoped that, by so doing, the whole structure of the remaining half was not weakened, for it was needed to house the remaining tenants until Phase Two could be completed.

With the seven units that comprised Phase Two of the development then constructed and the Vanalloys tenants securely housed in beautiful brick-built, airy units, came the day, in 1991, when the remainder of the Big Top was to be demolished.

Although Betty and John could look with great pride at the new units that stood in its place, there was a moment of nostalgia as they watched the historic building that had seen them through such lean times, razed to the ground.

There were further new units at the rear of the site too, for Toga had sold their development and Frank Scott, the contractor responsible for constructing the Vanalloys units, had bought the Toga site, demolished the buildings there and erected fifteen industrial units in their place.

The Searbys then felt the site worthy of a more modern, up-market appellation and renamed it the Vanalloys Business Park.

When he reluctantly retired in 1997, at the age of eighty-two, John Searby and his wife, Betty, held a party to celebrate their sale of the site to Leywood Estates Ltd. This company later finished the building of the last few units, including one along the front where Ronnie Hawkins' wooden bungalow had been.

The whole estate still remains a great credit to John and Betty Searby and all the hard work, thought and worry they put into it. It had all been especially demanding on John's wife because, although he had an excellent secretary in Nina Howells, Betty not only supported her husband at times of low morale, but she had also done most of the clerical work. Quite a change of career for a woman who, before her marriage had been a slim and glamorous dancer on the stage and later Manageress of several of the Richard shops which sold elegant clothing for ladies!

The Vanalloys Business Park, with its forty smart, airy brick-built industrial units now provides work for many dozens people from Stoke Row, Highmoor and the villages around. It is something of which Stoke Row is justly proud.

******

It was a bright, sunny Monday morning in October 1978 when Angela Spencer-Harper brought her parents down to Henley from her home in Chalfont St Peter, near Gerrards Cross in Buckinghamshire. They had come over for the weekend from their home in Stanmore, in Middlesex, where Angela and her brother, Tony, had been brought up and had reluctantly agreed to stay on an extra day to accompany their daughter to inspect 'yet another house'.

Angela and her husband Bob, who had grown up in Harrow Weald, a village adjacent to Stanmore, had met at a tennis party when they were nineteen and were married five years later in 1956 in St John's Church, Stanmore. They spent the first six years of their marriage in a semi-detached house in nearby Canons Park, where both their sons were born. Bob was based in Maidenhead, Berkshire, so in 1963, following a severe and very snowy winter, they decided to move, so as to be nearer to Bob's office. They bought a

440

newly-built, larger detached house at Chalfont St Peter with an excellent nearby preparatory school, Gayhurst. Their sons, Philip and Michael attended this school before eventually becoming boarders at Berkhamsted School for Boys.

By 1978, Philip was a student at Imperial College, London and Michael was all set to start his studies at St Catherine's College, Oxford, so it seemed to their parents to be a good time to move even further west. Philip quipped: "If we all keep going like this, like the lemmings, we'll finish up in the sea!" Nevertheless, the couple started looking for a house in which they would feel comfortable.

Michael asked them to "try and find a house with lots of little nooks and crannies in it!" but the task on all counts proved more difficult than they had thought it would be. Several times they found a suitable one for sale and on two occasions had started proceedings, but these fell through and so they continued their search. Fortunately, they were in no great hurry to change houses. Angela, who was happy in her work as Personal Assistant to Claude Baker, the Chief Architect for Trust House Forte Hotels, was reluctant to move, but Bob, who was Sales Manager to a mechanical engineering company, would have quite willingly relocated to anywhere that was accessible to Heathrow Airport and the main motorways as he travelled a great deal, supporting his many representatives and visiting their customers.

As they drove up the Fairmile from Henley and up through the beechwoods, Angela's mother was admiring the lovely colours of the trees, but her father, who had been a Quantity Surveyor, was closely perusing the particulars of the house they were on their way to examine. "I see it's called 'Old Place'," he said. "It looks like a large cottage to me. I thought you two were looking for a Victorian house?"

"Yes, we are." Angela replied. "But this is in the area we love, so we thought we wouldn't pass it over until at least I'd had a quick look at it. The house looks very attractive, don't you think? Actually, we're not serious about this one, that's why I haven't phoned the agent first. It's just a reason for me to take a day off work and bring you out to the Chilterns. I know you love this area."

Luckily, Sheila Bateman was at home and despite Angela's protest that they were only here for a cursory glance at the exterior, she insisted on inviting them inside and making them a cup of coffee.

The front of the house, with its huge dark green yews was not very enticing, but nevertheless, as soon as Sheila had shut her dogs in the dining-room, and brought her visitors into the sitting-room, they found themselves feeling very much at home. "This idea of having unplastered brick walls and keeping the old timbers is rather lovely." Angela's mother said to Sheila Bateman.

"Yes, and it saves a lot on the decorating, too." Sheila pointed out. "In fact the whole house was almost completely burned down about thirty years ago and then rebuilt, so although it's nearly four hundred years old, it has a damp course. John and I have been here about three years and we've put in central heating and painted all the walls and the kitchen units - believe it or not, they were all bright orange when we came here!"

As the time progressed, Angela and her parents became more and more enamoured with the cottage. "I see your name board says the house is called Old Place, but on the Simmons particulars they have called it The Old Place." Angela said.

"I don't know why they've done that." Sheila replied, but Angela suddenly had a feeling that this really was going to be The Old Place for them. Looking around the brick walls of the sitting-room and at the large old fireplace, she experienced the sense that she had been here forever, even though she knew it was a ridiculous idea.

"I see you looking at the fireplace." Sheila noticed. "Actually, we've only just opened that up. When we came here it had been bricked up and an electric fire put in. I think it was to conserve heat, because the original owner didn't have central heating. Incidentally we put in the shower, toilet and utility room as well."

Angela nodded and smiled, but actually she was trying to remember Daphne du Maurier's words on seeing her house, Menabilly, in Cornwall, for the first time. "It went something like 'This for me and me for this!'" she recalled to herself, but aloud she said: "Thank you very much for your hospitality, but I think we must be going now. I must talk to my husband and we'll let you know, through Simmons, of course."

She looked around for her parents and found her mother in the garden admiring the beautiful flowerbeds and her father looking at the drains. "I think we'd better be going now, Mummy," she said and, turning to her father asked: "What are you looking for?"

"I'm looking at the drainage system, it appears to be quite complicated." her father explained.

"Oh, drains, never mind about the drains, did you see the lovely cottage-style doors and the latch handles." Angela retorted.

"My dear girl," her father responded. "When you've been in this house a while, the drains may be far more important to you than the door handles!"

As they left the house at the foot of Witheridge Hill, they decided to go up to the Bull at Nettlebed, which they had seen as they were driving around trying to find Highmoor. "There," suggested her mother, "we should be able to get some lunch and you could phone Bob."

Her father, though, was still thinking about the house they had just viewed. "I didn't quite realise how many outbuildings there are, although I see now that they are all listed in the particulars. There is not only a large wooden double garage, but a small single one, too. That was probably constructed originally for a small pre-war car, like an Austin Ten. Then there's a sizeable work shed, as well as a potting shed and a greenhouse. All that and almost an acre of land; you'll be kept busy, if you do buy it!"

Angela was meanwhile thinking how to persuade Bob to leave his busy office and come down to see a house, which they had almost dismissed because it was so different from the Victorian type they had in mind.

Luckily he did agree to come, intrigued by his wife's enthusiasm. He was not disappointed. He agreed that he liked the house but most of all he was taken by the beautiful garden which was so reminiscent of the one at his parents' home where he had helped his father during the war to dig up a part of their lawn to grow vegetables under the *Dig for Victory* campaign.

The couple agreed to return two days later when John Bateman would be at home and it was then, after more discussion, and reaching an agreement, the Spencer-Harpers set the wheels in motion for the purchase of The Old Place.

In December, whilst the solicitors were making their searches,

Bob and Angela were invited to dinner by the Batemans, who had also requested their next-door neighbours to join them.

Sheila cooked a delicious dinner on the Aga and this included a large joint of pork, complete with crisp crackling and all the trimmings. Part way through this enjoyable meal one of the neighbours enquired: "Is this Matthew One or Matthew Two?" The Spencer-Harpers both looked perplexed until it was explained to them that the owners of both houses had clubbed together to raise two pigs, sharing their household scraps as well as the labour of cleaning out the sty, etc.

These animals were kept on a piece of land that belonged to the owners of Beech Hollow but was at the side of their garden and at the bottom of the one belonging to Old Place. Later the owners planted beech and larch trees there, but for the many decades since the outbreak of the war, it had been an area set aside for pigs. These two particular animals had been raised to maturity, killed and divided between the two neighbours who kept them in their freezers.

At the point where Matthew was mentioned, Bob had a fork full of steaming pork half way to his mouth and suddenly found it suspended in mid-air as he took in the scenario. Nevertheless, he soon regained his composure and continued to enjoy his meal. The incident did not really spoil the meal, or the relationship between the vendor and the purchaser of the house, but the event was sometimes recalled in later years, especially when the subject of roast pork arose!

About a week before Christmas, Bob was in his office one day when he received a telephone call from John Bateman who asked to come and see him. They met for lunch in a Maidenhead hostelry and John then explained that they could not proceed with the sale because some personal plans had not materialised and so everything would have to be suspended.

Bob and Angela admired the Batemans for their honesty in coming to explain their difficulty in person, instead of leaving the matter for the estate agents to sort out, as many would have done. Bob immediately rang the man who was buying their house and explained the situation and his impression of the purchaser was fulfilled when he, too, agreed to 'hang on'.

Christmas and New Year's Eve passed in a mist of uncertainty.

Angela had bought Bob a pair of antique bellows for the big old cottage inglenook as a Christmas present but when he put them by the more modern tiled fireplace in their Chalfont St Peter home, they looked completely out of place. Nonetheless, he rewrapped them and put them in the loft in the fervent hope that all would soon be resolved.

Equally suddenly, two weeks later, Bob received another phone call from John to say that the way was clear and he hoped all the parties could now proceed to completion. From then on everything went smoothly and both houses were bought and sold as planned, and the Batemans moved up to North Wales where they acquired a small hotel.

Angela and Bob, together with Philip and Michael, moved in on 17th February 1979, in two feet of snow. The next day they were only able to drive out of their house by grace of a local farmer who drove his tractor up the 'New Road' on Witheridge Hill ahead of them.

A few days later Bob sank a large post into the grass at the front. It proudly bore the new name of the cottage: The Old Place.

In the months that followed, Angela left her job with Trust Houses Forte and stayed at home to supervise the alterations and improvements that the couple made to their new home. These included complete new electric wiring and more sockets, new units in the kitchen and all the lofts insulated. Much work to the hitherto freezing diningroom, where a small east window was removed by Bob and replaced with brickwork. It was his first attempt, and done with his usual engineering precision. The walls were also lined with insulating board and a radiator added.

They also located and invited Mr Stephen Bertram, ARIBA to The Old Place and he was able to tell them how he had redesigned the dwelling after the fire in 1948 and the difficulties he and the builder had had in finding suitable materials for the task, especially as, due to the shortages which continued well after the war, building materials were still controlled by licence in 1950. He explained, too, how he found the little lattice-paned window which he had inserted in the wall between the sitting-room and the hallway to provide extra light, as well as the origin of the two curved posts that supported the main beam in the centre of the sitting-room.

As winter turned into spring Angela and Bob began to explore their garden, having wisely taken the advice of more horticulturally-minded friends: "Don't take out anything until the autumn." This became particularly pertinent to a large ball-shaped bush at the top of the garden which appeared to be dead and leafless, even up to the end of May, when it started to shoot orange tips which became lovely, deep, dark red leaves. They later learned that it was a Cotinus Purpurea and it was often commented on as being one of the oldest and best specimens of its kind in the locality, due to its rounded shape, which it owed to the care given to it by previous owners.

In fact, it became apparent that at some time, probably in the 1950s, after the house was rebuilt, the garden had been landscaped. The large lawn with its curved edges and surrounding herbaceous borders, the crazy-paved terrace and path leading down to a circular area in which a bird-bath had been set, as well as the many old shrubs and trees, showed that much thought had been put into its planning. Two large apple trees, a cherry and a greengage, all of which had been somewhat neglected, stood like sentries at the end of the garden and were backed by a privet hedge that concealed a sizeable vegetable garden.

The apples that fell to the ground that September seemed very poor in quality. Bob sent a sample from each tree to apple specialists in Brogdale, Kent and they were later returned, named as a Bramley and a Newton Wonder but with the warning that the trees were probably at least fifty years old and much in need of pruning. The Spencer-Harpers had this work carried out the following year. The greengage, like all trees of its kind, fruited well one year but gave little for the next twelve or fifteen years – what fruit there was soon became infested with wasps. It gradually deteriorated and later had to be felled.

By the end of the summer, the couple had worked for so many hours in the garden that they had almost managed to clear it of the ubiquitous and invasive ground elder, which they were told by a neighbour that the Romans had brought here for their gout! This had been achieved by deep digging all the beds, taking out the plants and tracing the long white roots of this pernicious weed. In so doing, though, they came across a number of interesting finds, especially old garden tools.

Pieces of clay smoking pipes appeared all over the place and

Angela set aside those that had any kind of markings on them. Later she studied several books on the subject and made notes about the makers, including one manufacturer, Hawleys of Bristol, whose name was found on one piece of a pipe stem. There were also many shards of Victorian pottery, some by Meakin of Hanley – most were blue or green. Part of a hollow silver-coated cross, possibly worn as a pendant was an interesting find for it appeared to have been made in the 'rustic' style.

The three most fascinating though were a 'Bun Penny', so named because when it was minted early in Queen Victoria's reign; it depicted the Queen with her hair drawn back into a 'bun'. Another was a copper token which Angela sent up to the British Museum. She had a reply informing her that it was an 'Angelsey Halfpenny Token', dated 1788-1792 and made in the reign of George III when very little copper coinage was issued and so trading firms and corporations produced their own. Again, how this came to be in an Oxfordshire garden was a mystery.

However, the most beautiful discovery was a flat brass plate which had holes drilled on either side. The whole was engraved with the details of a bird in flight. Mr North of the Metalwork Department in the Victoria and Albert Museum suggested that it was probably 'a mount to secure the cords of a window blind. The two cords would be passed through the twin holes and secured around a knob.... the work indicates a date in the early nineteenth century.' As it was highly unlikely that such an object would have been used in a poor cottage such as theirs was at that time, the conclusion was reached that it may have been an unwanted object brought home from a local country house by a parent to please a child.

In October, 1979, Maggie Saunders, landlady of the Black Horse at Checkendon suggested to Angela that, as she seemed interested in the history of her house, she might like to interview Miss Dolly Franklin who had lived there from 1906 to 1930 and was now in a retirement home in nearby Sonning Common. In due course Angela found the old woman and brought her back to The Old Place. There she tape-recorded Dolly's high-pitched voice as she recalled very clearly many details of life in the earth-floored cottage.

With her permission, Angela transcribed these memories and published them in the monthly village magazine, the Stoke Row

News, which was still A5 and rather thin. She was astounded at the reaction of the villagers. People came up to her in the street and suggested the names of many other people who had been born and raised, not only in Highmoor and Stoke Row but also in Nettlebed, Peppard, Checkendon and even Woodcote. She very soon came to realise that if she was to try and preserve some of these oral histories she would have to place a mental boundary around just one or perhaps two of them. Eventually she decided that, although their house was technically in Highmoor, the boundary between it and Stoke Row was very nearby and so she would concentrate on just those two villages.

The following spring, Angela took a post as Secretary to Professor Mike Jones, who headed the International Centre of the Henley Management College, a position she was to hold for four years. At weekends Bob and Angela started to explore the locality and often walked up through the woods to the top of Witheridge Hill. Up there, at the end of the footpath, they found a large old oak tree. "I'll bet that's hundreds of years old!" Bob exclaimed. "I'm sure it could tell you a tale or two, especially as it's just behind the old school."

By the summer, Angela had started to collect quite a few of the memories of the older residents of Stoke Row and Highmoor and had photocopied the photographs they had lent her. At first it was difficult to persuade them to part with their treasured pictures, but it was Mrs Ada Britnell who was kind enough to allow her to do so. Once 'Mrs 'arper', as she called the stranger, with her charming Oxfordshire burr, had returned them within a few days, Ada spread the good word that 'the wumman from Lunnon' was trustworthy, others soon followed suit, happy to have their memories recorded on tape and on paper as well as to loan their photographs.

Again with their permission, these stories were published in the *Stoke Row News* under the heading *Getting to Know your Neighbour*. It was after just a couple of months of continuing in this manner that Angela was introduced to David Beasley of Wallingford, himself a local historian and a talented photographer. He had a collection of over fifteen thousand photographs that he had amassed over a period of about forty years, but these were of Wallingford and nearby villages and were later contained in several books that he published. It was with his help that Angela was then able to borrow photographs from local residents so that David could make a negative and a positive of post-card size and very soon return the original to the owner.

Angela also spent much of her spare time up at Oxford where she was sometimes able to lunch with her son, Michael, who was studying at the University there. As well, she was able to carry out researches at the Bodleian Library, the Oxfordshire Archives and the Centre for Oxfordshire Studies. There she made many friends among the very helpful staff and learned a great deal about the two villages. During one such visit she found a postcard of Old Place in 1938 and came home with a copy of it, full of joy!

Postcards were very popular at the beginning of the twentieth century as they were almost the only means of communication between people before the invention of the telephone. Prior to 1901 they had not had a division for the address, but thereafter they did and the cost of posting one was a halfpenny. Around 1903 more than three million a day passed through the national sorting offices of the nation. It was quite common for someone to post a card in London in the morning, stating that the writer would be 'on the train arriving in Reading at four o'clock that day' and expect to be met by the addressee with a pony and trap. Another, written in 1902, told the addressee to 'call for me on the way to school' referring to the next day and was posted the previous evening, although it is true that it was in the same town – would this be the same today, Angela wondered to herself. Before 1913 all cards and letters were hand-franked with a rubber stamp, but after that the mechanical franking machine came into its own, just in time for the millions of cards, which were to be sent to and from France during the First World War. These and many more facts she recorded on cards and in files, using her secretarial skills on the typewriter during lunch breaks.

Computers were introduced into Henley Management College in 1981. Angela and her colleagues who had to constantly type similar letters every day, as well as retyping lists of details as they changed, found these machines to be 'God's gift'. However, when chatting one day to a friend in the office, Angela said: "I've just been reading that in the States people have these things in their homes, I wouldn't like that, would you?" Her friend shook her head in agreement but neither of them realized to what extent computers were soon to overtake and change not only their own country, but also the whole world.

Back at home Bob noticed that the old cherry tree, near the road was beginning to lean so badly that it was in danger of falling. A tree surgeon recommended it be felled and when it was, on New Year's Day, a canker in the core was discovered. Angela had recently found an entry in the Archives, which stated: 'On Wednesday 28 July 1813, Sarah Blackall of Witheridge Hill was killed by a fall from a cherry tree. The verdict by the Coroner, Mr G P Cooke was that 'she fell from a ladder'. He charged a fee of twenty shillings and this was paid, plus seven shillings and six pence expenses, by the Court'. Many of the references in the archives were to the occupants of a sole house at the foot of Witheridge Hill being occupied by the Blackalls, so Angela, in a sentimental moment, placed an urn on the stump of the old tree in memory of the sad event which may have taken place there.

By this time Angela had acquired quite a few artefacts as well as tape-recordings of some twenty or so residents. Her photograph collection was growing too and she therefore agreed to put on a display of all of these when the Maharajah's Well Committee decided to hold a Steam Rally in a Stoke Row field in order to raise money for restoring the well canopy and winding gear. Unfortunately, the whole affair was rather spoiled by heavy downpours of rain and the mud that was caused by it.

The first months of 1982 produced one of the worst snowstorms in twenty years and during the few days that Angela and Bob were not able to get out of their home. Bob had paperwork to do and his wife set about organizing her local history records into better order. When talking to older people about The Old Place they usually referred to it as 'the one what was burned down' or 'the one in the frost hollow'. The couple soon discovered that frost was one of their worst problems, as the earliest one recorded was on 29th September the previous year and the latest on 6th June that year. The mists rolled down the hillside in what one of their neighbours referred to as *the catabaric effect* that was so feared in wine-growing areas in Europe. They soon learned to buy 'hardy' plants and, as the beeches and larches that formed a patch of woodland just beyond their garden began to grow taller, they also found it necessary to look for plants that would be shade-tolerant.

To pass the winter evenings, Angela joined the Stoke Row Women's Institute and both husband and wife attended the Village Quizzes, soon Angela was enrolled as a team member and Bob as a scorer. About the same time Bob became Advertising Manager and subsequently Chairman of the *Stoke Row News* while Angela took on the role of Secretary. They were becoming more and more involved in the village by then. They had started to attend the Independent Chapel at Stoke Row soon after their arrival in the area, but now Bob joined the choir and, at the request of the charismatic and persuasive Padre Bernard Railton Bax, also agreed to become the Secretary.

Their younger son, Michael, gained his degree in Physics at Oxford where he had met a very attractive and brainy American girl called Victoria. The following year they went to the States and lived for a while with Vicky's father in New York. Their elder son, Philip, was still at Imperial College, and, having gained his science degree in Astrophysics, was now working on his thesis for a PhD in X-ray Astronomy. Angela typed this up for him and although it was almost incomprehensible to her, it did inspire her to take an evening class in Astronomy that spring term. However the teacher was already complaining that, although they could see the Milky Way and most of the major constellations from the grounds of Henley College, the 'light pollution' from Reading was already making this joy increasingly difficult.

The Spencer-Harpers loved the countryside in which they found themselves, especially in the long, hot summer of 1983, when they were able to walk in the woods and often caught glimpses of the lone Chinese water deer. This creature, the Muntjac, sometimes nicknamed the 'barking deer' was thought to be an escapee from the Wildlife Park at Woburn Abbey in Bedfordshire, which had learned to survive in the Chiltern uplands. Like the badger it was crepuscular and therefore rarely seen.

More often sighted were the fallow deer that loved to bask in the sunshine on Witheridge Hill. They travelled in groups of anything from five or six to twelve or fifteen. It was often their swishing tails or a glimpse of the vertical white stripes each side of their rumps as they departed that gave them away. The sound of their noisy rutting in October and the rhythmic grunting noises they made also indicated their presence. Unfortunately they took a liking to the roses growing in the garden of The Old Place and the Spencer-Harpers were forced to put up a green wire fence, largely obscured by the hedges, all around their property to prevent this happening. Later they had to add an electric fence of the agricultural type to deter the badgers from across the road.

All the bats, butterflies, dragonflies, and birds, both sighted and heard, were a joy to the couple. However, one evening in early May, they had a special privilege when they noticed a female tawny owl in the Newton Wonder apple tree. She had three juveniles with her and when she swooped to the ground to find grubs or worms for them, they alighted each side of the square topped bird bath and stared straight ahead at Angela and Bob who were standing silent and still in the sitting-room, behind the French doors The sighting lasted just a few moments but they were very excited at the vision of these three babies with their big eyes which seemed to be out of all proportion to their little soft bodies. So much so that Angela felt bound to do something to express her joy but could only grasp Bob's hand and squeeze it tight!

Later that year Philip was granted a Research Fellowship in X-ray Astronomy at Birmingham University and so his parents spent some time helping him to settle into a flat that he bought in Cotteridge, Kings Norton. Afterwards Angela spent a week up there, redecorating her son's new home and also enjoyed exploring the area, which she had never visited before. In time this work took Philip to NASA bases in Florida and Houston, Texas as well as to full-time work in Germany and Spain for the European Space Agency.

In her spare time the following winter Angela typed out Edward Anderdon Reade's manuscript on the *History of Stoke Row*. This work, hand-written in the 1870s, came to ninety A-4 typed pages and was, in some parts, rather tedious but her efforts did enable photocopies to be given to interested parties and one to be put into the Vestry of St John's Church, so that the original could be placed in the care of the Bodleian Library.

She also continued her work interviewing local people. Born and bred as she was, in the suburbs of London, it fascinated her to listen to these country people and to learn of some of the sayings that were used in the days of their forefathers. Ada Britnell told her that her father always spoke of his father as being a "long-headed [clever] man" and, one day, when Angela was taking the bottles from the milkman, a car went past at great speed and he said "'e ough'er a' been there afore 'e started!" Bill George told her about an old local who had been ill and when asked whether he was getting better, said, "Oi was bad a'bed and now oi'm wuss up!" Alan Cox, too, made her laugh when he recalled that, when his father was on his way to work at the local sawmill, he usually met another old villager who always asked: "'Ow be an?" [How are you?] To which the standard reply was always "Oi be an." [I am well]

One day in late April 1984, Bob received a phone call from the Chairman of his company group, requesting his company privately at lunch. This was not a common occurrence and Bob realised that 'something was in the wind'. Actually, it proved to be something more like a gale that took the couple down to Poole in Dorset that summer and an entirely new life. For Bob it was a great improvement, moving with his company to a new family-owned group and a Board of Directors who were much more engineering-minded and so he was constantly happy in the new situation.

For Angela it was quite a different story. She had to put all her local history work 'on the back burner' and leave the comfortable surroundings of Henley Management College. In Dorset she found herself unable to find a job. At fifty years of age, in a time of general recession, she soon realised that it was not going to be easy, but spent an interesting time, doing temporary work and job-hunting.

After some months of trying she did find a position with a small French engineering company in nearby Hamworthy, which had its Head Office and main manufacturing facility in Montelimar, France. The General Manager in Hamworthy was French and of Italian descent, who seemed to hate being in England and, since he spoke almost no English, was not slow to express his dislike of the British and everything about their country. Luckily, Angela's fluency in French was what enabled her to get the job and it was her role to translate everything, even making most of the telephone calls!

She did not care much for the atmosphere in this small office, with its adjacent engineering workshops and after a year managed to find a better post with a large car salesroom where she again acted as Secretary to the General Manager. Actually this turned out to be more 'Head Cook and Bottlewasher' type of work but it sufficed until she could find something better.

The Spencer-Harpers were very reluctant to leave The Old Place, even though Bob's new employers had hoped they would do so. After a few months they were able to buy a lovely flat in Corfe Mullen and thus began six years of living and working there all week and coming home to manage their house and garden at weekends. With the aid of many duplicated possessions and long lists of what to take home and bring back every Friday and Sunday night, the process gradually became quite smooth. In the evenings of that autumn, when Bob was not travelling, they drove out around many of the Dorset villages with delicious names like Sixpenny Handley, Melbury Bubb, Bedchester, Affpuddle, Minterne Magna and countless others. It was one of the happiest times of their lives in this respect.

However, they soon found that there was trouble with the freeholds of the flat they had bought. There were forty-eight flats in a group that were spread around in groups of about a dozen in Corfe Mullen. The Managing Agent who also owned the freehold rights had been paid management charges by each flat owner for many years and this included a reserve for the redecorations but the rogue absconded with the funds and went bankrupt, leaving all the owners with no money to pay for even the electricity that lit their hallways and operated their television aerials, let alone the redecorating that was now due.

Bob at once stepped into the breach. He went to the Receiver's meeting in Poole and the bank that held the freehold land rights under mortgage. He then bought the freeholds, and enabled each owner to purchase his freehold right for just £100. He had already formed a Residents' Association, which later became a limited company called 'Sableglade Ltd', with its Board of Directors, all flat owners. Bob himself became Chairman, Company Secretary and Estate Manager while Angela became Minutes and Correspondence Secretary. As the years went by they worked almost every evening on this project and kept up these roles for sixteen years. During the time they worked in Poole and even for several years after they returned, in fact until they sold their flat, they did this work voluntarily.

However, there was a brighter side to that year in that the

Spencer-Harpers were able to go out and stay with Vicky's father in New York and then go on to visit Michael and Vicky in their new condominium in Colorado. They hired an RV [Recreational Vehicle] and spent two glorious weeks all together touring the Rocky Mountain National Park. Angela later typed all their memories of this holiday, together with photographs and postcards into a couple of lever-arch binders and did this for every holiday they took from then onwards. She was later to find that these took up a lot of space in the house, but were much appreciated by their relatives and useful to lend to people who showed an interest, perhaps if they were planning to go to a particular country.

And so the years progressed. The couple were not able to do much more in Oxfordshire during this time, other than keep their house and garden in good order at weekends. Although they had to drop some things at Witheridge Hill, Bob continued to act as Secretary, caring also for general upkeep and maintenance of Stoke Row Chapel and they both continued their functions with the *Stoke Row News*.

For some years Angela and Bob had been sponsoring and writing to two Tibetan children in India and several members of their family did the same. In 1986 they decided to go and visit all these children who were living in a village at the foot of the Himalayas. They preceded their visit with a tour of the 'Golden Triangle', Delhi, Jaipur and Agra and learned much about India's history and way of life. They found the Tibetans to be a wonderful people, brought up to care for everyone and everything; even the tiniest insect was the subject of great love and attention. During their fortnight there, they had to live with very little water or electricity but managed to teach the schoolchildren something of England every day. They also had the pleasure of dining with several close relatives of the Dalai Llama and hearing about the trials of these people, banished from their homeland by the Chinese. The English couple felt themselves much richer in spirit after visiting this delightful children's village and on their return managed to find even more sponsors for this beneficent work.

Thanks to Professor Mike Jones, with whom she kept in touch after leaving Henley Management College, Angela continued to develop her lectures on Graphology and gave several each year whilst she was down in Dorset. By 1987, Mike was able to arrange for Angela to undertake the first of her lecture tours on board the *Queen Elizabeth 2*, accompanied and aided by her husband. At that time this ship was more often a 'liner' between Southampton and New York; cruising was only just beginning to be established. Unfortunately this particular trip across the Atlantic proved to be a 'baptism of fire' as the ship suffered one of its worst storms ever. Even though the Captain tried to skirt the force nine gale; the ship was five hours late into New York and lost much china, glass and even a piano which had not been fastened down securely enough, on that voyage. Angela had to learn how to cope with seasickness but nevertheless the couple enjoyed their trip enormously. It was to be the first of nine on the *QE2* in the coming years.

A year later Angela changed her job again and joined a small company that had been founded by Richard Branson and Anita Roddick. This was called 'Wellbeing' and sold healthcare insurance to both private companies and public organisations. The office was in the pretty New Forest town of Ringwood and Angela managed the office all day whilst her boss, Colin Swan, went out on business. It was for her the happiest period in the six years they spent in Dorset.

Also Michael and Vicky, who had married several years previously in Boulder, Colorado, came back to England in 1988. During this period, too, Bob and Angela were able to pop in on a Sunday, as they returned to Dorset, to see Michael and Victoria who rented a flat in Hampshire, where their first son was born on 31st January 1989 and named Ian. As Vicky preferred the name 'Milo', he was always called this and in his late teens decided to take the name legally.

Eventually, in 1990, the family engineering business for which Bob had worked for six years, decided to completely reshape the company. After helping them to do this, he suggested he would like to retire at that point. The family owners were appreciative of Bob's work in bringing the power transmission company into their business and made him a modest but generous 'Golden Handshake' at the culmination of thirty-four years service.

And so the Spencer-Harpers 'came home' and spent the first year reorganising their lives and their two homes. However, they had hardly started when Bob's mother became seriously ill with cancer and fortunately he was then free to help his middle sister, Olive, to nurse their mother to the end in her own home.

The following year they let the flat and set themselves up in businesses of their own. Bob formed a company which he called Spencer Enterprises and proved to be an umbrella for a number of roles, including the maintenance of the audio visual aids and computer networks of Gillotts School at Henley.

Angela's company became Highmoor Business Services and at first she did typing for various local small firms. Michael and Vicky had, by that time, bought a detached Victorian house in nearby Sonning Common. Michael had set up his own computer software business and suggested that he should employ Angela. Her role would be to sell the software products of his company 'Inside Information' over the telephone and so she started a role that was to last for over five years. To this end, he and Bob turned one of the two guest bedrooms into an office, where Angela was provided with an enormous bench desk and all the necessary computer and telephone equipment. This also, of course, enabled her to return to her local history work and to put on to computer all that she had previously kept written on sheets of paper and on cards.

Another interest came in the form of the Highmoor Well Restoration Committee which Angela set up in order to both raise money for this project and also to involve several of the new younger people who were coming to live in Highmoor. Over a period of about five years they raised nine thousand pounds, although various problems arose in the coming years over getting the actual work done.

At the same time, Angela became Secretary to the Highmoor Memorial Hall Committee. They were a splendid crew and put much work over a period of six years into restoring the old hall that had originally been constructed around an old First World War army hut. Before she retired from this post, Angela was able to find, frame and put up several dozen photographs of Highmoor, both to ornament the walls and to give visitors some idea of the village's history.

Very soon after this she also took on the editing and typing of the *Stoke Row News* and it was then agreed to turn it from an A5 to A4 format. This was because it was so much easier to type an A4 page on the computer as a master, and precluded the need for having to be so careful over the pagination. Not everyone in the village was happy about the change, but they soon became used to it, especially as Bob insisted on retaining the same colour and design for the cover.

At the end of 1990, after a very happy Christmas with the family, Angela's father died suddenly and for several months the Spencer-Harpers became engrossed in caring for her mother. Consequently almost all Angela's local history work had to be abandoned for a while.

As things improved in this direction another joy came along in the form of a second grandson, Quentin, who was born in June 1991. He was a beautiful baby with golden curly hair. Milo was enchanted with his little brother and, as they grew older, they usually played very happily together.

The following year, with the family situation being more settled, Angela was able to return to her local history researches, learning more about subjects less well known to her. She heard about the Seafire aeroplane that had crashed behind the church in 1950, the pilot losing his life in order to avoid killing the congregation that Sunday morning and other matters, such as the closure of Highmoor School in 1956 and the almost immediate subsequential loss of the village shop. She found that it was mainly this that led to the decline in the numbers of parents with children coming to live in the village and how that had changed the entire atmosphere of the community.

She also met a Stoke Row farmer, who had found a fourteenth century dagger in one of his fields and left it rusting in a barn for years. Luckily, she was able to persuade him to allow her to take it to the Oxfordshire Museum at Woodstock for safekeeping. She and Bob were told by a local taxi-driver that his father, who had the unlikely name of Bob Hope, was a blacksmith and had personally made the beautiful wrought-iron gate at the front of The Old Place. In fact, Angela's collection of documents, photographs and memorabilia were already filling her small study and she found it necessary to buy a third two-drawer filing cabinet in order to house them!

By 1993 she had amassed about fifteen hundred photographs and set up a Local History Day, so that the villagers would have an opportunity to see some of them and most of the artefacts that she had also been collecting. Among them were a number of Romano-British pottery shards found in a Highmoor wood, a white metal coin cast at the time of the opening of the Maharajah's Well in 1864 and a bottle of water drawn by the Duke of Edinburgh when he came for the Maharajah's Well Centenary Celebrations in 1964 as well as a commemorative mug bought on that day. This had been sent to her by an American who had been in a camp here just prior to D-Day in 1944 and had brought his wife to Stoke Row for the royal visit. There were also a number of items like an autographed tea-towel sold by the Stoke Row School as well as an item of the school uniform, both of which she realised would become memorabilia in years to come. She also put on display some of the many books she had acquired by then, relating to this area.

At this exhibition, the Vicar of St John's, Revd Donald Shepherd, asked her, "You say you have now amassed four filing cabinet drawers full of information from your researches. What's going to happen to all this stuff when you die?"

To which Angela replied, "I hope that Oxfordshire Archives will be able to take it all. They have said they will."

But David Shepherd's answer to that was brief. "Then the only people to see any of it will be family historians interested mainly in their own clan or perhaps students researching one subject, like the tent-peggers of Stoke Row. You should write a book and put as many of the photos and stories in it that you can." Angela was really daunted at the prospect, for she had never done anything like it in her life, but she did remember his words.

Also in 1993, the Spencer-Harpers had constructed a custom-built, brick and timber conservatory, with double-glazed windows. This was erected in lieu of the old aluminium greenhouse, and proved to be very useful in the cooler days of spring and autumn, both for potted plants and to sit in.

Two years later, again with Bob's help, she mounted another photographic exhibition and once more she received further loans of pictures and gifts of memorabilia, as well as corrections on the provenancing of the photographs.

She finally retired that summer and then she did make a start on her first book, using her secretarial skills to lay it all out, including the captions. Bob was also very helpful and his keen mind soon found any mistakes. This was in the days before computers could find errors for the writer! Although the work on it was spasmodic, it did progress gradually and she was glad of support from the British Museum, the Victoria and Albert Museum, the Oxfordshire Archives and the Centre for Oxfordshire Studies along the way.

A wonderful event occurred the following year when their eldest son, Philip, married a lovely girl who was an advisory teacher for children with special needs. Philip had his flat and Margaret had a semi-detached house of her own, so they sold them both and bought themselves a charming, comfortable detached house in Solihull, West Midlands. There they were quietly married in the local Registry Office in 1994 and held a reception for both their families in their new home.

The next year saw the birth of their third grandson, Gabriel, who actually entered this world on 27th July 1995, rather earlier than expected in the Addenbrooks hospital in Cambridge, where his parents, Michael and Victoria had gone to the wedding of a friend!

The principal project for the village throughout several months in 1995 was the Appraisal. Many people worked on it, including the Spencer-Harpers. The idea was promoted by the ORCC [Oxfordshire Rural Community Council] and consisted of distributing a question-naire to find out such things as how many bicycles or dogs each household owned to whether residents had any notions for new clubs or groups. The results were astonishing and led to the forma-tion of the highly successful and long-lasting Garden Club, among other ventures. The resulting booklet was truly impressive and won for the village the Best Appraisal award.

A year later she joined Yvonne Bax's Keep Fit class, held in the Chapel meeting-room and began a series of annual Litter Blitzes in both Stoke Row and Highmoor. Bob, assisted by his faithful garden-ing/handyman friend, Anthony Reford, reroofed the Workshop with a gabled roof and the addition of a Swiss-style log store. This was to house some of the many logs that he enjoyed cutting and storing and which provided them with lovely fires in their big fireplace every winter.

Another group formed about that time was the Sewing Bee, chiefly organised by the ladies of St John's Church and held in the home of Hazel Markham who also wrote a humorous page in the

Stoke Row News for many years. Angela made a tapestry kneeler for the church with a cross on it, in the centre of which was the number '2000'. When asked: "Why '2000'?" she replied: "Because it will take me until 2000 to finish it!"

Actually she completed it before that which was surprising because in 1998 an event occurred which was to take six months out of the lives of the couple at The Old Place. On Wednesday, 14th July, about nine o'clock, whilst it was still light, Angela and Bob were watching television after a busy day working in the garden. All of a sudden they heard a tremendous roar and jumped up to look out of their front window. An unbelievable sight met their eyes for, immediately behind their car a jet of water was rising some three feet wide and thirty feet high!

This gigantic fountain was filled with mud and flint stones that scraped the bark off the tops of trees and then fell to the ground, crashing through the roof of their car and filling it with water, mud and stones. In an interview with the *Henley Standard* next morning, Bob likened it to the recent eruption of the volcano, Krakatoa. What was most frightening was the realisation that, only a couple of hours before, his wife had been standing on that very spot.

Thames Water were quickly on the scene and confessed that the problem had occurred as a result of a burst to a nine inch water main only twenty-five metres from the house. It left the Spencer-Harpers with a terrible mess in their front and back gardens as well as a two-metre hole in their driveway and no car! However the water company were very good and arranged for a loan car and suitable financial compensation. In addition to this they arranged to have the road re-surfaced in tarmac. However, the couple had to forfeit a week's holiday they were just about to take and it took them many months to find an identical Mitsubishi Space Wagon to replace the one that had been their pride and joy.

Notwithstanding all these problems, the Spencer-Harpers continued to love life at The Old Place. They enjoyed the farces put on by the Stoke Row Drama Group in the spring and the Shakespeare plays performed by the Rising Sun Players in the summer. On Sundays they attended the little Chapel at Stoke Row where they found spiritual renewal as well as the pleasure of the company of other members of the congregation over coffee after the service.

The Chapel was fortunate in having received a bequest from local farmer William Brazil in the 1950s. This enabled it to be well maintained, even though numbers were lower than they had been in the middle of the twentieth century. Nonetheless, they were more than in most local churches and provided a happy relaxed yet respectful attitude towards their worship, encouraged by their Minister, Revd John Harrington. Moreover, both Angela and Bob liked the aspect of practical Christianity that was supported by the Chapel, as well as the wonderful music provided each Sunday by the Organist and Choir. The ever-practical Bob looked upon the building as being his 'second home' and cared for it accordingly, while Angela helped with the flower-arranging and secretarial work.

In their retirement they tried not to work on a Sunday afternoon but to go off a few miles to the west, where they could park their car on the escarpment and look upon large open views, different from the valley in which they lived. They would usually take a walk for an hour or so and come back to the car to read or to discuss some private matter in quiet seclusion. It was an afternoon of peace that seemed to set them up for the busy week ahead.

Although the cottage was not as sequestered as it might have been fifty years previously, it was still delightfully quiet at night, when one could stand outside and listen to the barking of the Muntjac and the various sounds made by the owls as they chatted to one another. It is true that by then one could only see the major stars and sometimes only the planet Venus, due to light pollution from Reading and Henley.

However, Angela still enjoyed finding the North Star and making out the form of the constellation of Orion as 'he' rose over Witheridge Hill in early September, a sure sign of approaching autumn. She often thought of how people through the ages had stood on that spot or nearby and looked at the same stars and the same moon and how, despite the many changes throughout the years, some things never altered.

Despite the water main burst, by the autumn of 1998, Angela had finally come to writing the closing chapters of the book which Revd Donald Shepherd, Vicar of St John the Evangelist, Stoke Row, had suggested she write some five years before. As she came near to completion, she and her husband, Bob, took the manuscripts down to Alan Sutton Ltd, in Gloucestershire, a company well-known for its local history publications.

The Acquisitions Editor was very complimentary on the work and on examining the front cover and the title of the book: *Dipping into the Wells, The story of the two Chiltern villages of Stoke Row and Highmoor, seen through the memories of their inhabitants*, asked: "Why two villages?"

Angela explained: "Although technically we live in Highmoor, the boundary between that village and its neighbour, Stoke Row, is very close by our house and so we have always felt allegiance to both villages. For the same reason I have interviewed and borrowed photographs from people who were born in Stoke Row and Highmoor as well as many other people who have lived here for many years or whose relatives have done so."

Turning over the four hundred or so pages and looking at some of the three hundred and ninety seven photographs, Ian murmured approvingly and enquired: "How many people live in these two villages?"

Bob answered: "In Stoke Row, I think about six hundred and fifty, but in Highmoor it's nearer two hundred and fifty."

Ian looked thoughtful. "We really do need a catchment of four times that number, so if you would like to add four more villages to this, we'll certainly take it, it's very good!"

Angela and Bob were dumb-founded. After a few moments, Angela found the breath to protest politely: "But this research has taken me over twenty years and these people are dying all the time. I couldn't possibly do that!"

At this point, Ian suggested they publish it privately. "If you can find the money," he said. "I think it would be worth it. After all, you've put a lot of work into it."

So the couple returned home and a few days later Angela started to examine local history books in her local library. There she noticed one called *The Changing Face of Oxford*, one of a series published by Robert Boyd Publications of Witney. She telephoned Bob Boyd as soon as she arrived home and he agreed to come to The Old Place some days later.

Bob Boyd had worked all his life for Oxford University Press and the Alden Press and the Spencer-Harpers realised that what he didn't know about printing and publishing wasn't worth knowing. He estimated a production cost of about twelve thousand pounds but suggested that if Angela were to teach herself 'desk-top publishing', she could save about two thousand pounds by getting it 'camera ready'.

He also made recommendations as to the type of paper necessary for the clear reproduction of the old photographs, as well as the use of a firm glossy card for the cover. Not only that but he was able to guide the couple as to the colour of the print and the background for cover. This was made having in mind the 1872 drawing of the Maharajah's Well that Angela suggested as an attractive picture for the front. This was taken from a greetings card, based on a drawing of the Maharajah's Well made by a correspondent of the *Oxford Times* in 1872. It had been sold by the Well Trustees some years before and hand-coloured for her by her friend and local historian, Laureen Williamson, as a birthday card.

Moreover, Bob Boyd went on to propose that Angela ask an authoritative person to write a Foreword and another to pen a few lines for the back cover. He also recommended having a photograph and a 'mini-biography' of the author on the back. All of this was quite new to the Spencer-Harpers but they realised that this man had far more experience than they and followed his suggestions to the letter.

Luckily, Dr Malcolm Graham, Head of the Centre for Oxfordshire Studies, whose department had been so helpful over the years, very kindly agreed to write the Foreword, which concluded:

'Such recollections may sometimes be fallible but the importance of this book is that it documents so much that could never be gleaned from other sources. We need many more Angelas delving as sympathetically into the histories of their villages before the process of 'gentrification' changes them beyond recall and the passage of time leaves us with only fragmentary records of what went before.'

Another very helpful friend, Dr Elizabeth A Finn, Senior Archivist at the Oxfordshire Archives wrote for the back cover:

'A book not only to read and enjoy now, but for 'dipping into' for years to come!

This book looks at aspects of the history of two adjacent Oxfordshire villages, focusing on the lives of ordinary people in the nineteenth and twentieth centuries. It is lavishly illustrated with contemporary photographs as well as many more, some dating back to the 1850s.

Based, among other research, on over sixty interviews with local people, this is a popular, anecdotal history, which should appeal to more than local readership.'

So, by early in 1999, the book on which Angela had been working for over five years was finally finished. She wanted to dedicate it to her husband who had been so helpful with the proof-checking, but decided in the end to remember those who had helped her with their memories and the loan of their photographs:

To: The late Bill George of Stoke Row and Ada Britnell of Highmoor, two people typical of the many that I have inter-viewed, some of whom have now gone on to 'higher service.' All of them have availed me of the richness of their experiences. Without their help this volume would never have been written.

Angela gave the 'camera-ready' manuscript to Bob Boyd in January 1999 and in the September of that year he brought the finished copies to The Old Place, where he and the Spencer-Harpers cracked open a bottle of champagne on the terrace at the back of their house. Angela likened the experience to "having a third baby; a lot of labour resulting in great joy!"

* * * * * *

Immediately after the following Christmas a little girl was born to Tarquin and Rosemary Caine, who lived in Watlington. The Caines were long-time friends of the Spencer-Harpers whom they had met whilst cruising on the QE2. They got on well together on board and were delighted to find they lived not far from each other. Although Rosemary and Tarquin were quite a lot younger, they had married somewhat late in life and this baby was their first and, as it transpired, their only child.

When Angela went to visit Rosemary and the baby in the Clinic, her friend suggested that she might like to be her Godmother. Holding the baby with care, and playing with her tiny fingers, Angela was delighted and asked: "Have you now decided on a name for this poppet?"

"Yes, at last we have, we're going to call her Jania!" Rosemary announced with pride. "And you will be her Auntie Angela."

"But I'm not her aunt, or indeed any relative." Angela protested.

"No, maybe not, but, as you know, I'm old-fashioned and I don't like children calling adults by their first names. We always called our parents' friends 'Auntie and Uncle' when we were young, like the announcers on *Children's Hour*."

Angela was so thrilled at the idea of having a God-daughter that she laughingly agreed. "As you know, I adore my husband, two sons and three grandsons, but they are all males and it will be lovely to have a little girl to spoil!"

"Right, that's agreed then. Now I'll have to get on with fixing a date for her baptism. We shall hold it in our church, of course, you know the Methodist one in Watlington?"

"Yes, I know the one." Angela said. "But why are you calling her Jania?"

"Because she was born in January, silly! As you know the name of the month comes from the Roman god, Janus, who was supposed to be able to see both ways at once and our little darling was born on New Year's Day, just as we left one millennium and came into another!"

"Oh, very clever!" was all that Angela could think to say.

Her happy friend burbled on: "As you know, she was due on New Year's Eve, but I'm glad really that she didn't come then, otherwise we might have missed seeing all the celebrations and fireworks all around the world - wasn't the Eiffel Tower spectacular!"

"Yes, indeed." replied Angela, trying to think of the celebrations they had seen on the television and, at the same time, endeavouring to envisualise herself as God-Mother to the adorable baby girl in her

466

arms. "It will also be quite an experience for our grandsons, to have a girl 'in the family' as it were. I'm sure Bob will be delighted, as well!" she concluded.

And so Angela and Bob found themselves with three new projects in the year 2000, to sell *Dipping into the Wells*, follow the progress of their new baby God-daughter and to help with the Stoke Row Festival 2000, planned for the month of May.

It was important that Angela try to sell her book as quickly as possible, as the couple had financed it from Bob's endowment policy that had matured in September 1999, and he had lent the money to her with the words: "Try to get it back in the bank within a year, if you can." Fortunately, she was remarkably successful and was able to return the sum within three months. In fact they sold the first edition of one thousand copies within the first year. It transpired that this was rare for such a substantial local history which normally only sell in editions of five hundred.

Part of the reason for the book's success was the third Local History Day that she held in the November of that year and the kindness of the inhabitants of the two villages in buying it so readily. Also the fact that the Stoke Row Village Store sold copies, along with a great variety of foods and household goods. This shop that had been bought by Peter and Pat Armstrong in 1993 was a great asset to the village, especially as it retained its Post Office and operated a small in-house bakery that produced newly-baked French bread and made some into lunches which were especially popular with local workmen. Not only that, this couple also ran a dry-cleaning agency, sold basic stationery and were always willing to help with local events, especially by displaying posters in the windows. It was a great meeting-place for the local folk and much valued.

W H Smith and the other bookshops in Henley, Wallingford, Reading and Oxford also stocked it continuously. The book went on to a second and a third edition, although some of these sales were made to local history societies and other clubs to which Angela gave illustrated talks in winter evenings. She was also able to add a series entitled *The History of Two Chiltern Villages* to her lectures on Graphology aboard cruise ships. In all this work she was assisted by Bob who attended to the technical side of showing the many slides created from the old photographs under such headings as the

Maharajah's Well, Local Inhabitants, Life on the Farms, Victorian Schools etc. The Americans in particular found such subjects fascinating.

This ability enabled the couple to enjoy over twenty-five years of cruises, going many times to the Baltic, Alaska, Scandanavia, the Mediterranean, the Canary Islands, Canada and many parts of the States. What had started out as an interest became an absorbing hobby, or as Bob said laughingly to Tarquin at the party which followed Jania's baptism in March, 2000: "I'm glad this baby is giving Angela something else to think about. I really do believe the history of our house and the villages around is becoming something of an obsession with her!"

In a way, her husband was correct. With the creation of her website, and putting on to the Internet the Census Returns 1841-1901 that she had transcribed, Angela was able to help family historians from all over the world, many of whom came to her personally for background information on their families and to see her collections of photographs and memorabilia. In answer to a question at the end of one of her lectures, she replied: "I didn't really set out to become a local historian. It was something that just started because of my interest in the history of our house and then spread out to the villages. In fact, I think I can safely, if not very modestly, say that I believe I arrived just in time to record all these memories and photographs, because the residents and the way of life in the villages today are actually quite different from those in the 1950s."

It was fortunate for them both that Bob was an excellent cook and provided delicious dinners every night. As he sometimes quipped: "It's a matter of survival, because Angela would otherwise forget to eat when she is working on her computer!" Then he would pause and confess, "Anyway she has done it for over forty years and I do enjoy cooking, especially on the Aga in the winter!"

They really did love The Old Place but when congratulated on the beauty of it and its setting, they always said: "We just look upon ourselves as being temporary custodians of this lovely old cottage."

******

The date for celebrating the Millennium was somewhat contentious, with some people saying that it should not be until 2001, for it was not until then that two thousand years would have passed since the birth of Jesus Christ. However, for most it seemed that the year 2000 had a better sound to it, and so this year was chosen for the whole world to celebrate the unique event.

For larger affairs throughout the nation, preparations had started several years before, but it was Revd Alan Johnson, Vicar of St John's Church, who suggested in 1999 that Stoke Row should celebrate the forthcoming Millennium in style. A committee was promptly formed and the title *Stoke Row Festival - A Celebration of Village Life* agreed upon. Several grants were made by various village organisations and individuals, as well as one for £1000 provided by South Oxfordshire District Council to form a backing fund. The great attraction was to be the opening of the event by no less a personage than Queen Victoria herself!

It was also decided to hold the Festival on Sunday 7 May 2000, a day that proved to be warm and sunny. In fact, it was almost too hot for Her Majesty, played by Mrs Daphne Stallwood, who found her black bombazine dress to be very warm and none too comfortable.

A bright yellow programme was produced and on the front of it was an excellent drawing of the Maharajah's Well done by local artist Avril Bryant. At the top of the inside were a few words which summed up what most people felt about their village:

Stoke Row, with its unique Maharajah's Well, donated in 1864,
is a village with a wonderful history and a great sense of
community.

It is a happy place in which to live and work
and the year 2000 gives us a good excuse to honour it.

Maria Brunsden, a reporter from the *Henley Standard,* summed up the joys of the day in her article, accompanied by many colour photographs, in the following week's edition. The pictures included those of three little girls who had had their faces painted, another girl dressed as a jester and the maypole dance in full flow.

"'If only we'd thought of it first!" read the messages of admiration and congratulation from neighbouring parishes at the Stoke Row Festival 2000. The day-long festival, held on Sunday last, was a celebration of village life and held in honour of Stoke Row's rich heritage and today's multicultural community. The event was blessed with glorious sunshine and around two hundred people from the community, plus friends, gather to participate in the celebrations.

The day commenced with an open air Ecumenical Service given in the Well Orchard by Revd Alan Johnson of St John the Evangelist, Stoke Row and the Revd John Harrington of Stoke Row Independent Chapel.

The service was followed by the spectacular arrival by horse-drawn carriage of 'Her Majesty, Queen Victoria', accompanied by Mr Brown. 'Her Majesty' entered the Orchard over a red carpet to an array of photographers and a flurry of loyal subjects eager to make her acquaintance.

While curry lunches were served in the Village Hall, out in the Orchard the Village Rock Band, led by Mr Tony Way, provided the musical entertainment.

Stoke Row Primary School contributed to the Festival with theatrical presentations and a traditional Maypole dance. Throughout the day many of the children could also be found wandering around the Orchard dressed as characters from the past.

Stoke Row Drama Group gave two humorous presentations that consisted of a hasty romp through the ages, and a number of Hindu dances were performed by 'Jeyanney'; a professional Indian dancer from Reading. The staging for these events was provided by Norman Cox & Partners, with the help of numerous volunteers.

Other attractions included a Flower Festival in the church, arranged by Avril Wood and a History Exhibition arranged by Angela Spencer-Harper. Traction engines, classic cars and bikes were also assembled for inspection; and there were a variety of stalls from refreshments by the Stoke Row WI and Arts & Crafts to sports, games and a small fun fair.

The Festival was such a success that many villagers would like to see it repeated.'

It was not intended that a profit should be made but there was about £2000 left over when all bills were paid and this was divided bwteeen the Maharajah's Well Trustees and the Village Hall.

Back in her study at The Old Place that evening, Angela wrote in the last page of her old blue Diary: "What a wonderful day we all had, it was well worth all the work. I do feel as if we really have now entered the Twenty-first Century!"

Very soon afterwards the Spencer-Harpers took a relaxing motoring holiday in South-West France which they thoroughly enjoyed. However, they returned to find that their house had been burgled. This was not the first time. In fact, it was the eighth in their married life time, despite their having taken increasing security measures. This occasion was really heart-breaking though, because the thieves took their antique furniture and numerous items that had been in their families for many years and were literally irreplaceable. Once they had recovered the insurance they decided to buy reproduction furniture and to try not to become so attached to material goods!

For her birthday in August, Bob gave his wife a beautiful new book in which to continue her journal. It had a red leather cover and on the front he had kindly had tooled in gold the words *Angela's Diary.*

Later in the year, as they sat up in bed drinking their early morning tea, looking out on the autumn tints of the beeches on Witheridge Hill, and watching the rest of the world go by in their cars to work, Bob asked his wife what she intended to do next.

"Well, first of all I must write up my holiday journals for this year, then there'll be the Christmas Family Party to plan. Every year, when I mention to the children and grandchildren that we might finish holding these big parties for seventeen of us, and only a week before

471

Christmas, they always protest. It is really rather lovely here at the festive season, I must say, with the big open fire and the brick walls festooned with cards. Milo loves the illuminated tree standing by the French doors, Quentin has great affection for you coming as Father Christmas and Gabriel told me he gets a thrill from seeing all the gifts under the tree, all wrapped in coloured papers. Yes, perhaps we'll hold one more this year and that really will have to be the last. Maybe Michael and Vicky will hold it at their house next year. They have offered and, theirs being a big old Victorian house it should lend itself well to such celebrations."

She took another sip of tea and continued: "But, after that, yes, I suppose I do need a new project to work on. In fact, I have been thinking. I've always thought it might be a good idea to write another book, one that would encompass a greater area than just the two villages. It could incorporate the four towns around here, Reading, Wallingford, Watlington and Henley. There's so much history in south-east Oxfordshire."

"Yes, I suppose that's true. It would need a lot more research, of course."

"It would, but that would be fascinating. I think I would base it on this house and all the people who have lived here through the ages, and even before the house was built. I could form each chapter around something that has actually been found in a particular place or has been recorded about a place in some way. I could start with the Stone Age and the Mesolithic Axe that was found up in Stoke Row and then come up through the ages, right up to the present day." she said and then, more slowly and meditatively, continued, "It would be even more fun to start fifty years from now and to imagine what might have happened here by then."

"Sounds a lot of work and a bit ambitious to me. What would you call it?" Bob asked.

Angela looked thoughtful for a while and then, smiling, suggested: "What about *The Old Place?*"

******

The story of the Vanalloys Estate is taken from the Memoirs of John and Betty Searby.

The story of Bob and Angela Spencer-Harper is largely biographical, with the exception of the references to Jania and her parents, who are fictional characters.

The account of the Stoke Row Millennium Celebrations was taken from the Henley Standard *and editions of the* Stoke Row News *in the year 2000.*